AGRICULTURAL ENGINEERING

ENCYCLOPEDIA OF AGRICULTURE – II

AGRICULTURAL ENGINEERING

By

Renuka Sharma

DISCOVERY PUBLISHING HOUSE PVT. LTD.
INDIA

Published by:

DISCOVERY PUBLISHING HOUSE PVT. LTD.
4383/4B, Ansari Road, Darya Ganj
New Delhi-110 002 (India)
Phone : +91-11-23279245; 23253475; 43596065
E-mail : discoverybooksindia@gmail.com
discoverypublishinghouse@gmail.com
namitwasan9@gmail.com
web : www.discoverypublishinggroup.com

First Edition: 2011

Reprinted: 2022

ISBN: 978-93-5056-020-4 (Set)

ISBN: 978-93-5056-022-8

Agricultural Engineering

Printed at:
Infinity Imaging Systems
Delhi

Preface

The breakthrough in science that permitted genes to be identified and manipulated as molecular ushered in the agricultural technology era, which is now more than a decade old. The new tools of agricultural technology are changing the way scientists can address problems in the life sciences; agriculture is one area facing major changes as a result of this new technology. The unanticipated rapid ratio at which discoveries and their applications in technology have unfolded has stored the capacity of society – more specifically, our agricultural research and educational institutions to absorb and adjust to change. We are challenged by pressing decisions opportunities, and problems that we face now and will continue to face in the future. Competition from abroad impels us to devise and use new technologies that can improve the efficiency and quality of agricultural production. These concerns led to this study – an overview of how the agricultural research system is responding to the latest technology and how it might prepare for future opportunities. Agricultural technology is moving in many directions with positive results – crop improvement, production of transgenic plants, vaccine development and diagnostic methods are some impending applications – but the development of genetic engineering's tools can be found in almost every agricultural discipline. The exception is that, through lessions learned, adequate food will be made available to the whole world in the future. The present title **"Agricultural Engineering"** has been planned, written, and edited with the intention of being useful for the beginners, researchers and scientists involved in the field of agricultural genetic transformation.

I would like to express my sincere thanks to Dr. M.P. Arora, whose continuous inspiration and encouragement initiated me in bringing out this title.

I am specially indebted to my husband Mr. Rajeev Sharma for his enthusiastic support, constant helpfulness and good spirit during the writing of this title.

Quite frankly, this book would not have been written without the aid of my daughter Shreya, who co-operated patiently during periods of neglect.

Special and sincere thanks to my parents and in laws for their blessings and continuous encouragement in bringing out this title.

To make the work more comprehensive and informative, I have consulted many authoritative books, research journals, abstracts, monographs etc., so there can be no claim to originality except in the manner of treatment.

I also express thanks to my friends and colleagues whose continuous inspirations have initiated me to bring out this title.

I express my gratitude to Mr. Wasan and staff of M/s Discovery Publishing House Pvt. Ltd. for their whole hearted co-operation in the publication of this title.

I acknowledge the fact that the development and publication of this book would not have been possible without the assistance and encouragement of colleagues, research scholars and students. They are so numerous to mention. I thank all of them most warmly for helping to create the present title.

Any worthwhile criticism and suggestions for improvement would be thankfully acknowledged.

Renuka Sharma

CONTENTS

IMPROVING FOOD QUALITY

The beginning of the *agronomic* revolution, some 10,000 years ago, was characterized by the collection of seeds from important staple plants for use in the next season. But a crop such as maize, which involves the cross between two *genetically* dissimilar wild plants, could not have survived in the environment without the *intervention* of man.

This is because it has no natural process for dispersing its closely bound seeds. The developments in fermentation to provide more diverse foods with longer storage capacity and its use in bread making were applications of *biotechnology*.

Thus, biotechnology was applied throughout history in the production of food without any real scientific understanding of what was occurring. It was not until the end of the 19th century that the principles *governing* inheritance influenced the process of plant *breeding* as we know it today. However, it is really only from the 1960s onward that high-yielding varieties with *agronomically beneficial* traits and other quality *characteristics* have been developed and introduced into the market.

This has resulted from applications of the *technologies* described in other chapters and forms the beginning of the biotechnological revolution. The effect of this *revolution* is most dramatically observed in the increase in yield of rice that occurred *throughout* Southeast Asia with a *continued increase* in yields from 1968 until 1983.

However, despite the application of these technologies to plant breeding, and the outstanding success they have had, problems remain that are best solved through the application of genetic engineering or are tractable only using this approach. Only whole *chromosomes* can be introduced into plants by "*conventional*" means, and in doing so both "good" and "bad" traits can be *transferred*. The whole process of

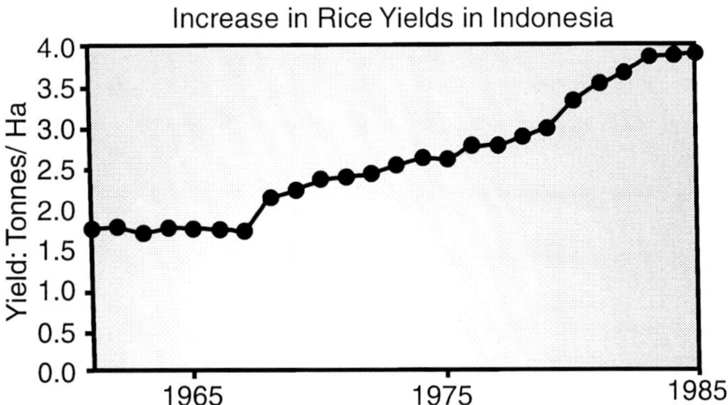

Figure 1.1: Increase in rice yields in Indonesia.

developing a new variety can take years with conventional approaches. Conventional plant breeding simply cannot ensure that a staple crop contains a *beneficial* constituent, such as an essential nutrient, if the *biosynthetic* machinery for that *consituent* is not expressed.

Conventional plant breeding does not readily provide the basis for determining the effect of specific genetic changes on quality because there is no control over the specific biosynthetic pathways that enable any relationship to be assessed.

Indeed, the current critics of the use of *biotechnology* ignore the fact that many plant products on the market are derived from *"wide crosses," hybridizations* in which genes are moved from one species or genus to another to create a variety of a plant that does not, and could not, exist in nature. Developments in *genetic* techniques have enabled molecular genetic approaches to replace gene identification by standard biochemical approaches.

As an example, *Arabidopsis* mutants have been characterized with altered production of a number of nutrients and *phytochemicals* that are important determinants of plant quality including *carotenoids,* flavonoids, tocopherols, and ascorbic acid. Information about their *biosynthesis* and the function of specific genes in *controlling* these quality *determinants* has been established.

The increase in use of *heterologous* expression has allowed the *functional* cloning or *characterization* of the steps in the synthesis of many nutrients and phytochemicals to be established. The carotenoid pathway has been cloned by colour *complementation* in *Escherichia coli.*

The enzymes involved in iron uptake and biotin, thiamine, and vitamin E synthesis have been cloned or functionally *characterized* using *heterologous expression* systems. Genetic *manipulation* provides the opportunity to look at the relationships between composition and quality in a systematic way.

It is this application of the technology in conjunction with the genetic *characterization* of mutants that needs to be fully exploited to advance the *effectiveness* of *conventional* plant breeding. Once a gene or gene product, either in isolation or acting in tandem, has been determined to confer a specific beneficial characteristic, a tool exists to screen potential new varieties. Modem gene, or genetic *engineering,* has really taken off only in the last decade or so.

Table 1.1: Recommended Dietary Allowances (RDAs) of Nutrients and Minerals Compared with Their Maximum Safe Intakes.

Nutrient	*Adult RDA*	*Upper safe intake (× RDA)*
Calcium	1200 mg	2
Iron	15 mg	5
Iodine	150 μg	13
Selenium	70 Ag	13
Vitamin C	60 mg	16
Vitamin B_8	2 mg	125
Folate	200 μg	50
Biotin	30-100 μg	300
Vitamin E	10 mg TE	100
Vitamin A	1 mg RE	5 (retinol)
		100 (β-carotene)
Vitamin K	80 μg	375

Large areas of genetically modified soybeans, corn, and canola have been successfully grown in the Western Hemisphere. In the United States alone in 1999, some 50% of all the soybeans planted were planted with GM-herbicide-resistant seeds.

Although in this initial period the benefits have been primarily directed toward farmers, with the greatest focus on improved *agronomic* characteristics, there are specific applications of genetic engineering with unlimited potential benefits to consumers in the food and nonfood sectors. Many of these are described in more detail in other chapters. This focus on producers' benefits has provided a reason, among many others, for opponents of the *technology* to argue forcefully against its use.

Considerable efforts are being expended *internationally* to detect *genetically manipulated* crops for the enforcement of effective labeling. The development of genetic engineering is being severely restrained through *sociopolitical* concerns over its widespread adoption and safety.

This is, in turn, leading to reticence in industry to make the long-term *investment necessary* to bring products to the market, given the strength of the opposition in the Western Hemisphere. In all of these areas the effects on food *composition* that have occurred as a consequence of the genetic changes have not been well documented. But it is clear that compositional effects will have occurred from the *application* of conventional plant breeding. Plant breeding, thanks to modern genetic *methodologies*, will be less "hit or miss."

It will be informed in the future about the consequences of a specific single-gene or multiple-gene alteration for the yield, the disease resistance, the *nutritional* value, and the flavor and texture of food plants.

This will allow much more targeted screening of beneficial *characteristics* in the future, as well as the introduction of *significantly* improved nutrition, for the developing world *communities* whose dependence on a single plant crop frequently causes *nutritional* deficiency disease. In practice however, it is unlikely that genetic *engineering* would ever supplant the more conventional *biotechnological* approaches entirely, especially in the context of improving the quality of our food supply.

Both conventional and genetic biotechnologies will continue to be exploited to achieve this goal. There are very many *commercial* and technical obstacles to the development of crops with multiple gene transfers. Yet many of the benefits that consumers might wish to see in their plant foods would require such an approach.

A seed company would have to be very convinced that either there were other benefits (e.g., resounding agronomic benefits) or the *potential* market size justified the investment before any such investment would be made. It is clear that some aspects of the quality of existing varieties of food crops could be *significantly* improved purely by conventional means, where multiple gene transfers are *commonplace*.

Examples in which significant variations in the nutrient content of genotypes have been documented include a Twofold variation in calcium *concentration* in beans Fourfold variation in β-catotene *concentrations* in broccoli Fourfold variation in folates in beetroot Two- to threefold variation in iron and zinc levels in maize.

PRIORITIES FOR THE FOOD SECTOR

In an international context, the priorities for the application of plant biotechnologies for the quality improvement of food vary depending on whether or not the *community* is in the developed or developing world.

The Developing World

Overwhelming proportions of the world's population are dependent on plants as their principal, if not exclusive, source of food. In such *populations*, the incidence of disease due to vitamin *deficiencies* is widespread. It has been estimated that over 100 million children *worldwide* are vitamin A deficient and that improving the vitamin A content of their food could prevent as many as 2 million deaths annually in young children.

This is apart from the deficiencies in iodine intake, resulting in goiter, and from iron-deficient anemia, which are estimated to affect millions in the *developing* world. There is also an important need to improve the amino acid content of legume proteins that are deficient in essential sulfur amino acids. There is evidence that the problem of vitamin A deficiency in *particular* has increased as a *consequence* of the application of traditional plant breeding.

While the focus on improving disease resistance and yields of rice has rid many of these *communities* of hunger, it has had an impact on the local traditions. Less effort has been placed on growing alternative crops that may well have provided a source of vitamin A but are more difficult to make money from or do not produce consistent yields under local *circumstances*.

This is particularly true of legume crops. With the focus only on this one aspect of basic food

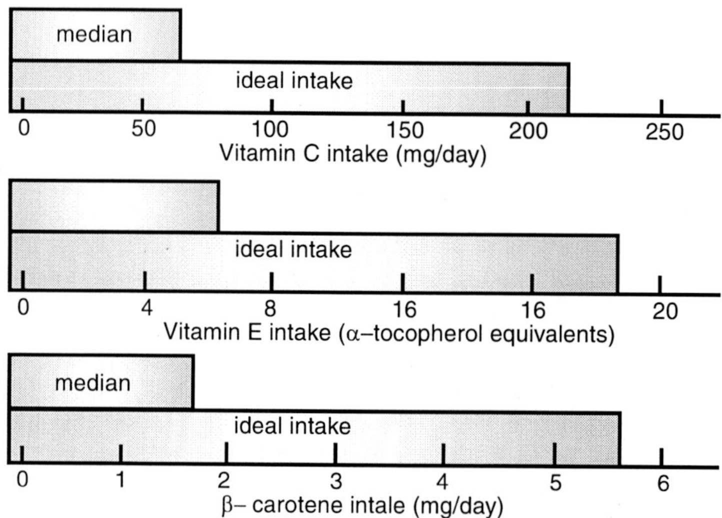

Figure 1.2: Plasma concentrations of selected antioxidant nutrients in the U.S. population.

production, the problems of *malnutrition* have not disappeared. Indeed, the incidence of nutritional *deficiencies* may have increased.

Improvements in Protein Quality

This is an area of crucial importance to the majority of the world's population and is covered in greater detail in other chapter of this book. Whatever strategies are adopted, there will need to be *assurance* that the introduction of any foreign protein into a plant will not increase the risks of an allergic response through the introduction of allergic epitopes.

For example, the strategy of *introducing* a methionine-rich protein into legumes from the Brazil nut had to be abandoned because of the risks of an acute allergic response by some *consumers.* Apart from this problem, the sulfur-containing amino acid content of the legumes is not substantially raised.

Suppression of synthesis of other methionine-rich proteins in the legume occurs. More information about the control of gene *expression* by the amino acid supply is required.

Reduction in Antinutritional Factors

The interest in reducing *antinutritional* factors in plants has been *predominantly* focused around improving the nutritional value of feeding stuffs. Phytates are present in many plant seeds and uptake of limit *phosphorus* or iron as well as other elements. The potential for introducing a phytase gene into feeding stuffs has been explored.

However, there are other strategies that seem to be of greater overall value in human nutrition. Thioredoxin is thought to be an activator of the *germination* process in seeds. It is able to activate proteins to *degradation* by proteolysis and results in improved *digestibility.*

It also has the potential advantage of being able to reduce allergenicity, presumably because of its capacity to break disulfide bonds by the action of the reduced thiol groups in the molecule and ensure that the tertiary structure of the protein is accessible to *degradation* by proteases.

The insertion of the wheat *thioredoxin* gene into barley has produced a transgenic plant in which thioredoxin accounts for 7% of the total protein content in the barley and is a good source of sulphur amino acids.

The Developed World

In contrast to that in the *developing* world, the incidence of known nutritional deficiency disorders in the developed world is low. Even in the case of vegetarians, there appears to be no appreciable problem. Classical nutritional deficiency diseases have been avoided through the widespread fortification of food when it was realized that many staple crops contained insufficient *concentrations* of many essential vitamins and minerals.

Fortification is also utilized to replace nutrients lost in the heat processing of staple foods and through oxidation. In addition, the *consumption* of nutritional *supplements* is becoming more widespread. Nonetheless, there is good evidence, as shown in figure elsewhere in this chapter, that even in a country such as the United States, where most nutritionally related disorders probably stem from *overnutrition*, there is inadequate intake of *micronutrients* compared with what would be found in the plasma if recommended dietary allowances (RDAs) were consumed.

For selected nutrients (iron, calcium, selenium, iodine, vitamin E, vitamin B_6, and vitamin A), the clinical and epidemiological evidence strongly supports the view that they play a *significant* role in *maintaining* health and are limiting in diets worldwide. The RDAs were first developed as *recommendations* to alleviate nutritional deficiency *diseases* and have been periodically revised in the light of further data.

A new set of values-to be known as dietary reference intakes-are expected to be published in 2000 soon by the U.S. Department of Agriculture (USDA). New values reflect the growing knowledge base in relation to the role of nutients in *optimizing* health. Diet is implicated as an important risk factor in the initiation or progression of many diseases of aging, particularly *cardiovascular* disease and cancer.

One of the most striking and consistent observations, in terms of the relationship to health, has been the decrease in cancer risk associated with an increasing intake of fruit and vegetables in the diet. There appears to be no single explanation for this effect, but there is growing evidence for the role played by nutrients (vitamins, minerals) and other *microconstituents* of plants in minimizing the adverse effects of the processes leading to oxidative damage and degenerative diseases such as vascular disease and cancer.

The basis for the protective effects of plant phytochemicals on *carcinogenesis* is the subject of intensive research *internationally*. This evidence needs to be taken into account especially in terms of reassessing overall nutritional needs *throughout* the human life span.

Table elsewhere in this chapter indicates the potentially large increase in intakes of certain nutrients that might bring additional health benefits without posing any additional health risks to the general population. It might be argued that because fruit and *vegetables* are known to reduce the risk of the development of cancer and *cardiovascular* disease, the only action that is required is to *encourage* the greater *consumption* of these foods.

Under such circumstances, the need to consider any specific enhancement of their *functional* benefits is pointless. This *argument* ignores a number of facts:

There is growing evidence that the augmentation of certain nutrients will have health benefits because RDAs of nutrients are based on requirements for healthy growth, not on optimal nutritional needs for the *prevention* of long-term disease.

Consumer choice is influenced by socioeconomic and cultural constraints. Freedom of choice ensures that foods are selected that are enjoyable and available, but these may not always be healthy. Enhancement of levels of nutrients in specific staple crops, or their *introduction* if absent, could meet *consumer* health needs without the need to change dietary habits radically, which is rarely a *practicable* option.

The consumption of fruit and vegetables may not provide optimal protection against the risk of disease.

Plant food *composition* is constantly changing as new *varieties* are marketed. Because the exact protective *mechanisms* that are induced by eating fruits and vegetables are not known, it is not possible to link composition to specific functional *mechanisms*. No criteria could be applied to the *development* of new plant varieties, in terms of their composition, other than that they remain the same. This is an unsatisfactory basis to proceed, from the perspectives of both the plant breeding sector and the consumer. Phytochemicals or vitamins vary by an order of magnitude or more in the gene pool. For the *prevention* of disease it could help to know in which direction this pool should be altered and with what likely consequences.

There needs to be a *systematic* examination of the factors that determine the biosynthesis in the plant of phytochemicals, including nutrients, that are bioactive and protective as well as the factors that determine their turnover and catabolism. Genetic *engineering* provides a tool from which to expand knowledge more rapidly than could be achieved in any other way.

APPLICATION OF GENETIC ENGINEERING TO FOOD QUALITY IMPROVEMENT

Potential strategies for the enhancement of specific metabolites could target on

1. Overexpression of enzymes that control the final steps in the biosynthesis of a metabolite
2. Overexpression of *rate-limiting* enzymes
3. Silencing of genes whose expression causes the metabolite to be degraded
4. Increased expression of genes that are not subject to metabolic feedback control
5. Increasing the number of plastids in a plant
6. Increasing metabolic flux into the pathway of interest
7. Expression in storage organs using site-specific promoters

The strategy that has had the greatest success at present is the first one, especially in conjunction with the last strategy. However, this *presupposes* that the metabolite of interest is the final one in a particular pathway.

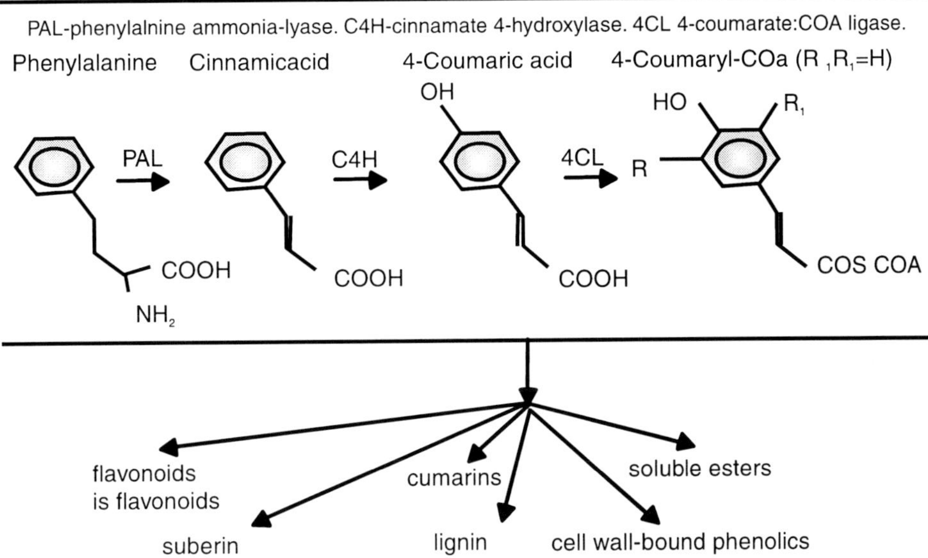

Figure 1.3: General phenylpropanoid metabolism.

In practice, if a substantial increase in the concentration of a metabolite is required, the use of specific promoters directing the synthesis to a particular organelle normally used for storage purposes, or where the plant normally *synthesizes* the metabolite, is essential. Failure to do so could cause toxicity in the plant by interfering with the production or function of other essential metabolites.

Because of extensive synteny among cereal crops, it is likely that information on the function of a gene in one cereal crop will be of direct *relevance* to its function in another. The differences in genome size between cereals are *predominantly* due to *amplification* of interspersed repetitive sequences, and knowledge of gene order and sequence in one cereal will enable the isolation and characterization of genes in another cereal.

Even the *characterization* of the genes in *Arabidopsis*, although only distantly related to cereals, has enabled functions and traits of similar genes in other food plants to be located and *confirmed*. No strategies have yet been applied where multiple gene insertions are necessary to produce the metabolite or where plastid numbers have been increased.

However, rapid *accumulation* of sequence data of both chromosomal DNA and expressed sequence tags of plants and other species is providing rapid advances in knowledge of the genetic makeup and functions of several plants, and it is expected that these other *possibilities* will soon be feasible.

PLANT SECONDARY METABOLITES AS DETERMINANTS OF QUALITY

There is considerable evidence that plant secondary metabolites are of crucial *importance* in determinining the quality characteristics of fruit and vegetables. Colour changes with maturity are characterized by the synthesis of chlorophylls and specific carotenoids and flavonoids (anthocyanins). Flavor and aroma are often *determined* by complex chemical changes centered on the production of terpenoids and aldehydes resulting from the action of lipoxygenases as well as changes in the composition of complex phenolics that can produce the ideal balance between *astringency* and bitterness in beer or wine.

Texture is determined by the structure of plant cell walls and the enzymic changes in their structure that can be induced during the ripening and storage process. Fortunately, a number of the pathways leading to the production of key *phytochemicals* of health interest are also important in *determining* these other quality characteristics.

The very diverse secondary metabolites in plants, which could have an important impact on food quality, are biosynthesized via two important pathways-the *phenylpropanoid* (PP) and the isoprenoid (IP) pathwayswith some common links. However, the way in which these pathways are utilized to produce specific metabolites in food plants and how these relate to the quality parameters described are at present *insufficiently* understood to undertake little more than a hit-and-miss approach to genetic manipulation.

THE PHENYLPROPANOID PATHWAY

Phenylpropanoids (PPs) provide the basic units from which a wide variety of plant metabolites are synthesized. From these basic units a series of important branch pathways result in the synthesis of flavonoids and *isoflavonoids*, coumarins, soluble phenolic esters, and cell wall polymers. The precise branch points are not known in all cases.

The functions of the PP derivatives are as diverse as their structures; they serve as pigments, *phytoalexins*, ultraviolet *protectants*, insect repellents, and signaling molecules in plant-microbial interactions; in the regulation of auxin transport; and in the *stimulation* of pollen *germination*.

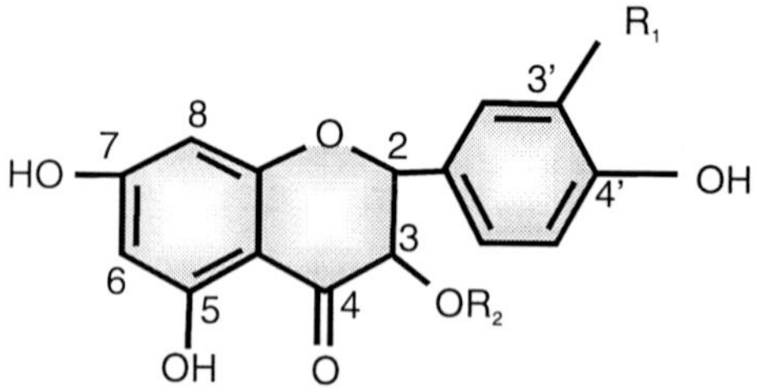

Figure 1.4: Basic structure of flavonoids.

They also produce structural support for plants, acting as the building blocks for the biosynthesis of suberin, lignin, and other cell wall components. Given this wide diversity in structure and function, there are major differences in temporal and spatial *distribution* of these metabolites in the development of the plant and between different plant organs and cell types.

The potential health interest in the majority of these metabolites lies in the fact that many of the simple and complex phenols that are present in foods have been shown to be powerful *antioxidants* in vitro and *demonstrate* a wide range of potential benefits in animal experiments.

They play an important role in the *determination* of flavor, colour, and taste. Clearly, given the *importance* of these metabolites to the plant, any proposed genetic *modification* must pay careful attention to a possible adverse impact on the plants' responses to *environmental* stress.

For this reason, most of the successful attempts at up-regulating the production of a specific

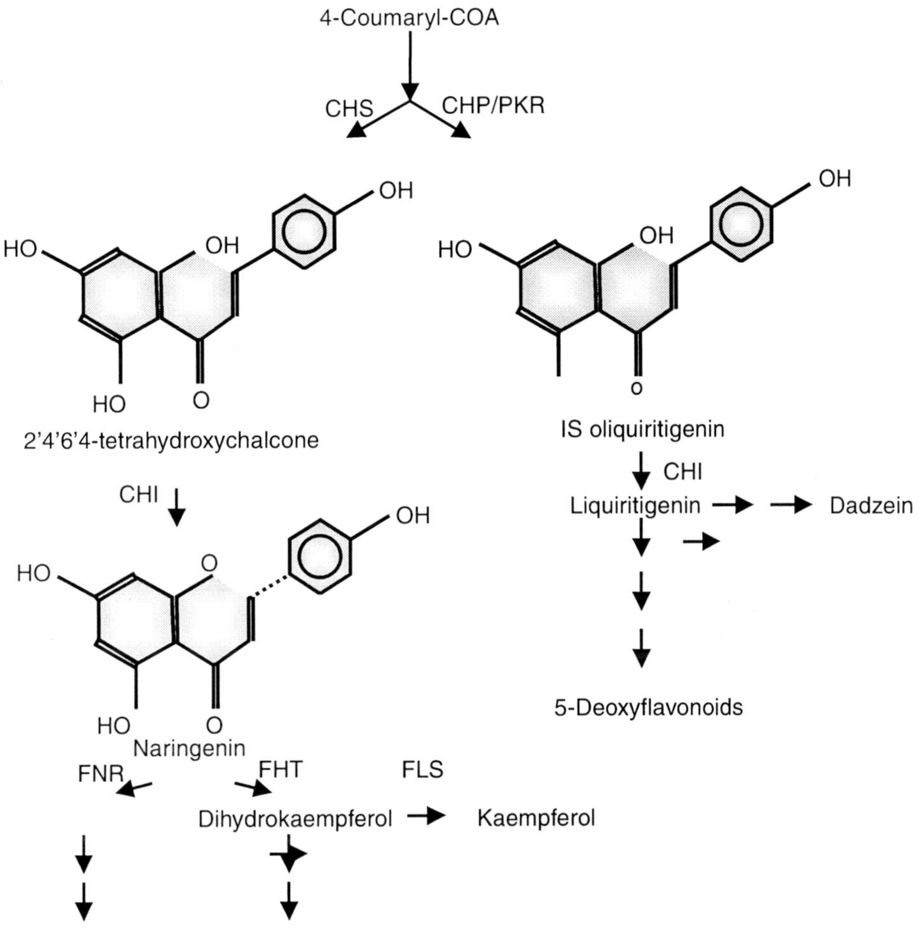

Figure 1.5: Biosynthesis of chalcones.

metabolite in the pathway have been where the gene is involved in the control of the end step in the *biosynthesis* rather than at earlier stages in the *biosynthetic* process.

Careful attention also has to be given to the choice of promoters for correct temporal and spatial expression. For the strategy to succeed, promoters must direct the *biosynthesis* to edible storage organs or organelles. Up-regulation of expression in all parts of a plant often leads to adverse consequences.

A great deal is known about the biochemical events that occur in PP metabolism. An array of mutants are available in which steps in the pathway are blocked, especially in the pathways to flavonoid pigmentation. *Complementary* DNA (cDNA) and/or gene sequences are also available for the early steps in PP *biosynthesis* as well as in flavonoid biosynthesis.

PAL deaminates phenylalanine to cinnamate, which is *subsequently* hydroxylated to *4-hydroxycinnamic* acid through the action of C4H. PAL is present constituitively, together with C4H and 4CL, in varying activities throughout plant development. The evidence suggests that these enzymes are highly regulated and exist in individual isoforms that may well be species and cell dependent.

Although PAL *overexpression* is likely to play a key role in increasing flux into total *phenylpropanoid* metabolism, it is probably too nonspecific and many biological functions would be affected. It has been found that overexpression of PAL in tobacco increases its resistance to microbial attack but decreases its resistance to insect larvae.

Similar problems are likely to be found with the *overexpression* of other enzymes early in the pathway. The free acids that are synthesized through this pathway rarely *accumulate* to high levels within the plant and are usually *conjugated* to sugars, cell wall carbohydrates, or organic acids. The texture of fruit and *vegetables* is closely related to the chemical and physical properties of the cell walls. The end point determinant of texture is related to the overall mechanical properties of the plant, which are determined by the structural characteristics of the cell wall, and the way in which these determine cell-to-cell adhesion.

An important factor in tissue softening is the separation of individual cells. Fruit ripening

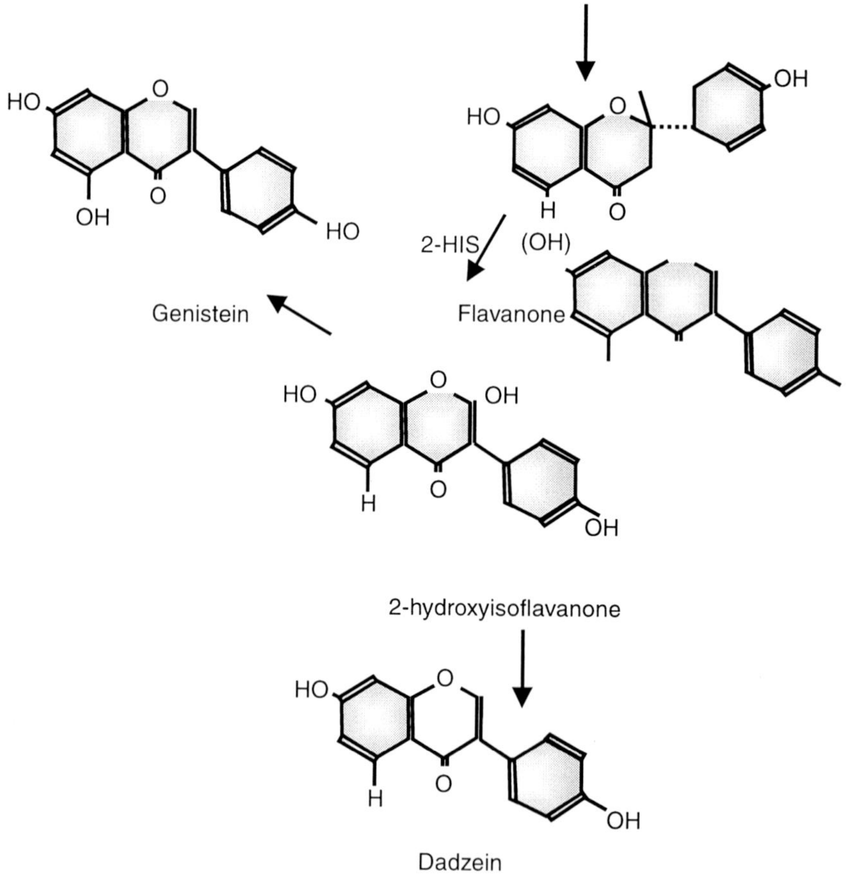

Figure 1.6: Biosynthesis of isoflavones.

generally results in the biochemical dissolution of the middle lamella pectic *polysaccharides*, which bind cells together.

Thermal treatment can also cause β-eliminative degradation of the pectic polymers involved in cell-cell adhesion. Ripening and thermally induced cell separation occur *predominantly* in nonlignified, thin-walled tissues. Tissues that fail to soften are frequently the result of secondary thickening and associated lignification.

However, some parenchyma-rich plant tissues with thin, nonlignified tissues soften only slowly on cooking. In any studies of the texture of fruit and vegetables it will be important to understand the factors that control the processes behind *maturation* within both the middle lamellar and the xylem tissues. The role of specific steps in the biosynthesis of these *structures* in fruit and *vegetable* textural *characteristics* is described further in other chapter of this book.

Flavonoids and Isoflavonoids

Flavonoids, whose basic structure is shown in figure elsewhere in this chapter, form an important class of metabolites of the PP pathway. They show protective effects against cancer *progression* in *experimental* animals. In vivo and in vitro studies have shown a range of potentially *beneficial* effects such as *antioxidant* properties, and they are effective vasodilators and platelet *disaggregators*. They are present in significant amounts in many food plants.

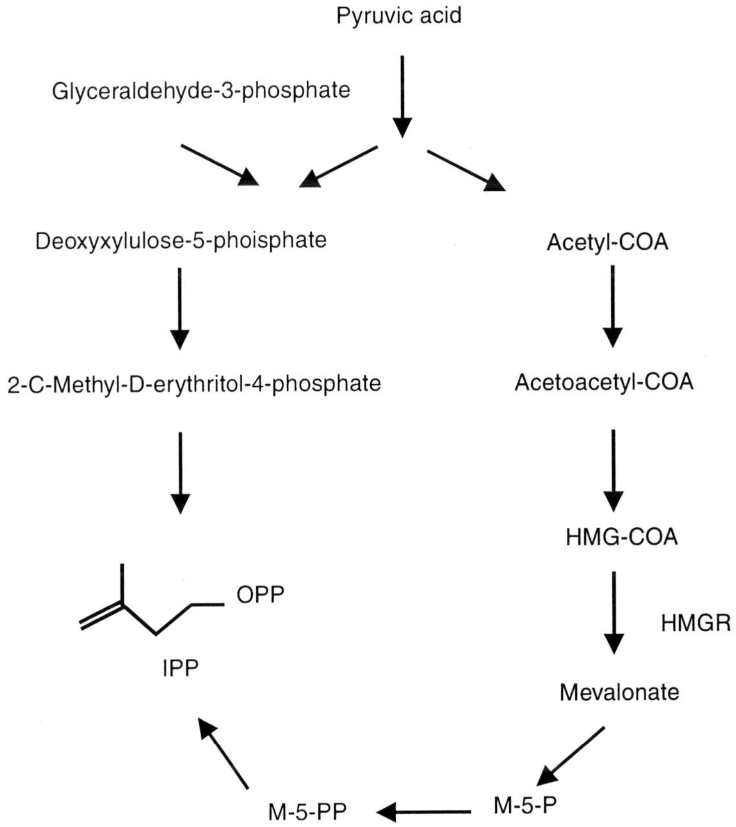

Figure 1.7: Biosynthesis of isopentenyl pyrophosphate (IPP).

They also illustrate extremely well the complex issues that need to be considered in focusing on specific metabolites in achieving the aim of improving food quality. All flavonoids are derived from a chalcone precursor, the product of condensation of 4-coumaryl coenzyme A (CoA) (derived from phenylalanine produced in the shikimate pathway), and three molecules of malonyl-CoA (derived from acetyl CoA through the action of a carboxylase) involving the enzyme chalcone synthase (CHS).

The CHS enzymes form a family of closely related multigene *enzymes* that produce a variety of secondary metabolites.

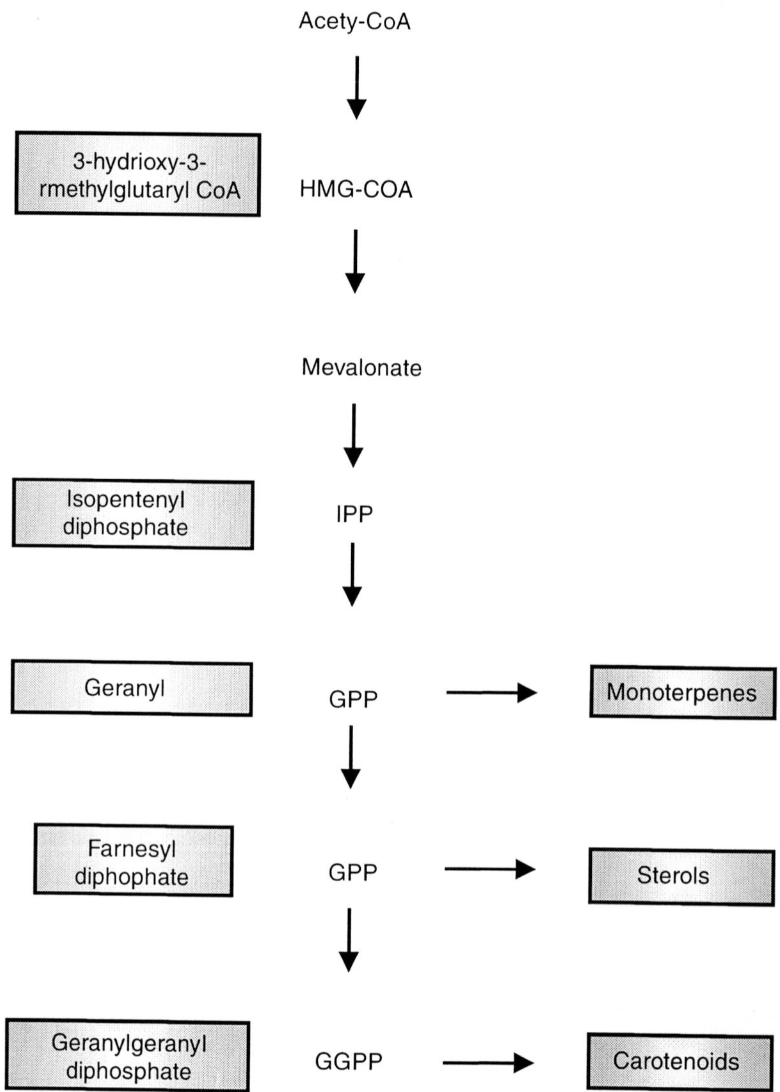

Figure 1.8: Synthesis of secondary metabolites through the isoprenoid pathway.

This is achieved through *variations* in the number of rounds of condensation and differences in the folding pattern of the intermediate polyketide.

Stilbene synthases from a variety of sources have exactly the same substrate *specificity* as CHS but the intermediate polyketide is folded *differently*, resulting in *decarboxylation* to form the stilbene. The stilbene resveratrol, which is found in wine, has been shown to possess *anticancer* activities in various cancer models. Resveratrol can be engineered successfully by genetic engineering.

The stereospecific cyclization of the chalcone, catalyzed by chalcone isomerase (CHI), provides a 2S-flavanone with the typical flavonoid skeleton. Chalcone reductase (CHR) isomerizes both 6'-

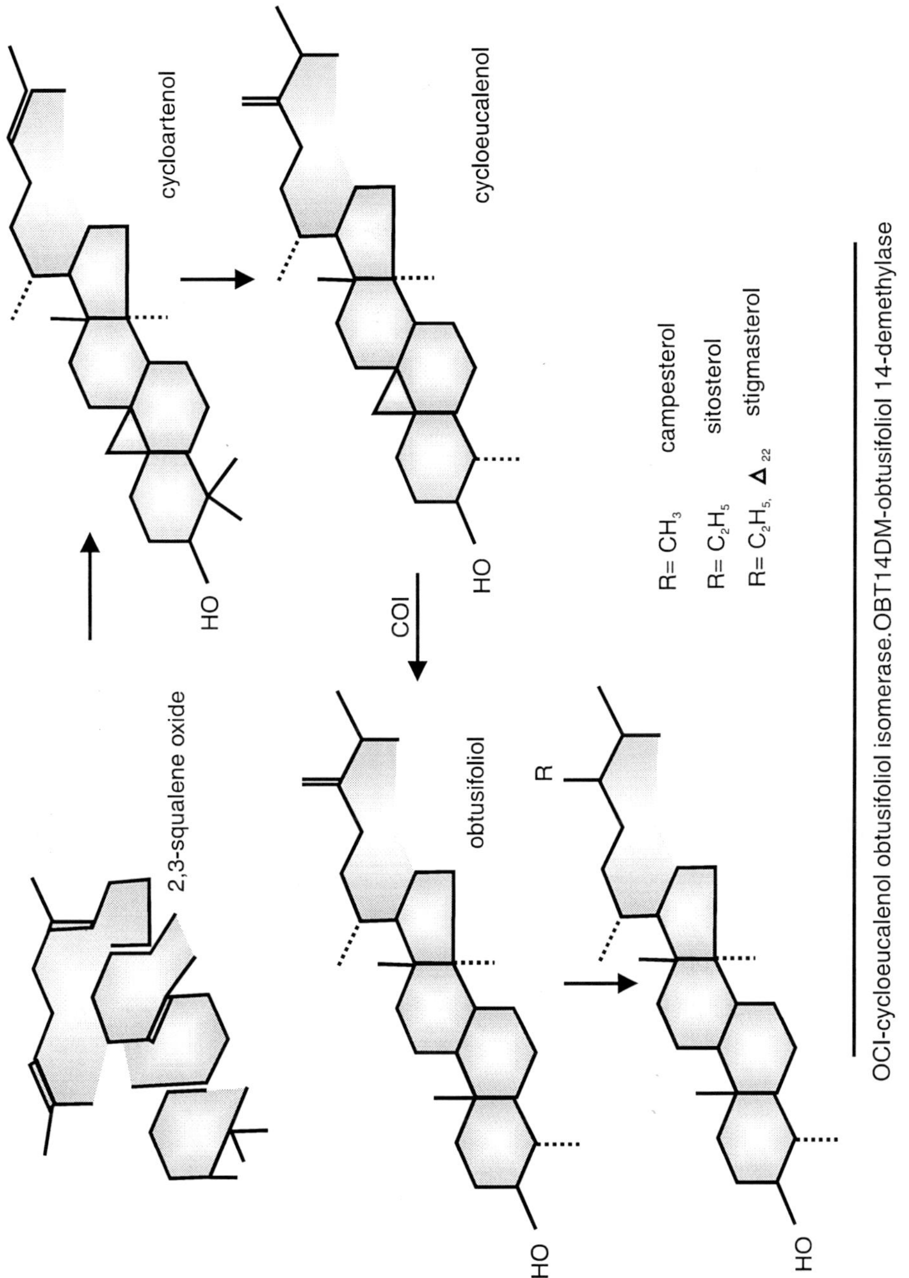

Figure 1.9: Biosynthesis of plant sterols in photosynthetic phyla.

hydroxy and 6'-deoxychalcone to 5-hydroxy and 5-deoxyflavanone, respectively. CHR and CHS are coinduced in elicited or infected cells, whereas CHS alone is expressed in the arial portions of *uninfected* plants.

Consequently, it is likely to be of greater importance in terms of its ability to influence food quality parameters. 2',4',4'-Trihydroxychalcone (the product of CHS and CHR) is a branch point for the synthesis in legumes of different flavonoids. Thus, chalcone isomerase (CHI) converts the chalcone to 4,7-dihydroxyflavanone and then to the isoflavones.

Another enzyme, chalcone O-methyltransferase (CHOMT), forms a chalcone that is a potent inducer of *Rhizobium* nodulation genes. Over 50 regiospecific O-methyltransferase *sequences* are known, which adds to the diversity of the flavonoids, isoflavanoids, and *hydroxycinnamates* found in plants.

The possibility exists of protein-protein reactions between all of these enzymes, the outcome dependent on many factors controlling their expression. In addition, there are enzymes that are crucial for determining the broad class of flavonoids that are produced (chalcone isomerase for flavanone production, flavanone reductase for flavone production, and isoflavone synthase for the isoflavones).

The highly species-specific nature of many of the biosynthetic steps makes it very difficult to predict the outcome of overexpressing any one enzyme. Instability has been observed in the expression of a transgene that can be exacerbated by environmental factors. Crosses between wild-type and transgenic plants in *Petunia* was exacerbated by *environmental* factors that caused methylation-mediated expression of the transgene.

This result is in contrast to the manipulation of *Arabidopsis* and tobacco with the regulatory gene controlling *pigmentation* in maize. The gene controls the expression of several steps such as CHS and CHI. In all cases, there was a substantial increase in anthocyanin production. Nonetheless, the situation is not *straightforward* and severe oxidative stress symptoms have been observed with plants overexpressing a transcription factor gene.

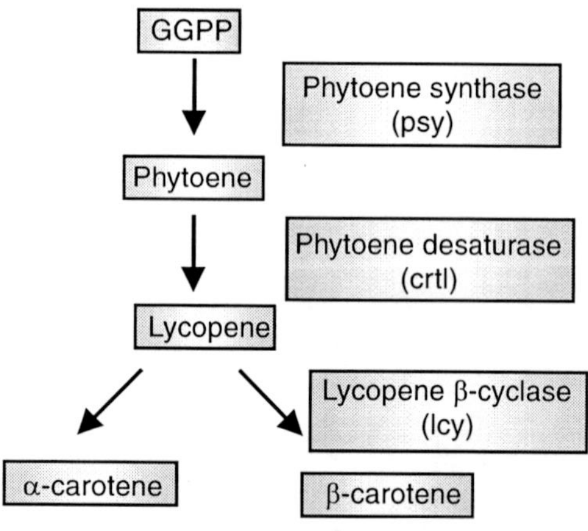

Figure 1.10: Biosynthesis of β-carotene.

Whereas very extensive information is available on the biosynthesis of flavonoids in terms of their induction, regulation, and tissue-specific expression in a wide range of species, very little is known about the *posttranslational* regulation of flavonoid biosynthesis. The simple flavonoids with a single hydroxyl in the B-ring can be extensively modified by hydroxylation, methylation, glycosylation, acylation, and a number of other modifications.

In terms of food quality characteristics, the enzymes that occur at the end of the biosynthetic pathway are likely to be of the greatest interest. The hydroxylases that are responsible for the conversion of kaempferol into quercetin and *subsequently* myricetin or pelargonidin into cyanidin and delphinidin result in an increase in colour, antioxidant activity, and potential *nutritional* value. Similarly the acyl- and methyltransferases increase pigment stability and may increase nutritional value.

The *glycosyltransferases* have an effect on taste (bitterness). Similarly, astringency is determined by the *concentration* and type of tannins, hydrolyzable tannins, and flavan-3-ols. Competing with these reactions are the enzymes that result in a loss of quality of the product, many of which involve some reaction with the phenolics present in the plant. Enzymatic browning is one of the main oxidative reactions leading to an undesirable loss of colour, flavor, and nutrients in some products (e.g., browning of apples or cut salads) and an increase of quality in others (e.g., prunes, dates, and figs).

The principal classes of enzymes involved are the peroxidases (PODs) and *polyphenoloxidases* (PPOs). PPO activity is found in all higher plant tissues and organs. A requirement of the processing of all frozen crops is that they be inactivated by blanching, before freezing, to prevent off-flavors developing as a result of their action and other quality deficits.

No satisfactory genetic *manipulation* approach to reducing their effects has been devised, and this may prove difficult given the important role they play in the overall physiology of the plant. Different plant families produce different chemical classes of PPs. Isoflavanoids are found *predominantly* in the *Leguminosae*, whereas the Solanaceae produce *sesquiterpenes*.

At present it is not possible to transfer the complete sesquiterpene phytoalexin of Solanaceae, such as tobacco, to a legume (or vice versa) as the biochemistry of the complex enzymatic pathways is not fully understood.

Isoflavones are less widely distributed and are found in highest concentrations in the soybean and food products *manufactured* from it. Genistein and daidzein are estrogenic and show a wide range of physiological responses as a consequence, including delaying the menstrual cycle in women and a series of beneficial effects on cardiovascular function and bone loss. Extensive screening of soy varieties is taking place to identify highand low-isoflavone genotypes.

Interestingly, the selection for *agronomically* beneficial allelles also appears to select for the varieties with higher isoflavone levels, providing an example in which the goals of farmers and consumers may be congruent.

The branch pathway for the formation of the isoflavones is almost completely *characterized* and has several common links with that for anthocyan-ins. However, the first reaction specific for isoflavone synthesis is unique.

The *2-hydroxyisoflavanone* synthase (2-HIS), which causes a *2hydroxylation*, couples to an aryl migration of the B-ring of a flavanone. The cloning of 2-HIS offers the possibility of intoducing isoflavone synthesis into other food crops.

The Isoprenoid Pathway

The IP pathway is responsible for the biosynthesis of a vast range of compounds that play a crucial role in maintaining membrane fluidity (sterols), electron transport (ubiquinone), *glycosylation* of proteins (dolichol), and the regulation of cellular development (gibberellins etc.). Terpenoids synthesized via the IP pathway are also used for more specialized purposes including defense (terpene-derived phytoalexins and volatile signals), pollinator attractants (monoterpenes), and *phytoprotectants* (carotenoids).

As far as food quality is concerned, among the most important characteristics determined by the pathway are flavor and aroma as well as colour. Antioxidant benefits are also likely from the carotenoid pathway as well as the capacity of terpenes to protect against the adverse effects of *procarcinogens* by inducing phase II enzymes.

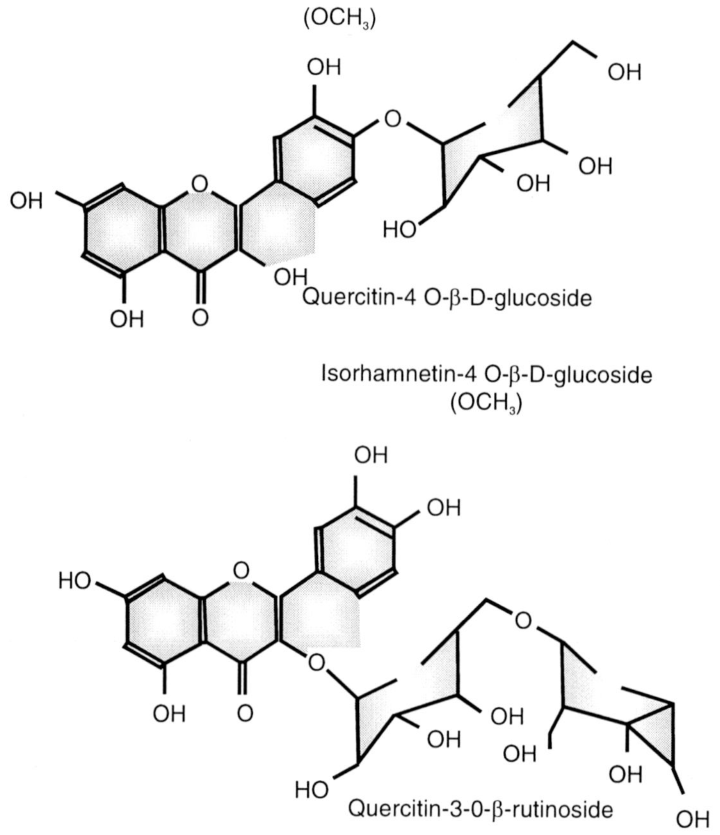

(OCH$_3$)

OH OH O OH OH HO OH O OH OH Quercitin-4 O-β-D-glucoside

Isorhamnetin-4 O-β-D-glucoside (OCH$_3$)

OH OH HO O O O OH O OH OH OH OH HO Quercitin-3-0-β-rutinoside OH

Figure 1.11: Structural features affecting the absorption of flavonoids.

The key metabolite from which this diverse range of chemicals is synthesized is *isopentenyldiphosphate* (IPP). This is formed by two independent pathways. The cytoplasmic acetate-mevalonate pathway appears principally responsible for the synthesis of sterols and *sesquiterpenoids.*

The second pathway-the GAP-pyruvate pathway-is responsible for the synthesis of carotenoids and mono- and diterpenes and is localized within the plastid. An exchange of cytoplasmic and plasticidal metabolites has been found in *Chamomilla recutita* that utilizes both pathways.

The extent to which this occurs could well depend on the tissue type and *developmental* phase, and IPP may move between organelles depending on numerous factors. Elucidation of the enzymology and regulation of the GAP-pyruvate pathway for IPP synthesis is a prerequisite to understanding and rationally *manipulating* terpenoid production in plants.

Multiple isoforms exist of the enzymes that are involved in terpenoid biosynthesis. These isoforms appear to direct subtle control over the biosynthesis of metabolites and can direct synthesis into specific organelles. One of the most important enzymes is 3-hydroxy-3-methylglutarylCoA reductase (HMGR), which is highly regulated and exists in many different isoforms that vary between species and tissues and during development.

A common aspect of the regulation of terpenoid biosynthesis is the coordinated modulation of many *enzymes* to affect necessary changes in flux of metabolites through the different branches of *terpenoid* metabolism.

Cholesterol synthesis in mammals requires the coordinated synthesis of HMG-CoA synthase, HGMR, and FPP synthase. However, the degradative turnover of these enzymes appears to be regulated *independently* of each other. This example of the effect of multiple enzymes to change flux in different pathways of terpenoid metabolism has been *demonstrated* in plants where exposure to specific metabolites can alter the production of either the steroid, glycoalkaloid, or sesquiterpene phytoalexin pathways, depending on the elicitor.

Sterol Biosynthesis

The nutritional interest in this class of phytochemicals derives from the fact that sterols have a similar structure to cholesterol and some sterols have a capacity to reduce the levels of total plasma cholesterol and low-density lipoprotein (LDL)-cholesterol. There has been a dramatic reduction in the morbidity and mortality from cardiovascular diseases with the use of *hypolipidemic* drugs (statins), and the interest in plant sterols lies in their potential to act as a natural, *preventative* dietary product.

The sterols are thought to act through their ability to limit the uptake of cholesterol from the diet as well as their potential to increase *cholesterol* excretion. This knowledge has led to the development of specific foods with *cholesterol-reducing* claims.

These are already marketed in some countries as Benecol® and Take Control®. Sterol biosynthesis begins with the conversion of famesyl *diphosphate* into squalene, which determines the channeling of the isoprenoid pathway into the branches that produce phytosterols.

The sterol pathway involves a sequence of more than 30 enzyme-catalyzed reactions, all of which are membrane linked. Nothing is known about the catabolism of plant sterols. Up-regulation of HMG-CoA in transgenic tobacco, corn, and tomatoes results in the *accumulation* of cycloartenol only, rather than sterols.

Targeting of enzymes upstream from cycloartenol results in a decrease in the total amount of plant sterols with potentially deleterious effects on membrane stability in the plant and the protection against infection. However, pentacyclic triterpenes (such as α- and β-amyrin) are formed by another route from squalene oxide, and inhibition of this route could increase free sterol *concentrations*.

Potential strategies for sterol production are, however, likely to focus on overexpression of terminal enzymes in the pathway. As far as the regulation of enzymes downstream from *cycloartenol* is concerned, the methylation of cycloartenol is a critical rate-limiting step. Inhibition of two of these enzymes, COI and OBT 14DM, leads to the *accumulation* of unusual steroids rather than natural A^5-sterols.

From the food quality perspective, the principal interest is in the *biosynthesis* of sterol esters, which give a more consistent cholesterol-lowering effect than the free sterols. The sitostanol esters were the first shown to be *consistently* effective in lowering cholesterol, but sterol esters appear to be equally effective.

Ideally, stages in the final phases of *biosynthesis* need to be studied to ensure that all the sterols are esterified and thereby ensure that they are more bioavailable.

Carotenoid Biosynthesis

Carotenoids are also derived from the general isoprenoid pathway. The first committed step in the carotenoid pathway is the head-to-head condensation of two *geranylgeranyl* diphosphate (GGPP) molecules to produce phytoene. The three enzymes responsible for converting GGPP into β-carotene are shown in figure elsewhere in this chapter. Carotene is of particular interest because it functions as a *metabolically* well-regulated precursor of vitamin A. Its importance to the health of children in the *developing* world has been discussed elsewhere in this chapter.

Although rice *synthesizes* GGPP, the enzymes required to convert it into b-carotene are not all present. In a *remarkable* feat of genetic *engineering*, three genes encoding these enzymes have been introduced into the endosperm of rice.

Phytoene synthase and phytoene desaturase were introduced using a construct that did not have a selectable marker. This was introduced through the *simultaneous* introduction of another construct, which carried the third gene of interest (lycopene β-cyclase) as well as a selectable antibiotic resistance gene. This *cotransformation* strategy should enable a segregation of the antibiotic resistance gene away from the phytoene synthase and desaturase genes.

This would eliminate one of the major issues that are raised when the safety of genetically *manipulated* foods is discussed. Fortunately, it has already been *demonstrated* that these plants will still produce β-carotene because these authors have demonstrated that plants engineered with standard *transformation* procedures to express only the first two enzymes in the pathway do not accumulate lycopene as would be expected. It seems that the enzymes needed to convert lycopene into β-carotene are *constitutively* expressed in normal rice endosperm or are induced when *lycopene* is formed.

RELATIONASHIP OF STRUCTURE TO NUTRITIONAL QUALITY (BIOAVAILABILITY)

The overall content of a given nutrient in a food is not always a useful indicator of its nutritional value as not all of the nutrient present is absorbed. Nutritionists must concerm themselves with *understanding* the proportion of an available nutrient that is digested, absorbed, and ultimately utilized.

In the case of nutrients or *phytochemicals* whose beneficial effects are directed toward inhibiting degenerative diseases, it is important to know whether or not the nutrient is reaching the particular target organ and in a form that is active. Otherwise, the claims concerning the health benefits of that chemical would not be justified, *especially* as it is difficult to *demonstrate* benefits from long-term human studies.

The diet plays an important role in the uptake of specific nutrients and *phytochemicals*. Those that are lipophilic are absorbed much more readily from a lipid-rich diet. Frying *tomatoes* in oil *dramatically* improves the uptake of lycopene compared with the consumption of fresh tomatoes. Raw carrots, which have high levels of *provitamin A* carotenoids, are poorer sources of b-carotene than gently cooked carrots.

The bioavailability of certain trace elements is increased by cooking or *processing*, such as the increased *bioavailability* of iron in canned spinach. The chemical form of the phytochemical present in food is very important in *determining* the uptake through the *gastrointestinal* tract. Quercetin-β-glucoside is more easily absorbed than the *aglycone* quercetin. Isorhamnetin-b-glucoside, which is chemically similar to quercetin, differing only by a single methoxyl group, is much more readily absorbed.

Flavonoid rutinosides (rhamnosyl 1-6 glucosides) are not easily absorbed. Sterol esters are more bioavailable than the free sterols. The chemical form of the *phytochemical* is of profound importance when considering the biological relevance of specific chemicals and their levels in the diet. Although some phenols might be better *antioxidants* than others when tested in in vitro systems, this is of little significance in terms of health relevance. What matters is whether the compounds are easily absorbed, are not quickly degraded in tissues, and are able to reach the target sites. Flavonoids that are not absorbed undergo extensive *degradation* by gut microorganisms and may play only a limited role in preventing oxidative damage in the colon.

SAFETY AND REGULATORY ISSUES

The safety issues related to new foods created by biotechnology were, until *comparatively* recently, reasonably clear. In general, food plants produced by modern plant breeding techniques were subject to no specific controls. However, the discovery that a new variety of potato (Lenape) with good agronomic *characteristics* contained higher than average levels of the potentially toxic alkaloid solanine was sufficient grounds to withdraw it from commercial use.

Similarly, in Sweden the variety Magnum Bonum was found to contain *potentially* toxic levels of *glycoalkaloids* and was withdrawn. In a number of countries, this led to voluntary codes of practice being adopted with the plant breeding industry to ensure that if there was more than a 10-20% variation in composition, the product would be referred to food safety agencies for evaluation.

As far as plants subject to genetic engineering are concerned, the principal concerns have been focused around the potential *allergenicity* of the modified plant and the use of antibiotic resistance genes for the selection of new strains. The possible variations in overall *composition* and the position to be adopted in terms of the need for safety evaluation have been considered by a number of *international* bodies.

In 1991 the United Nations Food and Agriculture *Organization* (FAO) and the World Health *Organization* (WHO) convened an expert panel to consider strategies for assessing the safety of foods produced by *biotechnology*. The expert panel *recommended* that genetically engineered foods should be evaluated for safety by *comparison* with that of their natural antecedents.

If the composition was similar to that of the traditional food and this food had a safe history of use, then the genetically modified food would be regarded as safe. This led to the concept of "substantial equivalence" being developed following a meeting of the *Organization* for Economic Cooperation and Development.

This concept assumes that if a genetically modified food can be characterized as substantially equivalent, it can be assumed to pose no new health risks and can be marketed without the need to undertake extensive *toxicological* and nutritional studies to determine its safety in use. The principle of substantial equivalence has been adopted into the European Union (EU) Regulation on

Novel Foods and Novel Food Ingredients. The Regulation excludes from its controls foods and food ingredients obtained through traditional *propagating* or breeding practices and which have a history of safe use. Genetically modified plants are considered as "novel" under the terms of the Regulation.

However, the detailed safety evaluation provisions of the Regulation do not apply to foods produced by genetic engineering "if on the basis of the scientific evidence available they are *substantially* equivalent to existing foods with regard to their composition, nutritional value, *metabolism*, intended use, and the level of undesirable substances present."

The Regulation regards food as novel if the *characteristics* of the food differ from the *conventional* food having regard to the accepted limits of natural variation of such characteristics. However, the principle of *substantial equivalence* is vague and difficult to define in many cases.

The U.S. attitude to regulation has so far been to regard safety as an issue that relates to the *characteristics* of the food and not to the process(es) that leads to it. Novel food products, of which products produced by genetic engineering are included in the definition, are not subject to any specific approval on safety grounds if the constituents of the food are the same as or *substantially* similar to those of substances currently found in other foods.

It is clear that it is never going to be possible to argue that a genetically modified plant is safe any more than to argue that a plant produced by conventional plant breeding is safe. The very concept can be addressed only in the context of a history of safe use as a human food. Clearly, the over whelming evidence supports the view that health benefits arise as a consequence of the regular *consumption* of a variety of fruits and vegetables, few if any of which have any close *compositional* relationship to the wild types from which they were bred.

Similarly, their production, storage, and distribution have depended on the use of a wide range of chemical fertilizers and pesticides. These chemicals are extensively tested for safety before approval is given for their *marketing* and use, but this has not removed the widely held view among consumers that "organic products" are better for your health.

There is no evidence to support this view, and any adverse health effects that there might be as a consequence of the use of pesticides appear to be outweighed by the beneficial effects from the *consumption* of fruit and vegetables. What determines "safety" is the overall effect of *consumption* over a period, not the effects of a specific chemical that might be present.

Food Chemical Risk Assessment

The historic approaches to assessing the safety in use of a chemical in the food supply continue in spite of the fact that a growing body of evidence suggests that this is an *inappropriate* way to assess the safety of a chemical that may be present in the diet in only trace amounts. Animal feeding studies of *fundamentally* benign foods cannot be used to determine a doseresponse relationship as in the case of a single chemical. Their usefulness is severely limited because of the differing diets of animals and the need to ensure that test and controls do not differ because of differences in weight or nutritional balance.

Many of the *phytochemicals* that are present in plants might be judged to pose an unacceptable risk if they were subject to the same approval procedures as are applied for synthetic chemicals. The value of doing so is highly questionable. It seems clear that any possible adverse effects of these phytochemicals are neutralized by other protective *phytochemical* factors in the plant. It is possible that the standardized toxicological bioassays do not reflect the mechanisms that are operating in vivo through low-dose exposure to these compounds in the *environment* of the food. The past *application* of toxicology to food chemical risk *assessment* provided a generalized basis for protecting the population.

Such a risk assessement process was strongly influenced by the need to ensure that there were no risks to consumers from the ingestion of food chemicals that were to be used in the production and processing of food. Thus, the only factor to consider was the inherent *toxicological* properties of the compound in question. The inherent *toxicological* properties of the compounds already in food and the influence they might exert in altering the toxicity of the added chemical were not considered.

Neither was it deemed of interest to determine whether, or under what circumstances, the same chemicals might exert some health benefit as opposed to risk. Although the safety in use of any food produced by genetic *manipulation* would be based on nutritionally based *experimentation*, there is likelihood of an insistence on applying traditional animal toxicological bioassays that have been designed to assess risk and not to make risk-benefit assessments.

This is especially so if the food is judged not to be *compositionally* identical to the "traditional food." The assumption that chemicals, be they natural or synthetic, must pose a health risk of some kind, no matter what the dose, should be *challenged*. Risks can arise when exposure to chemicals is high. But it does not follow that there is some degree of residual risk when *exposures* are low.

It is beholden on scientists to demonstrate that this is so through rationally based arguments that have a *biological* validity. Risk evaluation using animal bioassays *invariably* applies rules that overemphasize the likely risks. The process highlights low-level risks and is costly in terms of both manpower and the use of *experimental* animals.

The process might be justified if it resulted in providing consumers with total security over the safety in use of a food or of a chemical, but this is not the outcome. The very use of the word "risk" implies *something* unacceptable to many consumers. The application of extensive and rigorous approval procedures has done little to provide consumers with a sense of security in consuming food produced by using chemicals or other *technologies*.

None of the present methods for assessing safety take into account the fact that food is a complex mixture of chemicals, each of which has the potential to alter the overall risk-benefit ratio of consuming that food. *Assessing* the "risk" of chemicals in isolation and ignoring any *assessment* of "benefit" does not inspire confidence in the scientific process.

Lack of confidence in the scientific basis for regulating chemicals produces a lack of confidence in the regulatory process itself. Unfortunately although it is accepted that animal toxicological bioassays will play a diminishing role in establishing the "*wholesomeness*" of a food, there are presently no alternative or viable substitutes.

There is an urgent need to develop procedures for the safety evaluation of chemicals in food that are more realistic and that are developed from an understanding of the *mechanisms* that are occurring at usual exposure levels rather than on an empirical description of the phenomena and a focus entirely on perceived risk. Failure to do so will provide arguments for the opponents of any uses of genetic *modification* to impede progress toward its use in the development of even healthier plant foods.

CONCLUSIONS

There is little doubt that in terms of global health and nutrition needs, there is an urgent need to develop new plant crops with enhanced levels of iron, vitamin A, iodine, and the essential amino acids. This development will need to take place with plant breeders working closely with *nutritionists*.

The issues that will need to be considered include the magnitude of any *compositional* change that is possible, its potential impact on health, the effect on crop yields and other agronomic issues, the role of the *environment* versus genetic *manipulation* in increasing levels, consumer acceptance, and a thorough analysis of any possible risks.

Such an approach is already being adopted through the activities of the international *agricultural* research centers. For the 10% of the world where there is overnutrition, the major focus of the plant breeding community will have to be on *demonstrating* the importance of their science to benefits that consumers perceive to be worthwhile.

This is almost certainly to require a focus on health and nutrition issues. Any other application of genetic *manipulation* in food production is unlikely to be as effective in overcoming the current antagonism to its use. Again, this will require plant breeding institutes to work as part of *multidisciplinary* teams focused on specific targets that will improve the public health.

Chapter 2

IMPROVED NUTRITIONAL QUALITY

Considering recent controversies about genetically modified crops and genetically modified food, one frequently asked question concerns the real need for such *modifications*, especially if we refer to the first *commercialized* traits such as herbicide or insect resistance and the possible adverse effects of their utilization on the environment.

Creating crops by *transgenesis* with an improved nutritional value may represent a more positive example in the public perception and would result in better public acceptance of *biotechnology*. It can also be *emphasized* that such an approach holds a great deal of promise in terms of attaining more appropriate levels of quality food components, which can be particularly crucial for the developing world. Focusing on food nutritional quality, a series of targets can be identified.

A major goal of plant genetic *engineering* consists of improving the content of essential amino acids of edible crop organs to provide better food for humans and a balanced composition of feeds for domestic animals. Most of this chapter will be devoted to the progress that has been made to improve the amino acid composition of plants and in particular the lysine content.

Important results have also been reported on the qualitative aspects of a human diet, in particular vitamins, micronutrients, and *phytochemicals* relevant to human health. In time, plant *biotechnology* methods could lead to the production of feeds in which no addition of vitamins or minerals would be required.

To prevent deficiencies, the daily intake of such nutrients has to reach minimal levels that have been defined on the basis of the work of nutritionists. Unfortunately, a more or less acute lack of many of these nutrients exists in various countries of the developing world.

The diet of human *populations* is often essentially composed of a major staple food that does not fulfill the *nutritional* norms and may lead to severe illness and impair growth and development, especially in children. We intend to underline strategies that have been developed to improve the nutritive value of food by *increasing* the level of one or another of these nutrients and amino acids.

As such products are built up by the metabolic *machinery* of the plant cell, we will briefly mention a series of approaches that can be applied to redirect the metabolic flux toward increasing the level of a desired product.

Then we will envisage how these methods can be applied to modify the amino acid composition of plant organs through metabolic *engineering*. We will focus on the main limiting amino acids in terms of *nutritional* impact, essentially lysine and threonine in cereals and *sulfurcontaining* amino acids in legumes.

Finally, we will describe methods of improvement beneficial to human nutrition and health with examples concerning increases of vitamin A and E levels and *accumulation* of deficient *micronutrients* such as iron.

STRATEGIES TO MANUPULATE PLANT METABOLIC PATHWAYS TOWARDS THE PRODUCTION OF A DEFINED COMPOUND OF NUTRITIONAL VALUE

The definition of possible targets for *engineering* a primary metabolic pathway implies a sufficient knowledge of the whole pathway in terms of genes and enzymes involved and in particular *identifying* the critical regulatory points in the metabolic route. In the past, such studies have been developed for a series of amino acids as *exemplified* by excellent reviews in books and journals.

This acquired knowledge of the factors controlling the carbon flux through the *pathway*, such as identification of *rate-limiting* steps, enzyme regulation by feedback inhibition or repression versus induction, and the presence of *competitive* branches in the *pathway*, makes it possible to establish adequate strategies for *manipulating* the expression level of key enzymes in the pathway with the goal of provoking changes in flux toward the synthesis of a product.

We can now modify the expression of a gene controlling a *ratelimiting* enzyme by insertion in the plant genome of the *corresponding* homologous or heterologous gene under the control of a strong promoter, expecting that a higher level of the encoded enzyme activity will be obtained. The transgene can also be modified in such a way that it now encodes an enzyme with a higher affinity for the substrate used in the branch leading to the desired compound.

A mutated gene coding for a feedback-insensitive form of the enzyme could be obtained and introduced by transgenesis. This has already been achieved for both plant and microbial genes. Competitive branches of the pathway can be, at least partially, blocked by means of an antisense or knockout approach.

Silencing the genes that exert their effects at or beyond branch nodes is thus an effective way to increase the flux toward the production of the desired *metabolite* by avoiding or at least decreasing a wasteful flow of *intermediary* products in another pathway.

The lack of success in *accumulating* a metabolite can be also related to the fact that its catabolic rate is increased. Here also, antisense and down-regulation approaches may allow us to decrease the effects of such catabolic degradation. These methods that rely on *engineering* of at least some of the genes of the pathway of interest have now been extended to the regulatory network controlling the overall pathway.

The goal is to identify master control points that can influence the expression of a series of structural genes involved in metabolic conversions in the pathway to take advantage of this global effect on the synthesis of the product of interest.

Modifying the expression of a single *transcription* factor may affect the expression level of a battery of *biosynthetic* genes involved in individual branches of a complex *biosynthetic* pathway. Some examples showing the potential of this approach are already available in the case of secondary metabolism and also amino acid biosynthesis.

The increasing availability of regulatory genes and the dissection of signal transduction pathways *influencing* primary metabolism make this type of *methodology* particularly attractive for the biotechnologist. Finally, we also have to take into account the complexity of the biosynthesis we wish to orientate toward a defined direction. In that context, the development of functional genomics will provide us with invaluable information about the changes at the RNA, protein, and metabolite levels that occur when we modify defined steps of a specific pathway.

It will also allow us to monitor the *introduced* changes so that desired alterations remain compatible with the growth and development of the crop. Moreover, we have to mention the possibility of *engineering* not only nuclear genes but also organelle genomes, in particular in the case of plant chloroplastic DNA. Here we can take *advantage* of the impressive increase in the expression of an inserted gene due to the large number of copies present in each leaf cell of the plastid *transformed* plant.

As many steps of amino acid biosynthesis have been located inside the *chloroplast*, this represents a new avenue full of promise for *overexpression* of amino acid metabolism. All the forecast benefits of metabolic engineering may still be limited or annulled by the complexity of the regulation *controlling* many plant biosynthetic pathways that still have to be worked out before we can obtain the production of the desired metabolites *systematically* and reliably.

Besides manipulating gene expression of a pathway, the *compartmentation* of the metabolites in different cellular compartments and their transport inside the cell and to the different plant organs can totally alter the results of *manipulating* the properties of one key enzyme in the pathway.

In particular, better knowledge of how quantifying and directing metabolic flux obtained by nuclear magnetic resonance spectroscopy appears essential.

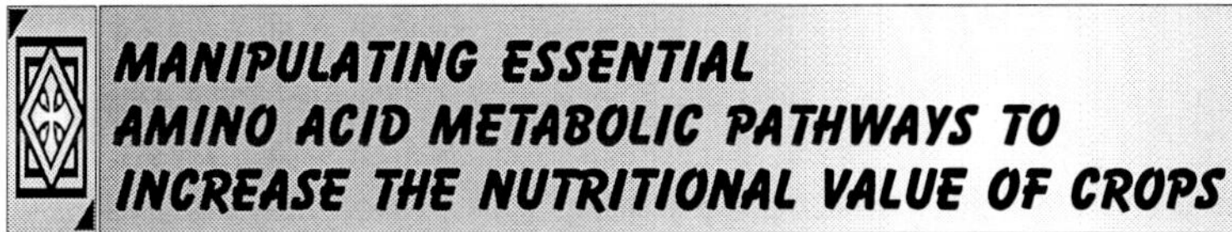

MANIPULATING ESSENTIAL AMINO ACID METABOLIC PATHWAYS TO INCREASE THE NUTRITIONAL VALUE OF CROPS

The nutritional quality of crop plants is determined by their content of essential amino acids provided as proteins in foods for humans or in feed for monogastric animals. Plant proteins are often deficient in some of the 10 essential amino acids that are required in the human and animal

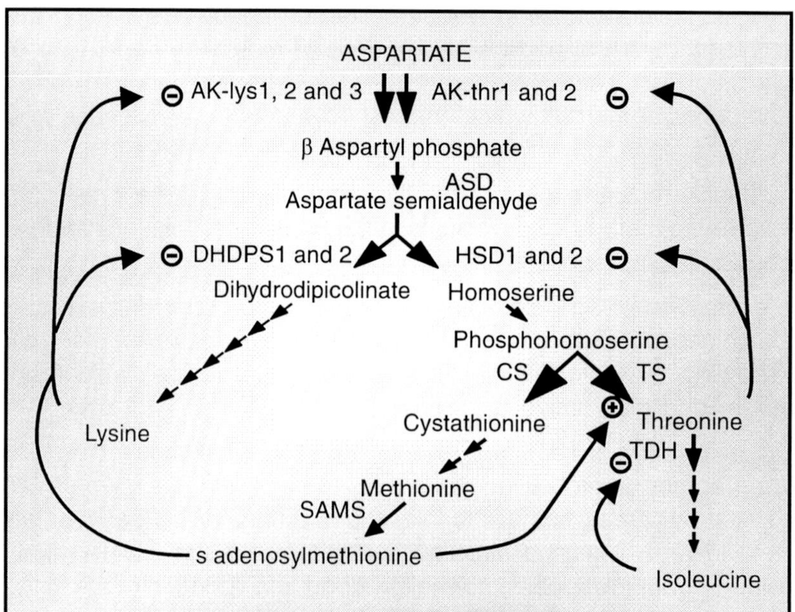

Figure 2.1: The aspartate family biosynthetic pathway. Enzyme abbreviations: AK-lys, aspartate kinase sensitive to lysine feedback inhibition; AK-thr, aspartate kinase sensitive to threonine feedback inhibition: ASD, aspartic semialdehyde dehydrogenase; HSD, homoserine dehydrogenase; DHDPS, dihydrodipicolinate synthase; TS, threonine synthase; TDH, threonine dehydratase; CS, cystathione-gamma-synthase; SAMS, S-adenosyl methionine synthase. Curved arrows indicate regulation loops by the end products. The (-) symbols indicate feedback inhibition and the (+) stimulation of enzyme activity.

diet. In general, cereals are deficient in lysine and legumes in the sulfur amino acids, *methionine* and cysteine. Several approaches have been presented and used with the goal of increasing the relative content of *essential* amino acids in plants, in particular the aspartate-derived amino acids, lysine and threonine. One of the earliest *approaches* consists of *screening* genotypes and induced mutants to identify plants with higher lysine levels in the seed.

This method was first applied *successfully* to maize and led to the high-lysine opaque-2 type . Later, similar types of mutants were reported in barley and *Sorghum*. The increase in total lysine content was due to a shift in the spectrum of storage proteins to the benefit of *lysinerich* albumins and globulins instead of lysine-poor prolamines.

However, this type of mutation was accompanied by a drastic reduction in yield and protein content. The introduction of gene transfer technologies opened new ways to alter the amino acid *composition* of the seed proteins, in cereals and legumes in particular.

In this case, genes encoding storage proteins naturally rich in essential amino acids or engineered genes leading to the production of "synthetic" proteins displaying a high content of defined essential amino acids were expressed in transgenic plants under the control of suitable promoters. In order to modify the *nutritional* value *significantly*, the foreign proteins must constitute a high percentage of the total proteins, so that in addition to high levels of transcription and *translation*, the stability of the additional proteins is crucial.

As underlined by Galili et al., although numerous attempts founded on such strategies have been reported, a significant, reliable *accumulation* of a stable nutritionally valuable protein still has to be convincingly demonstrated. In that context, it is worthwhile to mention the work of Chakraborty et al. on the expression in potato of an *AmA-l* gene coding for a seed-specific albumin from *Amaranthus hypochondriacus* with a well-balanced amino acid composition.

The authors reported that when this gene was put under the control of a granule-bound starch synthase promoter, a striking increase in most essential amino acids present in potato tubers was observed. Unexpectedly, the growth and production of tubers as well as the total protein content of this *accumulation* organ were significantly increased.

An alternative method consists of producing plants containing elevated levels of specific amino acids by *manipulating* their metabolism. This can be achieved through alteration of key enzymes from those biosynthetic pathways by mutation and transformation. We have focused on the *aspartatederived* amino acid biosynthetic pathway producing the four essential amino acids lysine, threonine, isoleucine, and methionine. Considerable research, aided by genetic engineering, has been devoted to this pathway, its enzymes, and their regulation with the aim of *optimizing* amino acid content.

Biochemical Regulation of Lysine and Threonine Biosynthesis

Higher plants synthesize lysine, threonine, isoleucine, and *methionine* from the common precursor aspartate via a complex branched pathway. Understanding the inner regulation taking place during this process is essential with respect to knowledge of basic plant *metabolism* but also to possibly modifying the nutritional value of crops. Close *examination* of the lysine and threonine biosynthesis revealed the existence of several enzymatic steps feedback controlled by these two end products.

Essentially, two enzymes play key regulatory roles in the pathway: aspartate kinase (AK), the first enzyme of the overall pathway, which is *retroinhibited* by either lysine or threonine, and *dihydrodipicolinate* synthase (DHDPS), the first enzyme of the lysine-specific branch, which is severely inhibited by lysine. The main limiting step in lysine production appears to occur at the DHDPS level via the feedback control exerted by lysine (K, between 5 and 20 AM).

Most of the biosynthetic enzymes of the pathway have been localized in the plastids on the basis of biochemical data and molecular evidence from genes encoding the majority of the *biosynthetic* enzymes, in which putative *chloroplastic* transit peptides have been identified.

Mutants Overproducing Free Lysine or Threonine

We will now focus on an approach based, as previously mentioned, on the deregulation of biosynthetic pathways of such essential amino acids, in particular in the case of lysine and threonine. In various species, mutants *accumulating* lysine or threonine in the soluble amino acid pool have been isolated by selecting for growth in the presence of the lysine amino acid analogue S-2-(aminoethyl)-l-cysteine (AEC) or toxic combinations of lysine and threonine in the culture medium.

Although threonine *overproduction* was detected in all tissues analyzed and in particular in seeds, the increase of free lysine was noticeable only in leaves and calli. Moreover, an aberrant phenotype characterized by reduction of the foliar surface, absence of shoot elongation, and sterility was observed when high levels of free lysine *accumulated* (25% and more of the total free amino acid pool).

The accumulation of both amino acids in leaves is also dependent on the *developmental* stage, reaching a maximum at shoot elongation. The biochemical *characterization* of these mutants has shown that we are dealing with deregulation at the level of the two key enzymes, DHDPS in the lysine overproducer mutant and AK in the threonine overproducer. These mutated forms are both fully insensitive to feedback inhibition by the respective amino acid.

Key Genes of the Lysine and Threonine Pathways

Aspartate Kinase Genes

At least five forms of aspartokinase have been identified in plants and may be classified on the basis of their differential feedback properties. One gene coding for a threonine-sensitive form (ak,-hsd,) was isolated by heterologous hybridization in *Arabidopsis thaliana*. The deduced amino acid sequence revealed the presence of a second region corresponding to the enzyme activity of homoserine dehydrogenase (HSD), the first committed enzyme in the branch of the pathway that leads to threonine synthesis.

We are thus dealing with a gene coding for a *bifunctional* protein with an AK activity at the NH_2-side and an HSD activity at the COOH-terminus. The expression of the A. *thaliana* ak,-hsd, gus gene was elevated in an array of young plant tissues containing actively growing cells (meristems, young leaves, cortical and vascula r stem tissues, anthers, gynoecium, developing seeds).

During the development of the embryo its expression appeared coordinated with the initiation

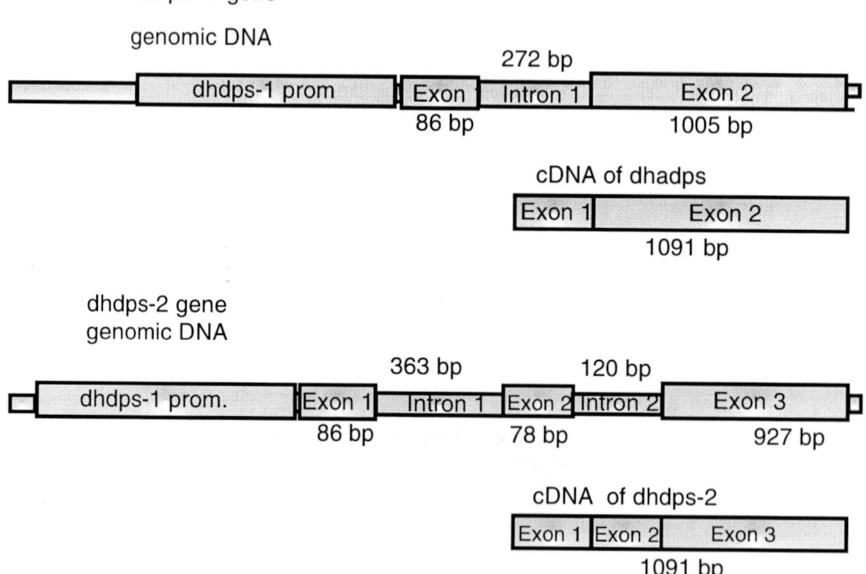

Figure 2.2: Structure of the dhdps-1 and dhdps-2 genes and cDNAs. prom, promoter; bp, base pair.

and onset of storage protein synthesis. A second gene showing a high identity (82%) with the ak,-hsd, nucleotide sequence was identified in a bacterial artificial chromosome (BAC) clone [European Molecular Biology Laboratory (EMBL bank)] and localized as ak_2-hdh_2 on chromosome 4 of the *A. thaliana* genome. As the major part of the AK activity is sensitive to feedback inhibition by lysine, attempts have been made to clone the corresponding genes.

Degenerated primers *corresponding* to conserved motifs between lysine-sensitive bacterial AKs were used to clone two genes *(ak-lysl* and *ak-lys2)* encoding monofunctional AKs in *A. thaliana.* The presence of two nuclear genes both encoding AK-lys proteins and both targeted to the chloroplast, as shown by the presence of a transit peptide, but with only 70% identity at the deduced amino acid level raises questions about their respective roles in plant development.

Therefore, *A. thaliana* and *Nicotiana tabacum* have been *transformed* with the 5' upstream region of either *ak*lys gene fused with the *uidA* reporter gene encoding glucuronidase (GUS). In *A. thaliana,* a comparison of the GUS patterns of *ak-lysl* and *ak-lys2* revealed strongly predominant expression of *ak-lys2* over *ak-lysl.*

Throughout the vegetative phases, *ak-lys2-GUS* expression reached a high level, especially in the vasculature, whereas *ak-lysl-GUS* plants showed a markedly reduced intensity of the histochemical staining. In the reproductive phase, both genes were well expressed in flowers, *ak-lys2* was the only one expressed in the fruits, and no staining could be detected in seeds in both cases.

The physical position of *ak-lysl* and *ak-lys2* could be assigned to chromosome 5 at two different loci at a distance of 2 cM. The *Arabidopsis ak-lys* gene family is thus composed of at least two different members. We identified a third *ak-lys* gene located on chromosome 3 of *Arabidopsis* using the Blast program to screen databases.

The deduced *ak-lys3* amino acid sequence showed higher identity with the *ak-lys2* (82.8%) than with the *ak-lysl* (68%) peptide sequence. The *ak-lys3* gene was reported to be highly expressed in leaf vein tissues. The isolation and characterization of *A. thaliana* mutants displaying an AK-HSD isozyme less sensitive to threonine inhibition or an AK-lys isozyme less sensitive to lysine feedback inhibition will make it possible to identify at the nucleotide level mutations that lead to threonine *accumulation.*

After incorporation into the corresponding copy DNA (cDNA), these mutated plant genes can be respectively expressed in an appropriate construct to obtain threonine accumulation in specific tissues, especially in seeds.

Cloning and Characterization of Wild-Type and Mutant Genes Encoding Dihydrodipicolinate Synthase

A mutant of *Nicotiana sylvestris* (*RAEC*-1) was shown to overproduce lysine because of a mutation in the DHDPS gene that causes the DHDPS enzyme to be insensitive to the normal feedback inhibition of lysine. The dhdps-rl mutation was identified as a *substitution* of two nucleotides changing asparagine in isoleucine in a conserved region of the protein.

In maize, a series of single amino acid substitutions were found to eliminate lysine inhibition of DHDPS. DHDPS-encoding sequences were cloned by functional *complementation* in a bacterial DHDPS-deficient strain. This first isolated clone made it possible to obtain and sequence a full-length *Arabidopsis* DHDPS cDNA. Constructs derived from the *Arabidopsis* cDNA allowed the generation through ethyl methane sulfonate in vitro mutagenesis of clones encoding fully *insensitive* forms of the DHDPS protein. Furthermore, the clones successfully isolated by functional *complementation* in a DHDPS-deficient *E. coli* mutant were all found to encode insensitive enzyme forms, which means that *complementation* selects for insensitive DHDPS plant enzymes.

In soybean, three mutants were constructed containing specific amino acid *substitutions* that lead to lysine-desensitized DHDPS. In a further step, the *Arabidopsis* promoter has been isolated and fused with the reporter gene gus to study the transcription properties of this upstream sequence.

Expression of *GUS* was detected in meristems and vascular tissues of roots, in vascular tissues of stems and leaves, and in the meristems of young shoots. In flowers, high expression was found in the carpels, pollen grain, and young embryos but not in endosperm of mature seeds.

No lysineinduced repression of the *dhdps* gene could be detected. An *Arabidopsis* genomic sequence encoding a second DHDPS enzyme was identified by screening the EMBL database. The *dhdps-2* coding sequence shows 84% identity with the nucleotide sequence of *dhdps-1*. The genomic *dhdps-2* sequence contains three exons and two introns, whereas only one intron and two exons are present in *dhdps-1*. Comparison of the promoter regions of *dhdps-1* and *dhdps-2* did not reveal boxes with any significant conservation.

The two *Arabidopsis* genes were localized on chromosome 2 for *dhdps-2* and chromosome 3 for *dhdps-1*. That *dhdps-2* encodes a functional protein was shown by the growth on a nonsupplemented medium of an *E. coli* DHDPS-deficient strain transformed with the *dhdps-2* apoprotein coding sequence.

Activity tests performed in the presence of increasing concentrations of lysine proved that the DHDPS-2 enzyme is also strongly feedback inhibited, with a 50% loss of activity at 30 μM lysine. Via promoter-GUS fusion, expression of the *dhdps-2* gene was observed during the whole *developmental* cycle and appears to be quite similar to that observed for the *dhdps-1* gene, although the *dhdps-2* gene is in general a little more expressed. DHDPS-2 activity was strongly detected in the vasculature of stems and leaves, in carpels, and in developing seeds.

Improving Lysine and Threonine Accumulation via Transfer of Bacterial Genes

The availability of bacterial and plant genes encoding feedback-insensitive enzymes allowed redirecting the expression of these genes in plants and in particular in storage organs. Initial *experiments* made use of constructs monitored by the strong cauliflower mosaic virus (CAMV) promoter harboring a bacterial *dapA* gene that encodes a DHDPS partially or fully feedback insensitive and mutated alleles of the *E. coli lysC* gene encoding a feedbackinsensitive AK.

Transgenic lines have been obtained in tobacco, potato, barley, *Arabidopsis,* and oilseed rape and soybean. As previously mentioned for *Nicotiana sylvestris* mutants, expression in tobacco of the bacterial AK led to *accumulation* of free threonine not only in vegetative tissues and in tubers in the case of potato but also in reproductive organs and seeds.

In the case of the bacterial DHDPS, the lysine *overproduction,* although present in vegetative tissues, was not expressed in mature seeds. Constitutive *overexpression* of the bacterial DHDPS gene was also accompanied by phenotypical alteration of the transgenic plants, as observed with the selected *N. sylvestris* mutants, at least when a high lysine level was reached.

Targeting the expression of these bacterial genes to sink organs such as seeds was then proposed as a way to alleviate such deleterious effects. Expression of the chimeric AK and DHDPS gene under the control of the β-phaseolin promoter obtained from the bean gene coding for this seed protein was thus evaluated.

Transgenic tobacco seeds showed an important increase in free threonine but no significant change in the amount of lysine in mature seeds, although the activity of bacterial feedbackinsensitive DHDPS was clearly higher than the DHDPS activity measured in *nontransformed* plants.

This lack of lysine *accumulation* in tobacco seeds was then ascribed to enhanced lysine catabolism as shown by higher activities of the major lysine catabolism enzyme lysine-ketoglutarate reductase (LKR). We have to underline that the lysine content present in mature seeds of transgenic plants appears to be the result both of increased *accumulation* due to high activity of a feedback-insensitive DHDPS and of the rate of lysine catabolism.

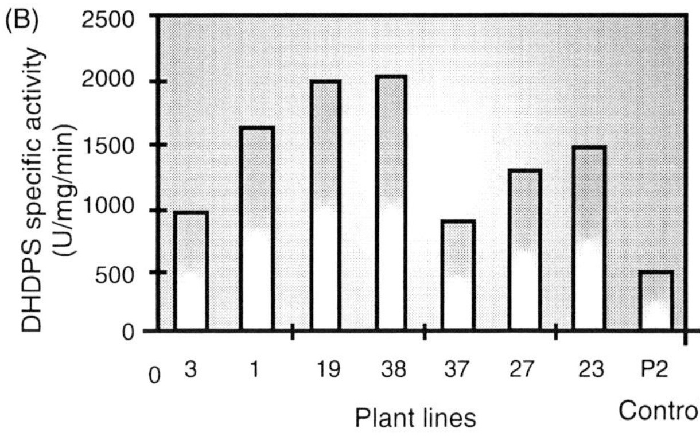

Figure 2.3: (A) Effect of lysine on DHDPS activity in leaf extracts of transgenic and wild-type (P2) Nicotiana plumbaginifolia plants. (B) DHDPS activity in leaves from transgenic lines and wild-type P2 plants.

According to the balance between enhanced *biosynthesis* and induced catabolic degradation, the *accumulation* of lysine in seeds may vary among plant species.

This is best shown by the results obtained by Falco et al. and Mazur et al. when similar bacterial ak and *dhdps* genes were *transformed* into oilseed rape and soybean. Alone or combined with AK, expression of the bacterial DHDPS resulted in a dramatic increase of free lysine (10-100 times the level of nontransformed plants) with a *significant* effect on the total lysine content, which increased more than twice.

In these last cases, *accumulation* of catabolic products such as saccharopine and α-aminoadipic acid was eventually observed but only at a minor level. However, in maize, when the bacterial AK and DHDPS were expressed with an endosperm or an embryo-specific promoter, lysine accumulation was detected only in the embryo but was sufficient to raise the overall lysine *concentration* in seed by 50 to 100%.

Bacterial enzymes can thus be expressed with success in vegetative and sink organs such

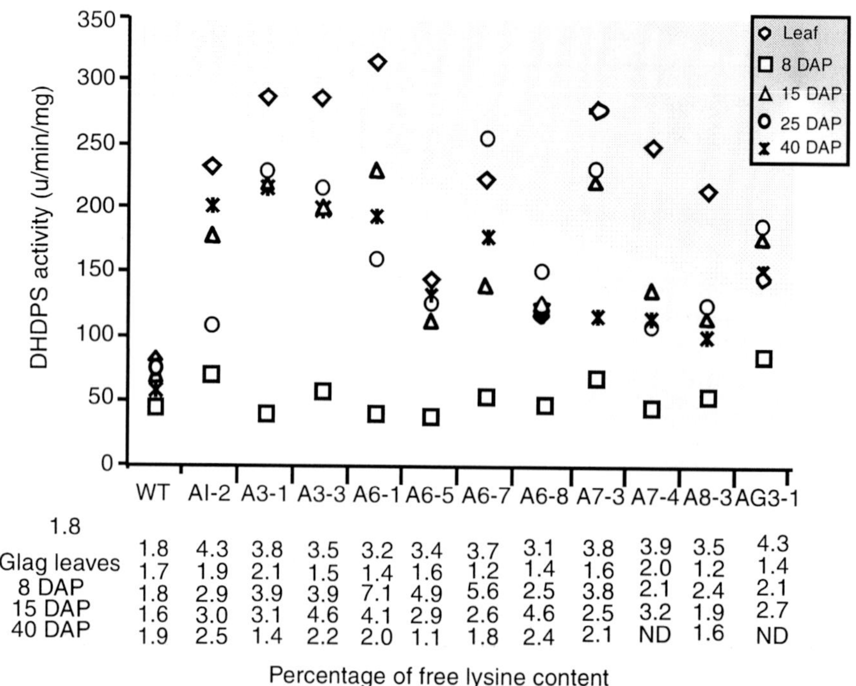

Figure 2.4: DHDPS specific activity measured in flag leaves and seeds of Sorghum, harvested on wild-type plants (WT) and T2 progenies of transformants (from A 1-2 to A G-3) at different developmental stages. Seeds were collected at 8, 15, 25, and 40 days after pollination (DAP) and were analyzed for DHDPS activity. Values at the bottom represent the percentage of lysine in the free amino acid pool. Each value is the mean of three independent assays from three individual T2 plants in each line.

as seeds leading to deep modifications in lysine metabolism.

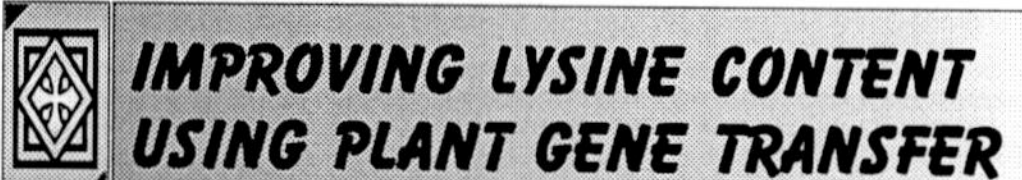

IMPROVING LYSINE CONTENT USING PLANT GENE TRANSFER

The cloning of mutated plant genes provided similar tools for metabolic *engineering* of plants. With the goal of increasing lysine *production*, several chimeric constructs harboring the *dhdps-rl* mutated allele have been developed under the control of the 35S CAMV promoter as well as tuber- or seed-specific promoters and transferred in a model species *(Nicotiana plumbaginifolia)* and crops such as *Solanum tuberosum* and *Sorghum bicolour.*

In *N. plumbaginifolia,* overexpression of the mutated *dhdps-rl* gene led to significant lysine *overproduction* in vegetative tissues, flowers, and immature seeds. Thus, the insensitivity of the mutated enzyme to feedback inhibition is critical for *accumulating* lysine, but the level of the enzyme also plays an important role in the increased lysine synthesis.

Transformants with high DHDPS activities are also characterized by high free lysine levels. The K_m and V of DHDPS thus represent determinant factors in the monitoring of lysine biosynthesis *(E. Haryanto, personnal communication)*. Constitutive overproduction of this insensitive DHDPS was

Table 2.1: Levels of Lysine Overproduction in Seeds of Some Transgenic Crops (Fold Increase Compared with Untransformed Control) As Refers to Amino Acids

Plant species	Inserted genes	Lysine	
		Free aa	Total aa
Brassica *napus*	*Corynebacterium dhdps*	3.1–140	1–1.75
Brassica napus	Corynebacterium dhdps + E. coli ak	4.7–38	1–2.0
Glycine max	Corynebacterium dhdps	12–25	1.25
Glycine max	Corynebacterium dhdps + E. coli ak	335	0.9–4.7
Hordeum sativum	E. coil dhdps	2	1.05

accompanied by abnormal phenotypes (multiple shoots, linear leaves, partial sterility) at least when high free lysine contents were reached in the transgenic plants, as already mentioned for lysine *overproducer* mutants of *Nicotiana sylvestris* and transgenic tobacco plants.

In potato, the same gene was introduced under the control of a patatin promoter to confine the lysine overproduction to tubers. In 23 analyzed tranformants, the range of lysine content varied from 0.9 to 13.7% of the total free amino acids while the control variety displayed a mean value of 2.6%.

Thus, *transformation* of potato resulted in a fivefold increase in free lysine content without any noticeable *modifications* in tuber structure and production. The properties of transgenic sorghum plants expressing the mutated *dhdps-rl* gene of *N. sylvestris* under the control of the 35S CAMV promoter were also determined.

Transgenic plants were produced by introduction of the gene into *Sorghum* immature embryos by microprojectile bombardment. These embryos were then selected on the lysine analogue 2-aminoethyl-Lcysteine (AEC) from callus initiation up to regenerated roots. As a result of the expression of the gene, an active DHDPS enzyme insensitive to feedback inhibition was produced in the primary transformants and their progenies.

In leaves of *transgenic* plants, a low but significant increase of lysine (1.5 to 2.5 times more than the control) could be associated with the expression level of the ectopic *dhdps-rl* gene. *Sorghum* seeds also synthesized higher levels of free lysine than observed in the original cultivar during the first phase of their development, from 15 to 25 days after pollination.

However, toward maturity the lysine content of transgenic seeds decreased and was almost comparable to the control value. This evaluation during maturation can be ascribed to enhanced lysine catabolism, as already mentioned for transgenic tobacco plants. A similar observation has been reported in corn, in which the expression of the deregulated bacterial *dhdps* gene under the control of an endosperm-specific promoter did not lead to any lysine accumulation.

The presence of LKR activity has been *demonstrated* in immature endosperm in maize and also in *Sorghum* seeds in our laboratory. In conclusion, these results show clearly that although we are dealing with a complex, highly regulated biosynthetic pathway leading from aspartate to four essential amino acids, the overexpression of a single gene encoding a feedback-insensitive form of the key DHDPS enzyme exerts a significant effect on the carbon flux through the aspartate pathway toward lysine.

This *accumulation* of lysine was in some species accompanied by phenotypical alterations, which should be avoided when this method is applied to crops. Organ-specific *overproduction* of lysine and threonine through the use of specific promoters can overcome the limitations due to the constitutive expression of deregulated genes in transgenic plants.

Although lysine synthesis can be increased in plants, the level of free lysine in mature seeds may be determined not only by the efficiency of the biosynthetic pathway (in terms of activity of a feedback-insensitive DHDPS) but also by the stability of the amino acid accumulated in the free pool.

In this case, the increased lysine catabolism due to the induction of LKR in endosperm tissues is a limiting factor leading to the reduction of free lysine *accumulation*. The genes encoding the two first catabolic enzymes, LKR and saccharopine dehydrogenase, have been cloned from *Arabidopsis* and maize. Therefore, by using an antisense or cosuppression approach, it might be possible to reduce the expression of LKR and the buildup of lysine degradation products.

Another complementary approach will be to produce transgenic plants, in particular cereals, that altogether overproduce free lysine and express genes encoding lysine-rich proteins in seeds. This would provide a sink for stable *accumulation* of the increased lysine supply as bound amino acid in the endosperm lysine-rich proteins, avoiding the induction of strong catabolic activity.

Manipulating Plant Micronutrients to Benefit Human Health and Nutrition

Plant foods also contribute to ensuring *sufficient* essential vitamins and minerals for the human diet. Such micronutrients are often poorly represented in staple crops, and attempts have been developed to increase the synthesis of these *compounds* by isolating genes required for their *synthesis* and *overexpressing* them under the control of pertinent promoters.

Lack of vitamin A and vitamin E and iron deficiency are common problems in developing as well as in developed countries, involved in a series of illnesses, *particularly* in children. In the major staple food rice, *provitamin* A is not *synthesized* in the endosperm, which represents the main part of the seed.

The latest precursor of the provitamin A carotenoid is geranylgeranyl diphosphate (GGPP). *Theoretically*, the synthesis of β-carotene from this early intermediate would require the expression of four additional enzymes: phytoene synthase, phytoene desaturase, carotene desaturase, and lycogene β-cyclase.

A phytoene synthase gene originating from daffodil was associated in a vector with the sequence coding for a bacterial phytoene desaturase that is capable of introducing the required double bonds. Lycopene β-cyclase from *daffodil* was carried by another vector, and cotransformed rice plants were selected.

The relevant genes were placed under the control of an endosperm-specific glutelin promotor or the constitutive CAMV 35S promoter in the case of phytoene *desaturase*. Transgenic rice harboring this combination of genes produced seeds with a yellow endosperm indicating *carotenoid* formation. Biochemical analysis confirmed the presence of provitamin A at a level of at least 2 µg/g in homozygous lines, which should ensure the necessary daily amount of vitamin A in a typical Asian rice diet (300 g of rice per day).

The grain known as golden rice is expected to be *beneficial* to people suffering from vitamin A deficiency. In the case of vitamin E, the example illustrates the power of a genomics-based approach. The final step of the pathway is of special interest here because the methylation of γ-tocopherol to α-tocopherol, the *biologically* active form of the vitamin E, is performed by γ-tocopherol methyl-transferase (γ-TMT), whose activity is a limiting factor in many seeds.

Therefore, the objective was to clone the *corresponding* gene and to *overexpress* it in seeds. This was made possible by a genomics-based approach by identifying probable orthologs of the γ-TMT of *Arabidopsis* using the protein sequence of a *cyanobacterium Synechocystis,* which also synthesizes α-tocopherol. In transgenic *Arabidopsis* plants overexpressing the γ-TMT enzyme, more than 95% of the total tocopherol pool was in the form of α-tocopherol whereas the wild-type seeds contain practically only γ-tocopherol.

Similar *manipulations* can now be used to improve the vitamin E level of important crops such as rapeseed, maize, and soybean. Iron deficiency is also a significant *nutritional* problem for 30% of the world population. Rice endosperm contains only low amounts of iron, which, combined with a high content of phytate (an inhibitor of iron *resorption* in the intestine), causes a dietary iron *deficiency* in *populations* with a rice-based diet.

One approach has been to express under the control of glutelin promoter a soybean gene coding for a ferritin protein used as a storage form of iron. Transgenic seeds have been shown to accumulate three times more iron than seeds from a control line.

With this modification can also be associated the reduction of phytate concentration in cooked rice via a transgene coding for a *thermotolerant* phytase from *Aspergillus fumigates.* Both vitamin A and iron-rich traits can be combined by sexual crossing, and such material is available for noncommercial use to developing countries. The low availability of phosphorus (P) in many soils is an important factor limiting agricultural production worldwide.

In an approach for developing novel crop varieties more efficient in the use of P, Lopez-Bucio et al. engineered plants able to produce more organic acids and in particular citrate by overexpressing a bacterial citrate synthase coding sequence in tobacco.

Citrate-overproducing plants yield more leaf and fruit biomass when grown under P-limiting conditions and require less P fertilizer to achieve optimal growth. In conclusion, we think that in time genetic *engineering* may lead to varieties carrying all the additional vitamins and minerals required in foods and feeds.

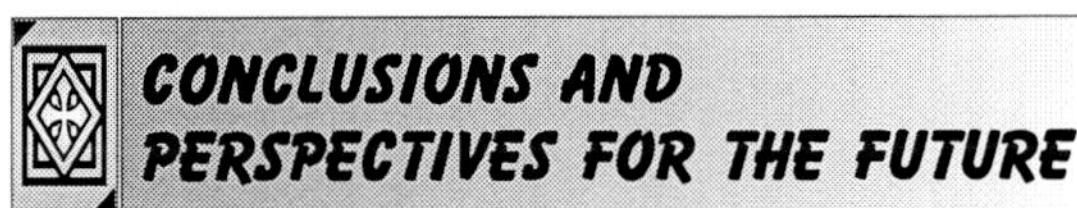

CONCLUSIONS AND PERSPECTIVES FOR THE FUTURE

Transgenic crops with improved nutritional value have already been produced by overexpressing homologous, heterologous, and eventually mutated genes involved in key steps of the metabolism of amino acids and vitamins. In the case of lysine and threonine, overproduction of these essential amino acids has been achieved by the expression of feedback-insensitive AK and DHDPS enzymes.

We stress that the overexpression of a single gene encoding a *feedback-desensitized* DHDPS exerts a significant effect on the flux through the aspartate-derived amino acid pathway toward lysine. With regard to metabolic engineering, this example is quite notable although direct *extrapolation* to other metabolic pathways will not necessarily meet with success.

Rigidity of the metabolic network, functional redundancy of genes, and posttranscriptional control processes can alter the expected results and lead to undesirable side effects. The desired metabolite may be degraded, limiting its accumulation, as exemplified for lysine in seeds of at least some plant species. Another constraint concerns the number of genes that have to be transferred in the recipient plant genome to reach or/and optimize the accumulation of a valuable product.

Coordinated *alterations* of rate-limiting enzymes associated with the overexpression of master regulatory genes will probably contribute to increasing the metabolic flux toward the desired metabolite. However, the expression of multiple genes involved in a complex biosynthetic pathway will require the development of vector systems and methods ensuring the integration and stable expression of gene batteries in the plant genome.

Further progress in *enhancing* the nutritional quality of crops will also rely on emerging technologies, and we can anticipate decisive advances through functional genomics, DNA *microarray* technology, and metabolic flux analysis to obtain more insight into *metabolic* networks and their regulation in plants.

It is important to obtain more information on metabolic sites of synthesis and storage and on *metabolite* transport between organs to learn how to exploit the possibilities offered by *biochemical* engineering and to apply them to *metabolic* processes relevant to the nutritional quality of crops.

3 Chapter

MODIFYING SACCHARIDES

Carbohydrates are a ubiquitous part of human and animal diets. Their *abundance* and omnipresence are difficult to overestimate. Carbohydrates provide clothing and shelter as the cellulose of cotton and wood, a means of *communications* as the cellulose of paper, dietary nutrients and fiber as starch and b-glucans, and the basis for most beverages ranging from fruit juice and soft drinks to cognac.

The starch of most plant-derived foods and beverages is derived from either seeds or tubers. The properties of these are determined largely by their carbohydrate and protein components. Humans throughout time, from the earliest hunter-gatherers to today's consumer, have chosen specific foodstuffs and processed them for consumption, generally unknowingly, in a way reflecting the *functionality* of their carbohydrate components.

Starch, as the major edible carbohydrate component of foods, a major industrial feedstock, and the most abundant edible biopolymer, attracts the greatest attention as well regarding its functional properties and the possibilities for their modification.

Besides their importance for food and beverage, plant carbohydrates are *increasingly* used in many industrial sectors including the production of *biodegradable* plastics. They can be seen as a "green" alternative to hydrocarbon-based polymers.

Carbohydrates contribute to many of the properties of novel "functional foods," ranging from *sweetening* to flavor *enhancement*, fat replacement, dietary fiber *supplementation*, texture *preservation*, and edible packaging. This chapter will concentrate on the synthesis and transgenic modification of α–glucans, in *particular* starch, and fructans in plants and leave aside the β-glucans including cellulose.

APPROACHES TO STARCH AND CARBOHYDRATE MODIFICATION

The various applications require starches with different *properties*, whether as raw starch granules, as gelatinized (cooked) starch, or as various hydrosylates. Suitable *starches* can be found by selecting either the appropriate plant source (tuber vs. grain), the particular plant variety, or the specific *postharvest* treatment.

Postharvest, chemical or *enzymatic* alteration ("modification") of starch structure and hence properties has begun to be replaced with alternative strategies. *Conventional* breeding is one approach. If germplasm with the desired properties exists, easily scored and closely linked markers are needed for *introgression* of the requisite genes into a breeding line with good agronomic *characteristics*.

Furthermore, a rapid screening method is needed for the trait. Often, insufficient variation in storage *carbohydrate* properties can be found in the existing germplasm pool for a given crop. In this case, another option is to create the exotic germplasm by transgenic methods. There are basically four *approaches* to *transgenic modification*.

The first is to change the quantity of *carbohydrates* in a seed or storage organ. Altering the relationship between the export strength of the carbohydrate source (generally, leaves) and the import strength of the carbohydrate sink (tubers, seeds) not only generally affects carbohydrate quantity and *ultimately* harvest yield but also may affect quality and *downstream* applications.

Modulation of the expression levels or *introduction* of the biosynthetic enzymes, or introduction of novel forms with different catalytic properties, for an existing pathway such as starch biosynthesis is a broad second category of approaches. Another is the *expression* of *degradative*, glucolytic or glycolytic *activities* to alter the structure of a native *carbohydrate*.

Lastly, an entirely novel pathway of branch can be introduced based on the metabolites present in the target tissue. These approaches will be *examined* in turn. Because starch is the major storage *carbohydrate* in plants, we shall concentrate on its biosynthesis, properties, and their *modification*.

STARCH STRUCTURE

Amylose and Amylopectin, the Two Components of Starch

Virtually all of the starch used by humans is storage starch, that which *accumulates* in seeds and tubers, and our knowledge of starch *structure* is mainly based on studies of this. Starch consists of two components, amylose and amylopectin, both of which are largely α–1,4-linked glucan polymers. Starch *structure* has been subject to many general reviews.

Generally, amylose constitutes 20-30% of the total and contains rare, α–1,6 branches, whereas amylopectin, which has frequent α–1,6 branches, makes up the rest. *Amylopectin* consists of linear, α–1,4-linked glucan chains *frequently* branched by α–1,6 bonds.

The average chain length (degree of polymerization, DP) in amylopectin is on average 21-25 *glucoses* which, because of the frequent branching, yields a weight-average *molecular* weight

Table 3.1: Starch Components and Their Properties

Property	***Amylose***	***Amylopectin***	***Phytoglycogen***
Degree of branching	Branches rare	Branched	Highly branched
Solubility in water	Insoluble	Insoluble	Soluble
Limiting viscosity number mL $(mg)^{-1}$	240-390	185-188	
Iodine affinity, mg I_2 (100 mg)$^{-1}$ starch	19-19.9	0.33-1.5	
Molecular size	10^5-10^6	10^7-10^8	10^7
Glucose residues (DP)	~103	~105-106	~10^5
Average chain length (CL)	100-1800	18-25	10-14
A-chains/B-chains		1.0-1.5	0.6-1.1
Iodine colouration (λ_{max})	660	530-550	430-450
β-amylolysis limit (%)	~70	~55	~30-45
α-amylolysis limit (%)	~100	~90	~80

(M_W) for amylopectin about 300 times larger than that of amylose. The branch points are not randomly *distributed* within amylopectin but rather are clustered. The chains of amylopectin are classified as the C-chain, the "core" chain *containing* the only reducing glucose in the molecule; the B-chains, which branch from the C-chain; and the A–chains, which are defined as the *outermost* branches of the molecule.

Progressive amylolytic digestion followed by *chromatography* has shown that the *B-chains* are *distributed* in several size classes. Chains of DP 15-20 are found in the linear portions of clusters, whereas chains of DP 45-60 extend between clusters.

A third form of starch, the highly branched "phytoglycogen," appears in certain mutants and is now thought to be an *intermediate* in the *biosynthesis* of amylopectin. The general properties of these *components* are *presented* in table elsewhere in this chapter.

Starch Granules

Starch is packed into granules whose shape and size are characteristic of each plant species. Starch granules in potato tubers, for example, are smooth, irregular, and 15-75 μm in diameter, whereas those from maize are *polyhedral* and 5-20 μm. The starches of the Triticeae cereals including barley and wheat are present in a bimodal *distribution* of large A-granules (15-30 μm) and small B-granules (2-5 μm). Starch granule form confers properties to the starches that are *important* in various *applications*, from paper coating to brewing.

In malting, the A- and *B-granules* are amylolytically digested in different manners, the A-granules by pinholing followed by internal *digestion* and the B-granules by surface erosion. This

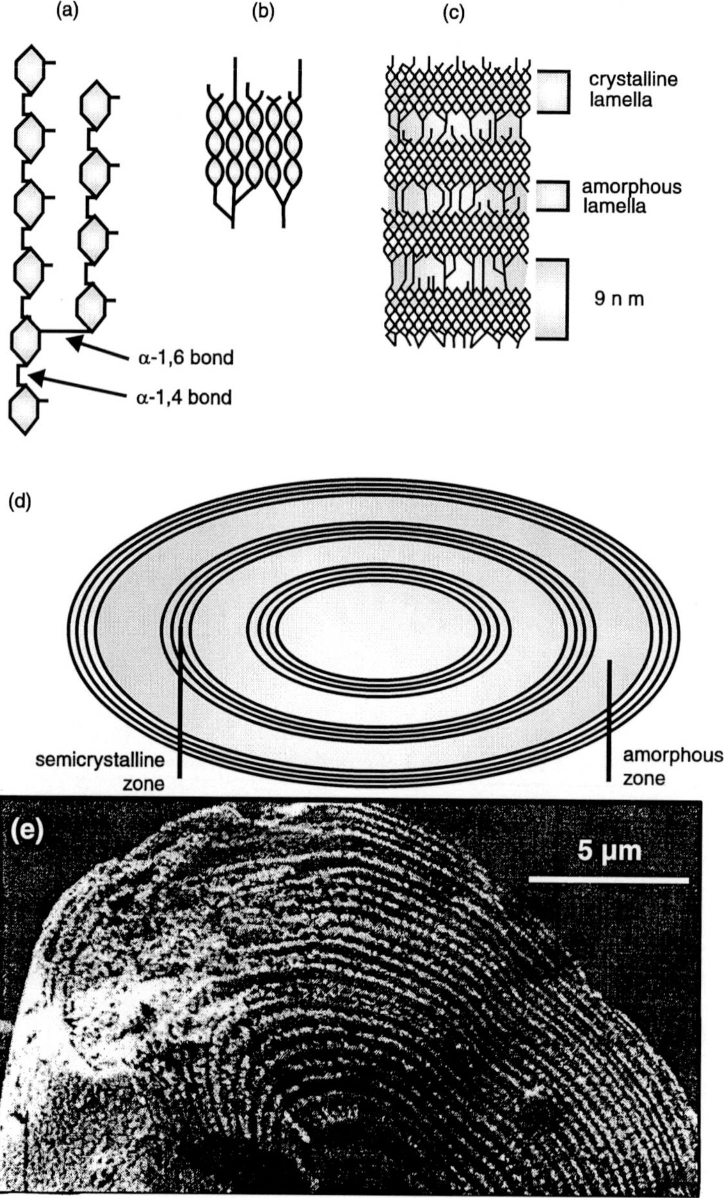

Figure 3.1: Current view of starch structure and its successive stages of organization within the granule, (a) Segment of amylopectin indicating the two bond types, (b) An amylopectin cluster showing the double helices formed between adjacent chains, (c) Helices are packed into crystalline lamellae spaced at intervals of 9 nm, interspersed with amorphous regions containing the parallel branch points, (d) The interspersed crystalline and amorphous lamellae form concentric semicrystalline zones several hundreds of nanometers wide. These zones are separated by amorphous zones lacking orderly packing of amylopectin helices. A pair of semicrystalline and amorphous zones form a growth ring in the granule, (e) Scanning electron micrograph of a potato starch granule showing the growth rings. The granule has been digested with α–amylase to remove partially the amorphous zones, which are more easily hydrolyzed.

leads to uneven *conversion* during malting, a problem in brewing. The existence of mutants affecting starch granule size distribution or *morphology* in various plants including barley and pea indicates that *engineering* of crops for specific granule size *distributions* is in principle possible.

The properties of starch, and the ultimate effects of biotechnologically induced changes in starch *biosynthesis*, largely reside in the organization of the starch granule. Work with advanced physical *techniques* and biochemical studies *extending* back almost 20 years have produced much insight into granule structure, the generally accepted view of which is *presented* in figure elsewhere in this chapter.

At the lowest level of *organization*, paired, adjacent amylopectin chains form double helices. The helices are *arranged* as clusters, and the clusters in turn form *crystallites*. The linear, helical regions of the α–1,4 glucan chains form, in a radial direction, crystalline lamellae.

These alternate at a *periodicity* of 9 nm with amorphous regions containing the α–1,6 branch points. Sets of these *alternating* crystalline and amorphous regions form semicrystalline zones hundreds of nanometers wide that alternate with broad amorphous zones.

Together, the *semicrystalline* and amorphous bands form concentric shells termed growth rings. Interspersed within the amylopectin structure is the amylose *component* of the granule. In addition, lipids are tightly associated with the helix cores and proteins, in particular granule-bound starch *synthase* (GBSS), are tightly bound to the starch.

The emergent properties of starch *granules* when treated with *enzymes*, solvents, or heat are greatly affected by the *organization* of the granule and by the bound lipids. These properties are related to the activities of the starch synthetic enzymes in complex ways, *complicating* rational approaches to specific targets in starch *functionality*. The genetic, developmental, and biochemical variations among plants *producing* storage starch result in a wide range of final properties of the starch.

STARCH DEPOSITION

In storage tissues, starch is *synthesized* within amyloplasts, which are derived as are chloroplasts from proplastids. Starch is also *synthesized* diurnally for *transient* assimilate storage in leaf chloroplasts. Starch biosynthesis is part of the complex process of *tuberization*, conversion of a stem into storage tissue, in potato and other crops *producing* storage tubers.

In the cereals, starch is deposited in the starchy endosperm, whereas in most dicotyledonous plants it *accumulates* in fleshy cotyledons. Within developing endosperm, starch granules appear *within* a day of the onset of *cellularization* and continue until the grain dries. Tubers, however, have no sharp end point for starch *biosynthesis*.

Source of Photosynthate for Starch Biosynthesis

Starch biosynthesis with its key *enzymes* and metabolites is *diagrammed* in figure elsewhere in this chapter. Photosynthate is generally supplied as sucrose via the phloem of the *maternal* tissues. Both source and sink strength are critical to starch yield in storage organs.

In some plants, breakdown and resynthesis of sucrose appear necessary to maintain a sucrose gradient and thus sink strength, although this is not the case in others such as barley. The sucrose taken into the endosperm is *subsequently* converted into *UDPglucose* by sucrose *synthase* (UDPglucose:D-fructose-2-*glucosyltransferase,* EC 2.4.1.13):

$$\text{sucrose} + \text{UDP} \rightarrow \text{UDPglucose} + \text{D-fructose}$$

This is a reversible reaction but, under the conditions found in storage tissues, the breakdown of sucrose is favoured. In many plants, sucrose synthase activity appears to be important to overall sink *strength* and hence yield. Antisense-mediated *reductions* in sucrose synthase levels in *transgenic* tomato and potato reduce overall starch biosynthesis, as do mutations to the sucrose synthase genes such as found in the maize *shl* and *sus1* mutants.

The UDPglucose product of sucrose synthase is then converted to glucose- l-phosphate by UDPglucose pyrophosphorylase (UTPglucose- l -phosphate uridylyltransferase, EC 2.7. 7.9). The UDPglucose pyrophosphorylase enzyme has been purified and the gene encoding it cloned from barley as well as from other plants. Glucose- l-phosphate is further processed to ADPglucose, the specific nucleotide sugar that serves as the substrate for the starch synthases. This is catalyzed

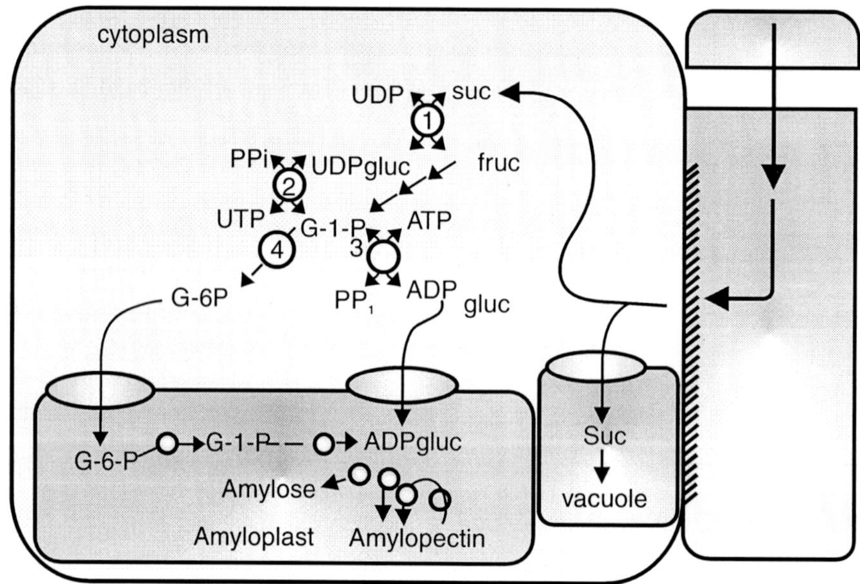

Figure 3.2: Schematic diagram of the currently accepted pathway for starch biosynthesis in storage organs. Photosynthate is transported as sucrose from source leaves through the phloem to the storage organ. It is then moved as sucrose into the storage tissues or cleaved in some plants by a cell wall invertase to glucose and fructose (not shown) to be resynthesized as sucrose by sucrose phosphate synthase in the cytoplasm. Storage as fructans in the vacuole represents an alternative to starch biosynthesis in temperate grasses. The key enzymes of starch biosynthesis are (1) sucrose synthase (SucSyn), (2) UDPglucose pyrophosphorylase (UGP), (3) ADPglucose pyrophosphorylase (AGP), (4) phosphoglucomutase (PGM), (5) granule-bound starch synthase (GBSS), (6) soluble starch synthase (SS), (7) starch branching enzyme (SBE), and (8) debranching enzyme (DBE). Not all alternative shunts in the pathway are shown. Fructose can be converted to glucose-1-phosphate via fructokinase (FK), phosphoglucoisomerase (PGI), and phosphoglucomutase (PGM). The relative proportions of ADPglucose synthesized in the cytoplasm and amyloplast vary from species to species. Translocators are shown as ovals on the organelle membranes.

by the enzyme ADPglucose pyrophosphorylase (AGP, glucose-lphosphate adenylyltransferase, EC 2.7.7.27) in the reaction

$$\text{ATP} + \alpha\text{–D-glucose-l-phosphate} \rightarrow \text{pyrophosphate} + \text{ADPglucose}$$

The Committed Pathway of Starch Biosynthesis

The conversion of glucose- I -phosphate to ADPglucose by AGP is considered the first specific, or committed, step in starch biosynthesis. The AGP enzyme has been extensively studied and reviewed since the 1960s and also is the target for engineering of the pathway as discussed in the following. The enzyme in all tissues is a heterotretramer of two regulatory (small) and two catalytic (large) subunits.

In most tissues, it is allosterically regulated, activated by 3-phosphoglycerate but inhibited by orthophosphate. Due in part to its regulation and also to the severely shrunken phenotypes of mutants of AGP, it has been seen as the major control point for the flow of carbon into starch. Flux analyses, however, contradict this interpretation. Until recently, it was universally held that AGP is nuclear encoded but localized in the plastids in all tissues, photosynthetic and storage.

However, at least for maize and barley *endosperm*, a combination of investigations on the *bt-1* mutant, studies of isolated amyloplasts, and messenger RNA (mRNA) *transcriptional* analyses has shown that up to 95% of the cereal AGP is cytosolic.

A reasonable explanation for the difference between *chloroplasts* and amyloplasts regarding AGP *localization* rests on *chloroplasts* being sources of energy whereas *amyloplasts* are sinks. If AGP were restricted to amyloplasts, the ATP would have to be imported and then converted to PPi and AGPglucose. This is *energetically* less favourable than movement of *ADPglucose* into the plastid and transport of ADP outward in return.

Nevertheless, some AGP is plastidic even in the cereals, where the majority is cytoplasmic; the relative roles of the two forms remain to be established. Furthermore, in potato tubers it appears that the majority of the carbon moves as *glucose-6-phosphate* into the amyloplasts, where it is *subsequently* converted to glucose- l-phosphate and then to starch.

The details of the pathway in any particular plant are important regarding the *possibilities* of modifying starch quantity or quality. Starch content as well as starch quality can be affected by modulating the activity and properties of the AGP present in storage tissues.

Synthesis of Amylose

Amylose consists of glucose subunits linked by α–1,4 bonds into linear chains, with occasional α–1,6 branch points connecting additional α–1,4linked chains onto a backbone. In barley, the average chain length is 1800 glucose units, but it may vary in the cereals between 1000 and 4400 glucose moieties, yielding a molecular weight of between 1.6×105 and 7.1×105. In most normal starches, amylose makes up 20-30% of the total by weight.

This is reduced to virtually none in the waxy mutants. The general features of amylose and the other main *component* of starch, amylopectin, are well established. The α–1,4 links in both amylose and amylopectin are made by the starch synthases (EC 2.4.1.21). The enzyme occurs in multiple forms, but all forms use ADPglucose as the glucose donor to the growing chain.

In the storage organs, namely *endosperm*, cotyledons, and tubers, amylose is synthesized by the form called granule-bound starch synthase I (GBSS or GBSSI). The "waxy" starches, perhaps the most common example of a modified *carbohydrate* created through both breeding and transgenic *biotechnology*, virtually completely lack amylose because of the absence of the GBSSI.

The other forms of starch synthase are unable to *compensate* in such mutants, called waxy ("glutinous" in rice) because of the *resulting* property of the starch (the gene for GBSSI thereby being wx). In nonstorage tissues, however, amylose continues to be synthesized in waxy mutants, a form of the starch synthase called GBSSII carrying out the task in the cases examined.

The gene or transcript for GBSSI has been cloned from many sources; alignments of these sequences revealed that these are highly conserved. The α–1,6 branch points in amylose are not synthesized by GBSSI or GBSSII but may derive from the action of a starch branching enzyme (SBE, see next for amylopectin) or from a branched oligosaccharide as the starch-synthetic substrate, with the poorly branched product *subsequently* elongated by GBSS. The substrate for amylose biosynthesis remains *controversial* and in vivo may be either amylopectin chains or soluble *maltooligosaccharides*, both, or neither.

Synthesis of Amylopectin

Amylopectin is considerably more complex as a molecule, and its biosynthesis is commensurately more intriguing. The linear, α–1,4-linked portion of the polymer is produced by the soluble starch synthases (EC 2.4.1.21), which catalyze growth of the α–1,4 glucan chain by addition of glucose residues from ADPglucose. Historically, these enzyme forms received their name because they are not bound tightly to the starch granule, in contrast to the granule-bound starch synthase or GBSS.

More recently, it has become clear that all forms of starch *synthase* are to some extent partitioned onto the starch granules or somehow become trapped in the growing, insoluble granule, so the *original* distinction is not very useful.

The amylopectin-synthesizing starch synthases are found in multiple forms in virtually all plants examined. Alignment of the proteins encoded by the sequenced soluble synthase form divides them into three main groups: SSI, SSII, and SSIII. Investigations of mutants and transgenics lacking or reduced in the activity of one of the SS forms indicate that each plays a specific, or at least preferential, role in amylopectin synthesis.

These efforts have been complemented by expression of specific forms in *E. coli* and analyses of the α-glucan products made in the bacteria. From such experiments, SSII appears to synthesize α–1,4 chains of intermediate length, whereas the SSI form in barley appears to be involved in initiation of new chains. Potatoes expressing antisense to SSII, *consistent* with this view, have reduced relative *abundance* of chains of DP 18-50.

The complexity of amylose *biosynthesis* from the perspective of *engineering* the pathway lies not only in the multiplicity of forms but also in their overlapping roles. Although one form may, because of its kinetics, be responsible for producing chains of a certain size class, in a mutant or transgenic plant where this form is absent another form may substitute but only partially or with *identical* results.

The combination of *overlapping* roles and *pleiotropism* can lead to novel or *unpredicted* amylopectin structures in engineered starches. The soluble synthases cover half of the story of amylopectin biosynthesis, however. The starch branching enzymes (SBEs, α–1,4-glucan, α–1,4glucan-6-glucosyl transferase, EC 2.4.1.18, Q-enzyme) are responsible for producing the α– 1,6 branches on the amylopectin molecule, which can then be further extended by the soluble starch synthases.

Because it is the branching of amylopectin that confers its specific functional properties and behaviour in food and beverage production, the SBEs have attracted *considerable* interest for the genetic tailoring of starch. The SBEs are transferases rather than synthases, detaching an α–1,4 -linked *oligoglucan* from the end of an amylopectin chain and moving it into an α–1,6 position elsewhere in the molecule.

Nevertheless, they stimulate soluble starch synthases by *increasing* the effective substrate concentration determined by the number of nonreducing α–glucan ends in the amylopectin. As with the starch synthases, multiple isoforms have been identified that show organ (usually leaf or storage tissue) or temporal *specificity* in their *expression* patterns. The various forms show differences as well in the length of chains transferred, which has implications for engineering of starch.

These forms have been characterized as A or B types by their distinct properties. Antisense work in potato indicates that SBE A is responsible for *transferring* shorter chains than SBE B because average chain length increases in its absence. The well-known *amylose-extender* (*ae*) mutants illustrate the profound effect SBE has on starch properties.

Rather than containing an increased amount of amylose as would be produced by the GBSS enzyme, these plants are in fact defective in amylopectin *branching*. Over the last several years, a revolution in thinking about amylopectin biosynthesis has taken place with the introduction of the *preamylopectin trimming* model. The model addresses the question of how the nonrandom distribution of branch points typical of amylopectin may arise.

It also helps to explain why mutants lacking a debranching enzyme such as the *sugaryl* of maize or a similar one in the alga *Chlamydomonas* and *Arabidopsis* contain a highly branched α–glucan referred to as phytoglycogen. In the model, SBEs and debranching enzymes (DBEs) carry out *discontinuous* steps of synthesis and amylolysis so that excess branches added by the SBE are removed.

Crystallization of the product removes it from the cycle and fixes the structure as, in essence, a partially debranched glycogen. An alternative, the *soluble glucan recycling* model, has been proposed. In this hypothesis, DBE plays only a subsidiary role in forming amylopectin, helping to turn over branched, soluble oligoglucans. This *hypothesis* explains the occurrence of *phytoglycogen* in DBE mutants but does not take the clustered branching of amylopectin into account.

The validity of the two models is currently difficult to test. Furthermore, the actual in vivo functions of the soluble starch synthases, SBEs, and debranching enzymes still remain to be disentangled from the pleiotropic effects seen in mutants and antisense experiments.

TRANSGENIC MODIFICAITION OF CARBOHYDRATE BIOSYNTHESIS

Efforts to alter carbohydrate biosynthesis extend back to about 1990 and have *proceeded* hand in hand with the use of *overexpression* and antisense inhibition to unravel *carbohydrate* biosynthesis in plants. The approaches can be divided into those that seek to alter starch quantity through affecting the strength of the carbon source or sink, those that attempt to convert starch to simple sugars, those with the goal of altering the amylose/amylopectinratio, those trying to alter amylopectin structure, and lastly those that seek to produce novel carbohydrates through the introduction of new *biosynthetic* activities.

Overviews of these efforts have been made several times from various perspectives. The key point is that grain or tuber quality and end use are related to the structures of the starch and protein components. These structures can be modified *transgenically* if suitable natural mutants are not available.

Alteration of Starch Quantity

Storage organs constitute net consumers or sinks for *photosynthetically* produced carbon, whereas leaves are the sources. Generally, source-sink balances are regulated by sugar levels (hexoses as well as sucrose) and by stress.

Willmitzer and his colleagues *demonstrated* that source strength in tobacco is inhibited by accumulation of sugar in the leaves. Expression of a yeast invertase in the cell wall of tobacco cleaved the sucrose normally loaded into the phloem and blocked its export, mimicking a very weak sink. This work was repeated later in transgenic potato plants, and photosynthesis was shown to be inhibited by sugar accumulation in the leaves.

Using a parallel approach, sink strength was investigated by the same team. Sucrose synthase was *demonstrated,* through its removal in plants expressing sucrose synthase antisense under the strong 35S CaMV promoter, to play a crucial role in *determining* the sink strength of a potato tuber. Similar results were obtained by inhibiting the next step on the starch biosynthetic pathway, glucose- l-phosphate synthesis, through the expression of *pyrophosphatase* and concomitant reduction in pyrophosphate (PPi) content. Following the pathway further, the *accumulation* of both starch and protein was inhibited by antisense *knockdown* of AGPase levels in potato tubers.

Instead, the tubers *accumulated* up to 30% of their dry weight as sucrose and 8% as glucose, resulting in their increased fresh weight but decreased dry weight as well as pleiotropic effects on the *transcription* of other genes on the starch synthetic pathway. Generally, the practical goal is to increase the *accumulation* of starch in tubers or grains rather than to block it.

Low-starch, high-sugar potatoes would be quite poor for a major market sector, chips, crisps, and fries, because sugar accumulation results in discolouration of chips or slices during frying. The postharvest *accumulation* of sugar in tubers has been limited by transgenic inhibition of UDPglucose *pyrophosphorylase* activity.

An alternative, more effective approach was taken more recently by the expression of a tobacco invertase inhibitor in tubers. This reduced conversion of starch to soluble sugars by up to 75%, which appears to be at levels sufficient for the practical improvement of potato processing. Increased sink strength has been engineered through expression of a yeast invertase in the tuber, promoting cleavage of sucrose and hence a stronger translocation gradient to the tuber.

One strategy to improve potato tubers is to increase starch levels. Besides increasing total yield in dry weight, a higher starch content is correlated with a decrease in fat uptake during frying and therefore a more healthful product. In an attempt to do this, a mutant *E. coli* AGP form has been expressed in tubers as a *translational* fusion to a ribulose bisphosphate carboxylase transit peptide and driven by a patatin promoter.

Other efforts using the same AGP form failed to increase starch content because of associated higher turnover of starch into sugars. As reviewed elsewhere, efforts to date to increase yield and hence starch biosynthesis through the *manipulation* of single enzyme levels have not been very predictable.

An example of the capacity of carbohydrate metabolism to yield surprising results is the effect of expressing viral movement proteins in tobacco and potato. The protein MP17 of potato leaf roll virus increased soluble sugar and starch amounts in source leaves but did not affect *photosynthesis* in the leaf blade because of *sequestration* of the sugars in the vacuole.

Although such experiments do not provide a ready recipe for engineering sugar or starch accumulation in plants, much can be learned about carbohydrate metabolism in the meantime, and in the end, effective quantitative manipulations may become straightforward.

Production of Simple Sugars in Storage Organs

As an outcome of analyses of sugar and starch metabolism and source-sink interactions, know-how has developed on the *manipulation* or production of simple sugars in storage organs. Work on cold sweetening of potatoes, a problem discussed in the previous section, examined the role of acid invertase in the process. Although the *experiments* showed that invertases do not control the *conversion* of starch to sugars during storage, they do determine the hexose-to-sucrose ratios.

Transgenic *expression* of soluble invertase could thus be used as a strategy to produce hexoses in vivo. Tomatoes and most fruits, in contrast to potato tubers, accumulate sugar rather than starch. In experiments with goals opposite to what was *attempted* in potato, natural invertase levels in tomato fruits were reduced by an *antisense* strategy.

Sucrose levels increased and hexose levels decreased in the antisense fruits, *accompanied* by a 30% reduction in *fruit* size. In very promising newer work, an alternative approach to the production of hexose, in this case fructose, in potato tubers has been taken. Rather than introduce single enzymatic activities or reduce existing ones, a fusion coding for α–amylase from *Bacillus stearothermophilus* and glucose isomerase from *Thermus thermophilus*, both thermostable, was expressed in transgenic tubers under control of the GBSS promoter.

The complex was not *enzymatically* active during tuber development. Instead, production of fructose and glucose was achieved by crushing the tubers and heating for 45 minutes to 65°C. A parallel approach, demonstrated in transgenic tobacco, was reported by a different group slightly thereafter. In related work, a heat-toleran *β-glucanase* has been transferred to two malting varieties of barley.

This approach should improve malting quality through reduction of the content of 6-glucans in wort, the source of filtration problems and of cloudiness in beer. The native β-glucanases do not withstand well the heating of the mashing process.

These experiments clearly demonstrate the potential of in planta starch *modification* and of transferring an industrial process into the farmer's field to create a novel product. An example of an unexpected effect on carbohydrate synthesis or turnover from a transgene was shown through overexpression of wheat thioredoxin *h* in barley endosperm.

Thioredoxin *h* has been known to be important in *germination* for mobilization of storage protein in the endosperm. The thioredoxin must first be reduced, and the NADPH needed for this can be produced through hydrolysis of starch in the endosperm. Thus, it is perhaps satisfying but *nonetheless* surprising that overexpressed thioredoxin *h* should lead to a fourfold increase in α–1,6-debranching (*pullulanase*) activity in *germinating* grains.

Although the authors do not present the glucan profile, this approach should greatly alter the limit dextrin profile of germinating grain and have an impact on malting. The disaccharide trehalose, known for many years to be produced primarily by fungi and some insects, attracted interest because of its potential use as an osmoprotectant or stress-mitigating agent.

Efforts were therefore made to engineer its expression in tobacco and potato through the introduction of trehalose-6-phosphate synthase (*otsA*) and trehalose-6-phosphate phosphatase (*otsB*) genes from *E. coli.*

Although only very low levels of trehalose (0.11 mg g^{-1} fresh weight) could be obtained in this way, it was discovered that this poor yield is due at least in part to the presence of native trehalase activity not only in the transgenic regenerants but also in the control plants.

It later became clear that the enzymatic machinery for synthesizing trehalose is in fact universal among the angiosperms, although in most plants trehalase blocks the *accumulation* of the sugar.

This would not have been realized if control *experiments* with the trehalase inhibitor validamycin A had not been carried out, and it illustrates that metabolic *engineering* in plants is still very much of an adventure.

Alteration of the Amylose Complement in Starch

Some of the earliest efforts at qualitatively altering starch biosynthesis were directed at the amylose-to-amylopectin ratio. This was because the abundance of natural waxy mutants showed that amylose could be *eliminated* by suppression of GBSS activity and because low-amylose starches had certain processing advantages.

The first successful creation of a low-amylose (*amf*) potato was achieved in the group of Jacobsen and Visser through mutagenesis rather than transformation. This was followed by antisense expression of GBSS by the same group. Often, antisense suppression of endogenous genes succeeds even without full sequence identity in the transgene.

In other experiments, the GBSS of cassava, bearing only 74% identity to potato GBSS, was able in some *regenerant* lines to inhibit native GBSS synthesis completely. *Glutinous*, or amylose-deficient, rice is important in the diet of Japan, but a range of amylose contents may offer broader uses in foods.

An antisense approach to GBSS *suppression* in rice yielded transgenic lines varying in their amylose content from slight reduction to complete absence. In plants more *recalcitrant* to *transformation* such as wheat, the more traditional approach of *combining* mutants by crossing has so far been more effective in achieving low-amylose lines.

Alteration of Amylopectin Structure

A major goal in many laboratories has been the transgenic tailoring of amylopectin structure. The reason for this is that much of starch *functionality* in cooking, baking, and extrusion is determined by the degree and pattern of *branching* in amylopectin.

Linear chains readily form *interchain* hydrogen bonds, producing crystalline regions in starch granules and falling out of solution in the process called retrogradation in *gelatinized*, cooked starch. Lower levels of *crystallinity* result in more stable, but more wettable, gels. In malting and *fermentation*, digestibility by amylase is also directly linked to amylopectin structure.

Exoglucanases, in particular β-amylase, digest inward from the *nonreducing* ends of α–1,4-glucan chains in starch. These enzymes are blocked by α–1,6 bonds, yielding a "limit" dextrin. In malting, the *endoglucanase* α–amylase is also present, breaking the α–1,4 bonds within the glucan chain.

Because α–amylase does not cleave terminal α–1,4 bonds or those near α–1,6 bonds, α–limit dextrins remain after digestion. Hence, the processing benefits of increased yield of monosaccharides and disaccharides in starch hydrolysis and of tailoring of starch behaviour during cooking have driven interest in using transgenic approaches. One of the first efforts in which starch structure was altered in a *transgenic* plant involved expression of the *E. coli* glycogen synthase (*glgA*) in potato.

Glycogen synthase carries out the same reaction as plant starch synthases, *transferring* glucoses into α–1,4 glucan chains. Total starch content in the tubers declined, and amylose was reduced from 23% to 8-9%. The short chains (A + B1) in the amylopectin increased from 66% of the total chains detectable following hydrolysis to 85%, while the long (B2 + B3) chains decreased from 33% to 15%.

In a complementary effort, the *amf* low-amylose potato, which had been developed earlier by mutation breeding, was transformed with the gene for the *E. coli* glycogen branching enzyme (*glgB*). As in the previous example, this enzyme carries out the same reaction as the *corresponding* starch branching enzyme of the plant, although the final product in bacteria is highly branched glycogen.

Up to 25% more branches were made in the transgenic amylopectin and average chain length dropped, associated with more short chains of DP < 16. For certain applications, it would be highly useful to obtain virtually pure amylose directly from the plant rather than through chemical *fractionation* of starch.

So-called high-amylose or amylose-extender cereals have long been known, but, as described earlier, this is due not to synthesis of more of the product of GBSS ("true" amylose) but rather to less SBE activity and hence a less branched, more amylosic, amylopectin.

Taking a cue from these mutants, a group at Unilever was able to produce potato tubers virtually lacking normal amylopectin but containing apparent amylose levels as high as found in any commercial cereal.

Potato starch is phosphorylated in the amylose fraction, the phosphorylation conferring increased solubility, and this transgenic starch contained fivefold higher *phosphorus* contents than normal.

Rather than knocking out the branching enzyme activity to alter *amylopectin* structure, the Kossmann laboratory expressed a chimeric antisense construct against the genes of both major soluble starch synthases, SSIII and SSII, in potato. Total starch synthase activity was reduced up to 90%, but amylose production was normal and amylopectin not eliminated.

Instead, the amylopectin contained more chains of DP < 15, fewer of 15 to 80 glucose units, and more very long chains. The effect of removing one or the other SS form was not consistent with *eliminating* both *simultaneously*, indicating a complex interaction between the SS forms during amylopectin biosynthesis. In a more direct approach, the Kossmann group was able to modify the amount of starch phosphorylation in a transgenic tuber.

The group began by *isolating* proteins bound to starch and raising *antibodies* to them, with the expectation that starch-bound proteins would in some way be involved in starch biosynthesis. A gene for one of these, a protein of -160 kDa, was cloned by screening a complementary DNA (cDNA) expression library with the antiserum. This protein, named Rl, bears no resemblance to any previously *characterized* enzyme of starch *biosynthesis*.

When the level of this protein is reduced in antisense-transformed potatoes, the level of starch phosphorylation is likewise lowered to 10-50% of normal. Glucose-6-phosphate was *commensurately* reduced, and the effect on starch phosphorus levels was seen at both C-3 and C-6 positions to an equal degree. When R1 was expressed in *E. coli*, it led to phosphorylation of the bacterial glycogen.

Coincidentally, cold-induced *sweetening*, discussed earlier, was decreased through a secondary effect on starch digestibility. Curiously, in the antisense transgenic plants, leaves accumulated starch in excess of normal.

It remains to be seen whether the gene can be used to phosphorylate starch in plants particularly. The authors reported that similar sequences are expressed in rice and *Arabidopsis*, yet these starches are not normally phosphorylated. If activation of phosphorylation becomes possible in the cereals, an important new class of starches will be available to the marketplace.

Production of Nonstarch Carbohydrates

The interconvertibility of many of the sugar metabolites on the starch biosynthetic pathway in leaves and storage organs by native and *exogenous* enzymes indicates that, in principle, many new carbohydrates could be synthesized in transgenic plants.

An early attempt at this was the production of cyclodextrins in potato tubers. Cyclodextrins are rings comprising six to eight glucose units produced by bacterial cyclodextrin glucosyltransferases from a starch substrate. This group at Calgene expressed a *Klebsiella* cyclodextrin *glucosyltransferase* in potato tubers driven by a patatin promoter.

They were able to produce both six-unit (α-) and seven-unit *β-cyclodextrins* by this approach, although the yield was exceptionally low, 0.001-0.01% of the starch being converted to cyclodextrins. A more promising effort was made to produce mannitol in transgenic tobacco.

Sugar alcohols or polyols such as mannitol and sorbitol are found in diverse plant species, where they are believed to confer osmoregulatory and stress-ameliorating functions, as well as in bacterial, fungi, and mammals.

An *E. coli* gene for mannitol-l-phosphate dehydrogenase (*mtlD*) was expressed in tobacco and drove production of mannitol in excess of 6 μmol $(g)^{-1}$ of fresh weight in the leaves and in roots. In further work by the same group, specific targeting of this enzyme to tobacco chloroplasts led to *accumulation* of up to 100 mM mannitol in the plastids of one *transgenic* line, which was otherwise *phenotypically normal.*

The mannitol increased resistance to oxidative stress induced by methyl viologen, apparently through improved scavenging of hydroxyl radicals. Useful as this may be for plant improvement, no one has yet attempted commercial production and harvesting of mannitol in this manner. Perhaps the greatest attention has been paid to the *biosynthesis* of fructans in transgenic plants.

Fructans are fructose polymers localized, unlike starch, in vacuoles rather than plastids. They are synthesized by disproportionation, whereby a fructosyl residue is first *transferred* from one sucrose to another to make the shortest fructan, gluc-fruc-fruc. The process *proceeds* by further fructosyl *transfers* from sucrose as well as by transfers between fructans.

Mature fructans are found with a wide variety of branching patterns. In temperate grasses such as barley, fructans are an alternative to starch for carbon storage. This *accumulation* of fructans appears to contribute to yield stability under conditions unfavourable for starch biosynthesis because the fructans can later be converted to starch when *conditions* improve.

They also accumulate early in *endosperm development* but are turned over to support synthesis of starch as the grain matures. If starch biosynthesis is reduced by cold temperatures or blocked such as in the *shx* mutant of barley, fructans rather than starch may persist or accumulate. Aspects of fructan biosynthesis have been *summarized.* The focus on fructan engineering derives from its use as a potential pro- or prebiotic, *antitumorigenic* component of the human diet.

The most common sources of fructans, in particular inulin, have been the Jerusalem artichoke (*Helianthus tuberosus*) and chicory. However, initial efforts at engineering production of fructans in transgenic tobacco employed the bacterial *SacB* gene, encoding levan sucrase, from *Bacillus subtilis.* The transformed plants *accumulated* 3-8% fructan of the levan type found in the bacterium.

In a second effort with a bacterial transgene, the Willmitzer group *expressed* levan sucrase from *Erwinia amylovora* in the transgenic potato line *previously* engineered to be starch free with an antisense AGP. When the levan sucrase was targeted to the vacuole, 12 to 19% of the tuber dry weight was present as levan. However, yield was not increased relative to the parent line lacking starch. The first fructan synthetic enzyme to be cloned from a plant was sucrose-fructan *6-fructosyltransferase* (6-SFT) from barley. The group then expressed this clone in tobacco and in chicory.

Chicory normally produces fructan of a different type than those, the *graminans* and phleins, found in barley. The transgenic tobacco was able to synthesize the trisaccharide kestose as well as *unbranched* fructans of the phlein type. Chicory, normally making inulin, gained the ability to make graminan fructans, in *particular* the tetrasaccharide bifurcose, which is the main form in barley leaves.

In further experiments, chicory was transformed with a gene for an enzyme from onion, fructan:fructan 6G-*fructosyltransferase* (6GFFT), a key enzyme in the synthesis of the inulins found in the Liliales, which had been cloned by screening with a 6-SFT probe from barley.

Expression of the onion gene in chicory led to synthesis of the expected oniontype branched fructans as well as of linear inulin. Following similar lines with potatoes, a clone encoding a 6-SFT-like enzyme was first isolated from a cDNA library of the globe artichoke (*Cynara scolymus*).

When transformed into potato, the transgenic tubers produced high levels of 1-kestose along with nystose and traces of *fructosylnystose*. In subsequent work, the same group expressed both the sucrose: sucrose 1-fructosyltransferase (1-SST) and the fructan:fructan *1fructosyltransferase* from *C. scolymus* in transgenic potatoes.

The tubers produced up to 5% of their dry weight as high-molecular-weight inulins of a range identical to those found in the native artichoke, and some fructan was also detected in leaves. The tuber fructans were synthesized partly at the expense of starch production. An obvious choice as the transgene host for fructan biosynthesis is the sugar beet, which stores sucrose, the very substrate needed, rather than starch, for fructans.

When the gene for 1-SST, cloned from *H. tuberosus* together with that for 1-fructan:fructan fructosyl transferase (1-FFT), was transferred into sugar beet, the expected small fructans up to DP 4 were obtained. Remarkably, more than 90% of the sucrose of the beet was converted into fructans, and no deleterious effects on plant growth were observed under greenhouse conditions.

CONCLUSIONS

Plants are well suited as producers of modified starch and novel *carbohydrates*. Photosynthesis supplies a sucrose feedstock to carbohydrate storage organs, and the many intermediate steps in the conversion of sucrose to starch represent potential branch points at which the sugar may be shunted to new products. Storage starch, being insoluble, is not *physiologically* active, and the many *mutations* affecting starch synthesis *demonstrate* that a wide variety of structures can be tolerated by the plant.

Tubers and storage roots (beets) are not required for propagation, so the storage starch in these organs need not be accessible to the plant for turnover. Cereal grain starch is, however, important in *germination*; therefore, modification or *replacement* of this carbon source must take physiological needs into account.

To date, the main efforts in carbohydrate engineering in plants have been directed to alterations in starch yield, to increasing or decreasing the effective amylose content, and to changing the degree of branching in amylopectin.

Antisense approaches have been highly effective in bringing about *qualitative* changes in starch, although the type of starch produced has not been fully predictable. Great progress has been made over the last several years in *understanding* amylopectin *biosynthesis*.

However, the intricacies of the interactions between the various isoforms of starch synthase, starch *branching* enzyme, and debranching *enzymes* continue to dog attempts at rational starch design based on the functional properties desired in the final product.

Part of the difficulty lies as well in the elaborate nature of the starch structure itself, our limited ability to determine the structure fully as can be done for proteins or nucleic acids, and the complex relationship between gelatinization and *retrogradation* thermodynamics and rheology and starch structure.

The most success in producing novel carbohydrates has been achieved by the transfer of fructan *biosynthesis* from plants where it is common to other crops, *particularly* sugar beet and potato, where these carbohydrates are not normally found.

Fructans attract increasing interest as functional foods. Ultimately, the position of starch and other plant carbohydrates as "green," greenhouse-neutral replacements for petrochemicals offers great potential for the farming of crops containing *specialized* storage products.

In addition to nonfood uses, applications ranging from fat substitutes to fiber (as "resistant starch") in novel foods promise to create new markets for plant carbohydrates and new demand for their creation.

At present, however, the rejection by the public of genetic engineering in general, widespread in Europe and growing in North America and elsewhere despite the *environmental* benefits it can bring to agriculture, is *discouraging* growth in the production of transgenic carbohydrates.

It remains to be seen whether modified starch and *carbohydrates* produced in transgenic plants but destined for nonfood products can escape such pressures.

IMPROVING SEED PROTEINS

The protein content of seeds varies widely, from about 10-12% in cereals to 20-25% in pulses and oilseeds and up to 50% in soybean. It can be calculated that the total protein yield of the major seed crops amounts to over 350 million tonnes per annum, with cereals accounting for about 70% of the total. Seeds therefore form the major source of protein for the nutrition of humans and livestock.

In addition, seed proteins are largely *responsible* for the *processing properties* of many seeds including the use of wheat for making bread and other processed foods such as pasta and noodles. The impact of seed proteins on the nutritional and processing quality of seeds has provided a major stimulus to their study over a period *exceeding* 250 years since Beccari first described the isolation of wheat gluten. Seed proteins also provided an attractive model system to study gene structure and expression, as their synthesis is tightly *regulated* with high levels occurring in *specific* seed tissues and at specific stages of development.

Consequently, *complementary* DNAs (cDNAs) and genes for seed proteins were among the earliest to be cloned from plants, providing a basis for longer term strategic studies of the structures and functional (i.e., processing) properties of the encoded proteins.

This has led over the past few years to success in *improving* aspects of seed quality by genetic ngineering, although no improved varieties have so far reached the level of commercial production. Furthermore, the capacity of seeds to synthesize and store high levels of protein, combined with *well-established* systems for seed *production*, harvesting, storage, and fractionation, has led to the use of seeds as bioreactors to produce novel proteins and peptides, notably high value products for *biomedical* applications.

These form the subject of other chapters in this volume and we will, therefore, focus on the manipulation of seed proteins to improve their properties for traditional end uses (i.e., food and feed). However, before *proceeding* with this we will briefly discuss the structures of seed proteins and their impact on quality.

SEED PROTEINS

Seed proteins can be broadly classified into two groups, storage and nonstorage. Storage proteins can be defined as proteins that have no biological role except to provide a store of carbon, nitrogen, and sulfur that is mobilized during *germination* to support *seedling* growth.

The amounts of storage proteins present vary between seeds of different species, accounting for about half of the total seed proteins in cereals but a higher *proportion* in more protein-rich oilseeds and legumes. Furthermore, the amounts also vary with the nutritional status of the plant, with high levels of nutrient *availability* resulting in increased accumulation.

Storage proteins are invariably deposited in discrete protein bodies, where they form dense *masses* and do not interfere with essential cellular processes. They usually *accumulate* in cotyledonary and/or endosperm tissues, although storage in the perisperm or hypocotyl may also occur. Storage proteins are usually *classified* into four groups on the basis of their solubility properties and *sedimentation* coefficients *($S20,_y$)* following a system and using a *nomenclature* standardized by Osborne.

GLOBULIN STORAGE PROTEINS

The most widespread storage proteins are globulins, which are defined by their *solubility* in dilute salt solutions. These comprise 7-8S and 11-12S types that are often called vicilins and *legumes, respectively, reflecting* their *characteristic* presence in legume seeds. The 7-8S globulins are typically trimeric molecules with three subunits of M_r about 40-50,000 forming a protein of M_r about 150-190,000.

However, in some species *post-translational proteolysis* and/or *glycosylation* of the subunit chains results in a much more complex spectrum of components. For example, pea contains *unprocessed* subunits of M_M about 50,000 and a range of smaller *components* (M_r 12,000, 13,000, 16,000, 19,000, 25,000, 30,000, 33,000, and 34,000), the latter all being derived from M_M 47,000 precursor subunits.

The 78S globulin storage proteins occur in many but not all legumes, in other dicotyledonous plants such as cotton and cocoa, and in the embryos and aleurone cells of cereals. The 11-12S globulins differ from the 7-8S globulins in being hexameric, typically *comprising* six subunits of *M* about 60,000. Posttranslational *proteolysis* results in cleavage of the subunits into acidic (also called α or A) chains of M_r about 40,000 and basic ((β, B) chains of *M* about 20,000, which remain associated by a single disulfide bond.

Further proteolysis does not occur and glycosylation is rare. The 11-12S globulins are widely distributed in legumes and other *dicotyledonous* seeds (e.g., *composites, crucifers, cucurbits*) with related proteins forming the major storage protein fraction in oats and rice and minor components in wheat.

Although they have little sequence homology, the 7-8S and 11-12S globulins have similar *three-dimensional* structures, which may facilitate packing in the protein bodies, and appear to be derived from a common ancestral protein.

Prolamins

Prolamins are characterized by their *insolubility* in water or dilute salt solutions but solubility in alcohol-water mixtures. They are major storage proteins in most cereal species (except oats and rice, where they are minor components) and vary widely in their structures and properties.

The individual components are characterized by high contents of proline and glutamine (from about 30 to 70% of the total *residues, respectively*) and the presence of repeated amino acid sequences, while some individual subunits may be *assembled* into oligomers or polymers stabilized by interchain disulfide bonds.

2S Albumins

These are typically low-M_r proteins derived from single polypeptide chains that are posttranslationally cleaved to give subunits of M_r about 4-5000 and 8-9000 that remain associated by two interchain disulfide bonds. They are widespread in dicotyledonous plants (e.g., legumes, crucifers, composites), where they occur together with 7-8S and/or 11-12S globulins.

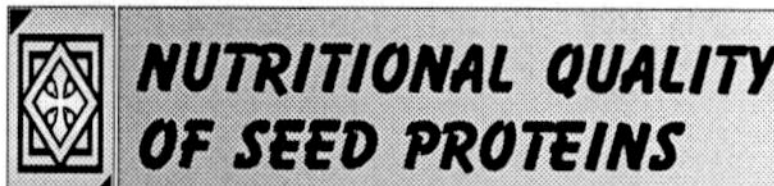

NUTRITIONAL QUALITY OF SEED PROTEINS

Animals are able to synthesize only about half of the 20 amino acids commonly found in proteins, the remainder being required in their diet and hence termed "essential." If only one of these is limiting, the *remaining* amino acids cannot be *utilized* but are broken down and excreted, leading to poor feed conversion and *environmental* pollution.

This is not usually a problem with ruminants, in which the rumen bacteria provide all 20 amino acids, but is a problem for nonruminants such as pigs and poultry. Comparison of the amino acid compositions of seeds with the requirements of essential amino acids for humans and *nonruminant* livestock shows that both legumes and cereals are deficient in one or more amino acids.

Furthermore, these *deficiencies* are *determined* by the amino acid compositions of the storage protein fractions. The prolamins of wheat, barley, and maize contain low levels of lysine ($\cong$1 mol % or less), and this is the first limiting amino acid in all three species.

The prolamins (zeins) of maize also contain little or no tryptophan, which is the second limiting amino acid in this species, and all three also contain low levels of threonine. In contrast, the 7S and II S globulins of legumes are severely deficient in cysteine and methionine, resulting in *deficiencies* in these amino acids in the whole seeds.

Because cereal and legume seeds are largely complementary in their contents of essential amino acids, they are often used in *appropriate* mixtures to provide a balanced diet of essential amino acids. Nevertheless, there is considerable interest in producing high-lysine cereals and high-sulfur legumes to provide more *flexibility* in producing low-cost diets for livestock.

HIGH-LYSINE CEREALS

Interest in improving the nutritional quality of cereals was stimulated by the discovery in the 1960s and 1970s of a range of high-lysine mutants in maize, sorghum, and barley. The first of these were the *opaque2* and *floury2* mutants of maize, followed by the lys gene of Hiproly barley and *hl* mutant of sorghum. These are all spontaneously occurring mutant genes; a range of other *spontaneous* high-lysine genes were *subsequently identified* in maize, and a range of chemical and physical mutagens were used to generate further high-lysine genes in sorghum and barley.

Despite initial optimism, only one of these mutant genes, *opaque2* of maize, has been successfully exploited in plant breeding programs, using genetic modifiers to convert the soft starchy endosperm to a normal type.

Although the other mutants have failed to be exploited because of *associated* deleterious effects on yield, analysis of their composition and molecular basis has contributed to our understanding of the regulation of seed protein biosynthesis and allowed us to make more informed decisions on strategies for improving quality. The high-lysine phenotype of most mutant lines is due, at least in part, to a reduction in the proportion of the lysine-poor *prolamins* and increases in other more lysine-rich proteins.

It is, therefore, tempting to suggest that high-lysine cereals could be engineered by down-

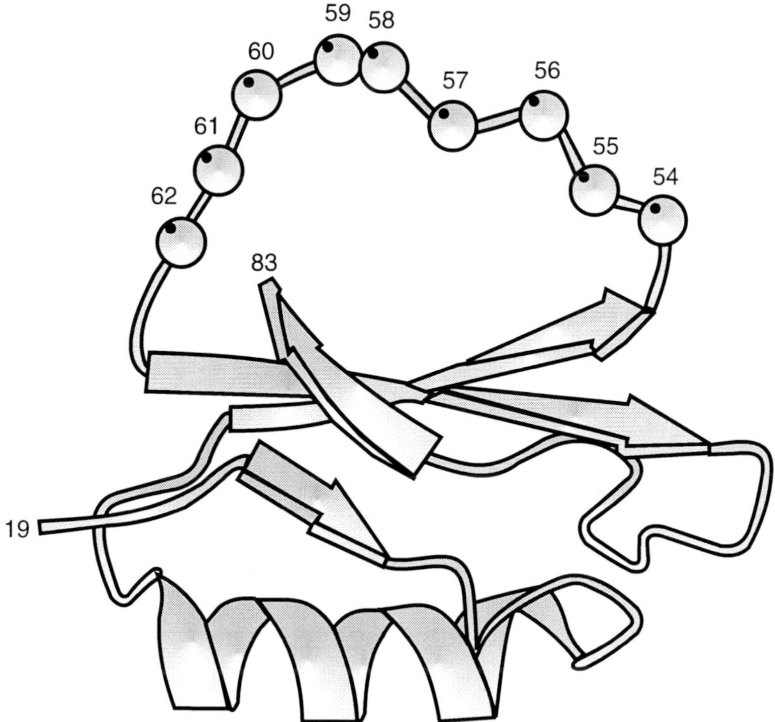

Figure 4.1: Ribbon diagram of the three-dimensional structure of the barley chymotrypsin inhibitor CI-2, showing the residues in the reactive (inhibitory) loop.

regulation of prolamin gene expression using *antisense* or *cosuppression technology*, as described for 2S albumins (napins) and globulins in transgenic oilseed rape.

In this work, antisense technology was used to down-regulate either napin or 12S globulin gene *expression* in developing seeds, resulting in compensatory increases in the remaining protein group. However, in all high-lysine cereals the decreased prolamin content is associated with reduced starch synthesis and hence lower yield, and this has proved difficult to separate from the high-lysine character by plant breeding.

Consequently, reduction in prolamins is not generally considered to be a valid strategy for engineering high-lysine cereals. Instead, three different strategies have been proposed.

Manipulation of the Amino Acid Composition of Prolamins

Wallace et al. designed modified maize prolamins (zeins) containing single and double substitutions of lysine for neutral amino acids; insertions of oligopeptides (five to eight residues) rich in lysine, threonine, and tryptophan; and insertion of an M_r 17,000 peptide derived from the SV40 VP2 protein.

All except for the latter (included as a control) were synthesized and *aggregated* into dense particles when the messenger RNA (mRNA) was injected into egg cells of the frog *Xenopus*, indicating that the *proteins* should also be stable in transgenic cereals.

However, the drawback of this strategy is that zeins account for about half of the total protein in the maize seed and appear to be *encoded* by up to 100 genes. Consequently, it would be necessary to express the mutant zeins under control of a highly active promoter and possibly also to combine this with *down-regulation* of the endogenous wild-type zeins. A similar strategy could be applied to other cereals.

Expression of Specific Lysine-Rich Proteins

Detailed analyses of the high-lysine barley mutant Hiproly demonstrated that about half of the increase in lysine resulted from elevated levels of four specific lysine-rich proteins, which together account for about 17% of the total grain lysine, compared with about 7% in normal lines. These proteins are (β–amylase (@5.0 g % Lys), protein Z (now known to be a serpin proteinase inhibitor) (@7.1 g % Lys), and chymotrypsin inhibitors CI-1 (^9.5g%Lys)andCI-2(@11.5g%Lys). CI-1 and CI-2 were both purified from Hiproly, providing a basis for molecular cloning.

This demonstrated that both proteins occur in two isoforms with the major form of CI-2 comprising 84 residues with an M_r of 9,380. This form contains seven lysine residues (8.3 mol %) but no cysteine residues (and hence no disulfide bonds).

The three-dimensional structure of the protein shows a wedge-shaped disc of about 28 × 27 × 19 Å with a single α–helix of 3.6 turns and four strands of β–sheet with a lefthanded twist. The reactive (inhibitory) site (Met-59) of CI-2 is present on an exposed nine-residue loop (Gly-54 to Arg-62).

Perutz and coworkers have shown that it is possible to mutate or extend this loop region, inserting up to 10 *glutamine* residues at Met-59 in order to explore the role of glutamine repeats in neurodegenerative diseases. More recently, Roesler and Rao have described the design and expression in *E. coli* of five mutant forms of CI-2 containing 20-25 mol % lysine, based mainly on

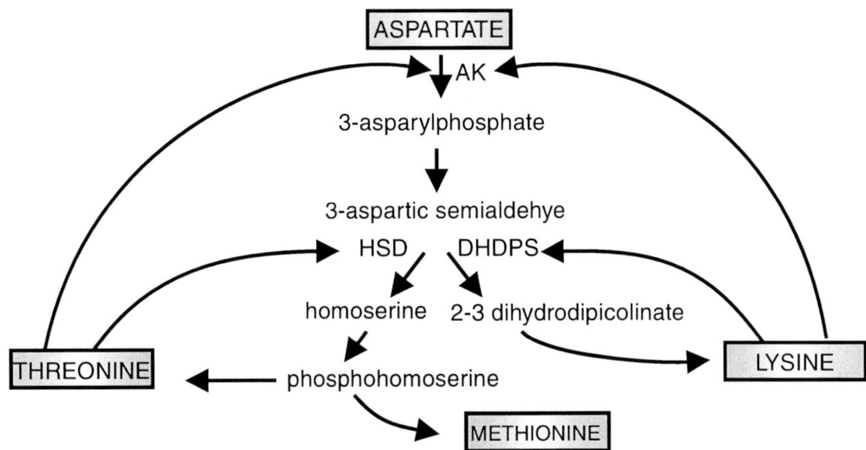

Figure 4.2: The pathway of lysine biosynthesis in plants showing feedback regulatory steps as arrows. AK, aspartate kinase; DHDPS, dihydrodipicolinate synthase.

mutation of surface-exposed residues. Although all the mutants appeared to have conformations similar to that of the wild-type protein, as *determined* by circular dichroism spectroscopy, they had lower *thermodynamic* stabilities. Nevertheless, at least one of the mutants was *considered* to be suitable for expression in transgenic plants.

The thionins are another group of lysine-rich seed proteins. Rao et al. designed high-lysine analogues of barley α–hordothionine, a 45residue protein containing five lysines (11 mol %). These included an analogue *containing* seven additional lysines (i.e., a total of 27 mol %), which was synthesized and shown to exhibit *antifungal* activity similar to that of the wild-type protein.

The authors have not, however, attempted to express any of the mutant proteins in transgenic plants, and such material would perhaps be unlikely to be accepted by consumers or regulatory authorities because of the wide biological activity of thionins. Pea legumin *contains* about 5 mol % lysine, which is similar to the nutritional *requirements* for humans (5.5 g %).

Sindhu et al. reported that pea legumin was stably accumulated in the seeds of transgenic rice plants but did not determine the effect on the lysine content of the grain. An alternative approach to using naturally occurring high-lysine proteins, or mutant forms of these, is to design *high-quality* proteins ab initio.

Keeler et al. demonstrated the feasibility of this concept by *designing* low-M_r proteins (3600 to 6700) with an α–helical coiled coil structure and containing up to 43 mol % lysine accompanied by high levels of methionine and in some cases also *tryptophan*. The proteins were initially synthesized in *E. coli* and one protein containing 31 mol % lysine and 20 mol % methionine was then expressed in tobacco seeds under control of the bean *phaseolin* and soybean β–conglycinin promoters.

Increases in lysine of up to 0.8 mol %, compared with a wild-type level of 2.56 mol %, were observed in the primary *transformants* and were inherited through three generations. No impact on seed *methionine* levels was reported, and the work has not so far been extended to cereals or other crop plants.

Table 4.1: The Essential Amino Acid Contents of Soybean, Maize, Wheat, and Barley Seeds and Their Major Storage Protein Fractions Compared with the WHO Recommended Levels.

	Soybean			Maize			Wheat			Barley		
Amino acid	Total seed	7S conglycinin	12S glycinin	Total seed	Ethanol-soluble zein	Ethanol-insoluble zein	Total seed	Gliadins	Glutenins	Total seed	Hordein	WHO
Cysteine	1.3	0.3	1.4	3.1	1.7	5.0	2.6	3.0	2.4	2.9	1.9	3.5
Methionine	1.3	0.2	1.8	2.0	1.6	7.9	1.3	1.7	1.4	1.7	1.1	
Lysine	6.4	7.0	4.9	3.5	0	0.1	2.0	0.6	2.3	3.1	0.8	5.5
Isoleucine	4.5	6.4	4.7	3.6	4.4	2.5	3.6	4.3	3.7	3.6	0.4	4.0
Leucine	7.8	10.2	7.2	11.6	23.0	13.9	6.7	6.8	6.6	7.2	7.8	7.0
Phenylalanine	4.9	7.4	5.7	4.9	7.1	3.6	5.1	5.5	4.8	5.5	9.3	6.0
Tyrosine	3.1	3.6	4.1	2.3	6.5	6.3	2.6	2.6	3.6	2.7	4.3	
Threonine	3.9	2.8	3.4	3.9	3.1	3.7	2.7	2.2	3.1	3.3	1.7	4.0
Tryptophan	1.3	0.3	1.6	0.9	nd	nd	1.1	0.7	2.1	2.0	nd	1.0
Valine	4.8	5.1	5.1	4.9	3.7	4.6	3.7	4.1	4.2	4.6	3.5	5.0
Histidine	2.5	1.7	2.2	3.2	1.2	4.8	2.2	2.2	2.3	1.9	1.8	—
Notes	b	c	d	e	f	g	b	g	9	b	h	i

Increased Accumulation of Free Lysine

The most spectacular success in increasing the lysine content of cereals has been achieved by *increasing* the amount of free rather than protein-bound lysine. This is based on eliminating the feedback regulation that normally limits the pool of free lysine by *transforming* with genes for feedback-insensitive enzymes from microorganisms. Two enzymes are important in this respect: aspartate kinase (AK), which catalyzes the first reaction in the pathway, and *dihydrodipicolinate* synthase (DHDPS), which controls the branch point leading to lysine.

Falco et al. initially showed that a twofold increase in total lysine occurred in seeds of oilseed rape (canola) expressing a DHDPS gene from *Corynebacterium* and a fivefold increase occurred in soybean seeds expressing the same enzyme together with an AK gene from *E. coli.*

More recent work, described in a patent application, has shown that expression of the DHDPS gene in maize under control of the embryo + aleurone-specific globulin-1 promoter resulted in increases in free lysine from 1.4 to 15-27% of total free amino acids, representing increases in total lysine from 2.3 to 3.6-5.3%.

In contrast, no effect was observed when the same gene was expressed under control of the starchy endosperm-specific glutelin-2 promoter, which was thought to be due to increased lysine *catabolism*. It was concluded that down-regulation of lysine catabolism would be required in order to achieve *accumulation* of lysine in the maize starchy endosperm.

HIGHT-METHIONINE LEGUMES

Legume seeds are deficient in both cysteine and methionine. However, animals are capable of converting *methionine* to cysteine but not vice versa.Consequently, there is interest in increasing the *methionine* content of *sulfurdeficient* legume seeds.

A range of sulfur-rich proteins has been characterized from plant seeds including the β–zeins (4.4 mol % Cys, 11.4 mol % Met), γ-zeins (over 7 mol % Cys), and γ-zeins (23-27 mol % Met) of maize. In addition, Chui and Falco have described the molecular cloning of a protein that appears to be related to δ-zeins but contains over 40 mol % methionine.

Similarly, the M_r 10,000 prolamins of rice contain about 10 mol % Cys and 20 mol % Met. The methionine-rich δ-zein gene has been used to increase the *methionine* content of maize seeds by up to 30%, but neither this nor any other sulfur-rich cereal prolamin genes have so far been used in *transgenic* legumes.

Instead, the main interest in improving the sulfur amino acid content of legume seeds has been focused on the 2S albumins. Youle and Huang demonstrated that the 2S albumin fraction from Brazil nut *(Bertholletia excelsa)* contained over 17 mol % Met and 13 mol % Cys, and subsequent studies showed the presence of at least six closely related components.

Methionine-rich 2S albumins have since been reported in sunflower, cotton, and amaranthus and cysteine-rich components in quinoa and pea. Expression of the Brazil nut albumins has resulted in significant increases in the methionine content of seeds of oilseed rape, tobacco (by up to 30%), *Arabidopsis* (by 20%), narbon bean *(Vicia narbonensis)* (by up to threefold), and soybean.

However, it is now known that the Brazil nut protein is allergenic to humans and the commercial

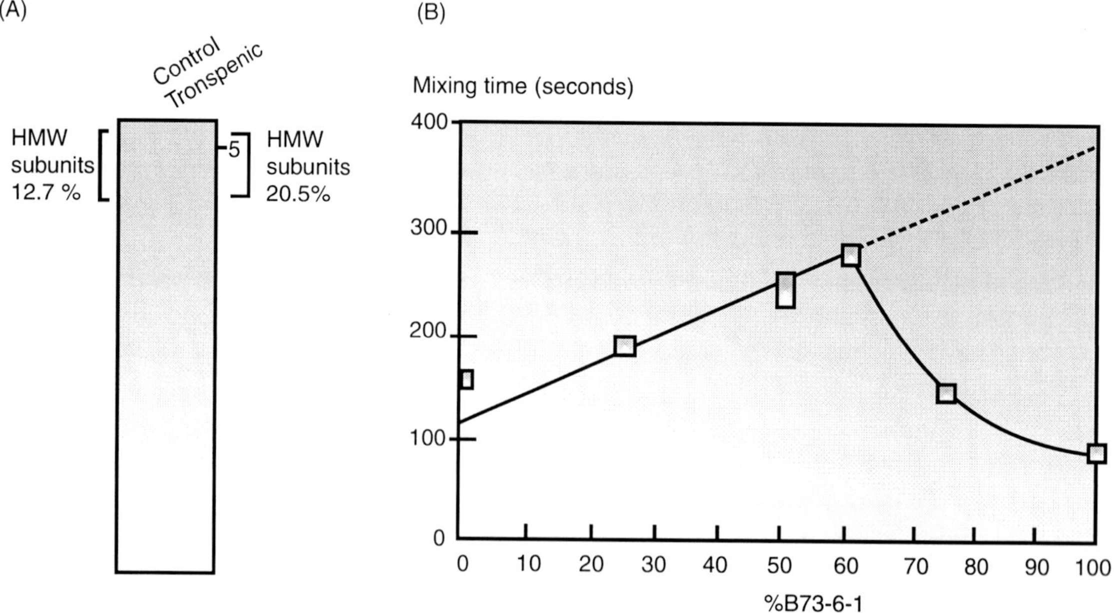

Figure 4.3: The mixing time determined using a small scale(2 g) mixograph is a measure of dough strength. Blending of flour from the transgenic line B73-6-1 with flour from the normal bread wheat cultivars Banks results in increased mixing time (i.e., dough strength) up to about 60%, after which the dough become "overstrong" and the mixing time falls.

development of seeds expressing this protein has therefore been suspended. Although a number of other (i.e., methionine-poor) 2S albumins are also allergenic (e.g., from mustards, castor bean, cotton), there is no evidence that this applies to the *methionine-rich* albumin (SFA8) of sunflower, which contains 16 Met out of 103 total residues (but see note added in proof).

Molvig et al. reported that the expression of this protein in seeds of lupin resulted in an increase in methionine by 94%, although there was no effect on total seed sulfur, the increase being at the expense of cysteine (reduced by 12%) and sulfate.

Feeding trials with rats showed that the nutritional quality of the seeds was improved significantly, with increases in live weight gain, true protein digestibility, biological value, and net protein utilization. These results *demonstrate* that the *methionine* content of legume seeds can be increased by genetic engineering but that the extent of this may ultimately be limited by the availability of sulfur within the seed.

Further increases may require the manipulation of the sulfur economy of the plant to increase the transport of sulfur into the developing grain. This will require further basic studies to identify the *underlying mechanisms* and their regulation. Other approaches can also be proposed to increase the methionine content of legume seeds, some of which have been tested in seeds of model species or other crop species.

Saalbach et al. showed that a methionine-enriched 7S globulin from *Vicia* was stably accumulated at levels of 1.5 to 2.2% of the total protein in seeds of transgenic tobacco plants, whereas methionine-enriched 11S globulin from the same species did not accumulate and was subsequently shown to be degraded. Similarly, Utsumi and co-workers have shown that wild-type and *methionineenriched* 11S globulins of soybean accumulate stably in seeds of transgenic rice.

De Clercq et al. constructed modified 2S albumins from *Arabidopsis* and chimeras comprising parts of the Brazil nut and *Arabidopsis* albumins and expressed them in seeds of tobacco, *Arabidopsis,* and oilseed rape.

Down-regulation of the sulfur-poor 11S globulins (cruciferins) in oilseed rape has also been shown to result in compensatory increases in more sulfur-rich proteins. Similarly, Kjemtrup et al. demonstrated that mutant *phytohemagglutinins* of bean containing four *additional* methionine residues were stably *accumulated* in seeds of transgenic tobacco although the level was not reported. However, none of these approaches has yet been *successfully* applied to grain legumes.

SEED PROTEINS AND FUNCTIONALITY

Although some seeds are consumed by humans with little or no processing (e.g., boiled rice), the vast majority are processed by the food industry into a wide range of products. The ability to process seeds is determined by their functional properties, which in turn depend, to a large extent, on the seed proteins.

For example, Kinsella has identified 10 *functional* properties that are conferred by soybean proteins used in food systems: solubility, water absorption and binding, viscosity, gelation, cohesion-adhesion, elasticity, *emulsification,* fat absorption, flavor binding, and foaming.

Similarly, the viscoelastic and cohesive properties conferred by wheat gluten proteins allow flour to be processed into bread, pasta and noodles, other baked goods, and various other food products. Because these are biophysical properties determined by the structures and/or interactions of seed components, they are difficult to define in molecular terms and to manipulate.

Nevertheless, good progress has been made with the two most important seed protein systems exploited in food processing, the gluten proteins of wheat and soybean globulins.

GEL FORMATION AND EMULSIFICATION PROPERTIES OF SOYBEAN GLOBULINS

Gelation forms the basis for making tofu, which is an important food product in the Far East. Gels result from the formation of an ordered protein network that is capable of holding water. In contrast, *emulsification* properties are important for *stabilizing oil-water* mixtures in products such as mayonnaise, dressings, and spreads, and protein emulsifiers usually have *amphipathic* properties that allow them to orientate at the oil-water interface. Utsumi and co-workers have explored the molecular basis for the gelation and *emulsification* properties of soybean 12S globulins (glycinins), using protein engineering and expression in *E. coli.*

A range of mutations and additions, and deletions of single residues and short sequences were made, focusing on five variable regions identified on the basis of sequence comparisons. Several mutant proteins were purified and their gelation and emulsification properties determined.

These contained deletions of l 1 or 8 residues from the protein N- and C-termini, respectively; the addition of blocks of four *methionines* into two of the variable regions; and the mutation of two cysteine residues involved in disulfide bond formation. All mutations showed greater *emulifying* activity, which was increased twofold in two of the mutants, while four of them formed harder gels. Furthermore, the presence of additional methio-nine residues in two of the mutants raised the possibility of *simultaneously* improving the functional and nutritional properties.

The wild-type glycinins and one of the *methionine-containing* mutants have been expressed in transgenic tobacco at levels up to 4% of the total protein. The proteins were correctly processed, assembled into hexamers, and accumulated in protein bodies, although about half appeared to be partially degraded.

More recent work from the same group has shown that the normal and *methionine-containing* glycinins can be expressed in transgenic rice seeds at levels up to about 5% of the total protein. The protein was colocated in protein bodies with the *structurally* related "glutelin" storage proteins of rice and assembled into 7S (trimeric) and I 1 S (hexameric) forms similar to those observed in developing soybean seeds. Some of the glycinin also appeared to form hybrid *oligomers* with the rice glutenin. Effects on the composition and digestibility of the grain were reported (61) (see earlier) but not on the functional properties.

THE VISCOELASTICITY OF WHEAT GLUTEN

The gluten proteins of wheat correspond to the prolamin storage proteins and account for about half of the total nitrogen in the mature grain. They are initially deposited in protein bodies in the cells of the developing starchy endosperm, but these deposits coalesce during the later stages of grain maturation to give a continuous matrix *surrounding* the starch granules.

When white flour (i.e., starchy endosperm cells) is mixed with water to form dough, the gluten proteins form a continuous network that confers cohesive and viscoelastic properties. This network is crucial for processing; in particular, it is expanded by fermentation of leavened bread to give a light porous structure that is then "fixed" on baking.

Highly elastic (strong) wheats are required for making both bread and pasta, and poor *processing* quality often results from low elasticity. Wheat gluten is a complex mixture of proteins that are classified into two broad groups. The glutenins consist of individual subunits that form high-M_r (above 1×10^6) polymers *stabilized* by interchain disulfide bonds.

They are the major *determinants* of gluten elasticity, appearing to form an elastic network. In contrast, the gliadins are monomeric proteins that interact with each other and with the glutenin polymers by strong noncovalent interactions (notably hydrogen bonds). They appear to be the major determinants of gluten viscosity, acting as plasticizers. Evidence from genetic and biochemical studies indicates that one group of glutenin proteins is particularly important in determining the elasticity (i.e., strength) of gluten. These high-molecular-weight (HMW) subunits of glutenin comprise between three and five individual proteins in hexaploid bread wheat and usually one or two proteins in *tetraploid* pasta wheat.

Each expressed subunit accounts for about 2% of the total protein, and quantitative differences in the total amount of subunit protein associated with variation in the number of expressed genes (three, four, or five in bread wheat) appear to contribute to differences in dough strength between cultivars. However, differences in dough strength are also associated with allelic variation in expressed proteins (particularly those encoded by genes on the D genome of bread wheat). These are presumed to result from subtle differences in subunit structure and interactions. The demonstration of a *relationship* between subunit gene *expression*, protein amount, and dough strength has provided a rationale for attempts to improve gluten elasticity by introducing additional genes for HMW subunits.

This has, so far, been achieved for bread wheat in four laboratories, which have introduced genes for wild-type HMW subunits encoded by chromosomes IA and 1D of bread wheat or a chimeric gene produced by combining parts of two subunits encoded by *chromosome* 1D. Similarly, He et al. *transformed* pasta wheat with the same genes from *chromosomes* IA and 1D of bread wheat.

In all cases, the transgenes were controlled by their own promoters and expression levels up to or above those of the endogenous genes were observed. Expression of HMW subunit *transgenes* resulted in increased dough strength in a poor quality bread wheat line *containing* only two subunits and also in pasta wheat when the transgene levels were similar to those of the endogenous genes.

However, very high level expression of a chromosome 1D encoded subunit in a bread wheat line expressing five subunits or in pasta wheat resulted in unusual mixing *characteristics* that were similar in some respects to those of "overstrong" varieties.

In both cases the flour could be blended to increase the strength of a poor quality bread wheat flour, indicating that such lines may be of commercial value for fortification of weak flours. This work demonstrates that *transformation* with HMW subunits can be used to manipulate the functional properties of wheat flour, either to improve its quality for traditional end uses (bread, pasta, noodles) or to confer new properties for food (e.g., ingredients) or nonfood (e.g., packaging, films) applications.

However, a deeper *understanding* of the *relationships* between the amounts, structures, and functional properties of proteins is required to allow changes to be specifically targeted. Furthermore, attention should be paid to other groups of glutenin subunits and gliadins in addition to the HMW subunits.

CONCLUSIONS

In the present chapter we have focused on four aspects of seed composition that determine the quality for major end uses: the nutritional quality of cereals (lysine content) and legumes (methionine content) and the processing properties of wheat gluten proteins and soybean glycinin.

These examples illustrate the range of approaches that can be taken to improve quality, including the expression of genes encoding novel proteins from other plant species, the up-regulation (by inserting additional gene copies) or downregulation (by antisense or cosuppression) of endogenous genes, and the *construction* and expression of mutant or ab initio designed genes.

It is not surprising that amino acid composition has been one of the early successes as this can be readily defined at the molecular level. Similarly, wheat gluten and legume globulin proteins are probably the best understood seed proteins in terms of the *molecular* basis for their functional *properties* in food systems. There are, of course, many other protein quality targets that can be addressed in the future, and there is no doubt that diet and health will have a major impact on the selection of these.

Examples are the removal of proteins that are toxic, allergenic, or involved in *intolerance* (e.g., coeliac disease) or the introduction of novel proteins with beneficial properties. Such manipulations will be of direct benefit to the consumer and may *consequently* help to increase the acceptability of transgenic crops and food.

5 Chapter

FLAVOURS AND FRANGRANCES FROM PLANTS

The sensation of odor is triggered by highly *complex* mixtures of small, rather hydrophobic molecules from many chemical classes that occur in trace concentrations and are detected by receptor cells of the olfactory epithelium inside the nasal cavity. The nonvolatile chemical messengers of the sense of taste interact with reporters located on the tongue and impart four basic impressions only: sweet, sour, salty, and bitter.

In scientific Anglo-Saxon usage, all sensory (*odor, taste, colour* and *texture*) attributes of food have been classed under the general term "flavor." Fragrances, as used in perfumes, *cosmetics*, and toiletries, are *distinguished* from volatile Flavours mainly by the different range of *application*.

According to European food legislation, aroma compounds derived from a natural source by physical means are classified as "natural"; their synthetic counterparts are "nature-identical," and compounds without a natural prototype are "artificial." Most of the natural Flavours currently processed by the flavor and fragrance industry are originally derived from plant sources. Naturalness of Flavours started to become *increasingly* important *particularly* for the food market about two decades ago.

Today, the U.S. demand for natural Flavours accounts for about 70-80% of all flavor-added products. Europe also favours natural Flavours, and a widespread growth in Asia over the next few years was predicted. This rising demand cannot be covered by means of traditional flavor recovery processes, which mainly revert to extraction and distillation of field-grown plant material.

Thus, this gap of supply represents one major push for plant biotechnology for the production of natural Flavours. Although the specific

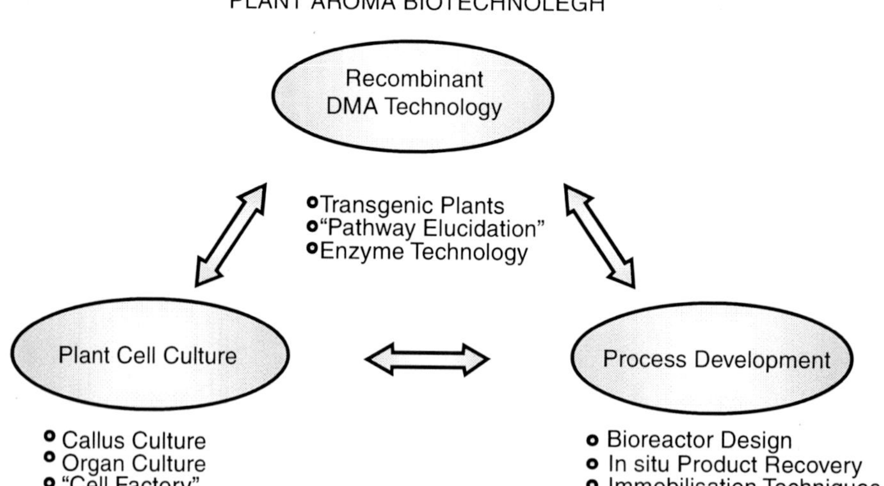

Figure 5.1: Research fields of plant aroma biotechnology.

fields of research overlap and interact to a wide extent, an attempt to structure plant aroma biotechnology is presented in figure elsewhere in this chapter. *Recombinant DNA technology,* although discussed controversially in public, raises multifaceted expectations.

Since the introduction of the first genetically engineered whole food, the FLAVRSAVRTM tomato, in 1994, recombinant *DNA technology* has developed rapidly. The majority of genetic *engineering* imparted pest or pesticide resistance to the plant, whereas improved flavor quality has been aspired to only recently. Notwithstanding the long breeding history of aromatic fruit, we still lack essential information on the molecular, cellular, and physiological events that control the processes of flavor genesis.

With the help of *recombinant* DNA technology, the genetic *information* responsible for flavor *formation* in plants can be *characterized* and isolated. Afterward it may be either transferred into a suitable microbial host strain or used specifically to modify food plants. The *understanding* of these fundamental biochemical principles is indispensable for the development of competitive industrial processes through *manipulation* of precursors, enzymes, and horticultural and storage conditions.

Leahy and Roderick and Takeoka published *comprehensive* articles with numerous references on general and on fruit- and vegetable-specific principles of flavor genesis from nonvolatile precursors. The employment of stable isotope-labeled precursors to trace their integration in the target compounds or the modification of enzyme activities expanded the *methodology* for elucidation of biosynthetic pathways leading to fruit Flavours.

Last but not least, the recent advances in analytical chemistry vitally contribute to deepen our knowledge of biochemical pathways of aroma genesis and *furthermore* permit the detection of new powerful aroma compounds as potential target molecules for biotechnological processes. Usually, only a few *constituents* of a complex plant flavor determine the overall flavor profile.

Aroma dilution analysis combined with coupled gas chromatography-olfactometry aids in detecting these so-called character impact compounds. Only trace *concentrations* of an impact molecule are required to modify a flavor or fragrance composition. The great potential of *plant cell and tissue cultures* for the production of food ingredients was emphasized by Fu et al..

Tremendous progress in the basic understanding of plant metabolic pathways and regulatory mechanisms and in the development of lucrative high-yielding cell lines has been made.

In particular, the short culture periods in comparison with the whole plant and the facile accessibility of the genome are attractive merits. An exciting field of application is the *bioconversion* of externally applied substrates, which is facilitated by the *saprophytic* nature of most plant cell culture systems.

The refinement of abundant *agrochemicals* from industrial waste streams to high-priced flavor compounds is within reach, as is the precise direction of the flavor profile by addition of potential aroma precursors. The use of plant cell cultures for flavor production has been reviewed by Scragg.

As the overall secondary metabolite profile of callus and organ cultures may differ *significantly* from that of the parent plant, exhaustive application and safety *considerations* and, where necessary, safety testing have to be undertaken before the commercial use of cell culture extracts as food additives.

Far-reaching *process developments* are necessary to translate ideas from recombinant DNA technology and cell culture systems into industrial practice.

Detailed economic considerations regarding the difficult interplay between technical and business factors may be found in the report of Goldstein.

Process developments may comprise bioreactor design or the provision of an external accumulation site. The *immobilization* of cells or enzymes on solid supports may both increase production of secondary metabolites *decisively* and simplify product purification.

Table 5.1: Genetically Engineered Plants with Modified Aroma Profile

Plant species	*Genetic modification*	*Altered properties*
Lycopersicon esculentum	Overexpression of a yeast A-9 desaturase gene	Levels of (Z)-3-hexenal and (Z)-3-hexen-l-ol increased
Lycopersicon esculentum	Insertion of a tomato alcohol dehydrogenase cDNA in increased sense direction	Hexanol and Z-3-hexenol levels
Cucumis melo	Transformation with a 1-aminocyclopropane-1-	Reduction of ethylene synthesis, delayed ripening carboxylic acid oxidase antisense gene
Cucumis melo	Expression of a brazzein-encoding gene	Enhanced sweet flavor component

 RECOMBINANT DNA TECHNOLOGY

Genetically Engineered Food Plants

In contrast to numerous efforts to establish pest- or pesticide-resistant field crops on the world market, few genetically engineered plants that provide benefits such as improved flavor properties or enhanced vitamin supply have been developed up to now.

A major breakthrough in consumer acceptance of genetically modified food plants could possibly be achieved by the work of Ye et al., who *transferred* the entire provitamin A (β,βcarotene) *biosynthetic* pathway into the endosperm of rice.

In a single *Agrobacterium-mediated* transformation, two plant genes from daffodil (*Narcissus pseudonarcissus*), phytoene synthase and lycopene, β -cyclase, and a bacterial phytoene desaturase from *Erwinia uredovora* were introduced into the rice genome.

The resulting genetically engineered "golden rice" is capable of forming β, β-carotene from endogenous *geranylgeranyl* diphosphate and thus may *counteract* vitamin A deficiency, which is a serious health problem in many third-world countries. Carotenes may act as precursors not only of vitamins but also of Flavours. Common flavor impact compounds such as the C_{13}-norisoprenoids α–ionone, β-ionone, and grasshopper ketone can be *structurally* traced back to *carotenoid* progenitors.

Overexpression of a yeast A9 desaturase gene in tomato (*Lycopersicon esculentum* Mill.) increased not only monoenic fatty acids but also polyunsaturated fatty acids in tomato fruits. The changes of the fatty acid profile were accompanied by changes in certain flavor compounds derived from enzymatic fatty acid degradation.

Especially the linolenic acid *peroxidation* products (Z)-3-hexenal and (Z)-3-hexen-l-ol, derived from (Z)-3-hexenal by alcohol dehydrogenase, were *increased* in transgenic fruit. An approach to the directed *modification* of the flavor profile of tomato fruit was reported by Speirs et al.. Tomato plants were transformed with gene constructs containing a tomato alcohol dehydrogenase complementary DNA (cDNA) in a sense orientation relative to the tomato *polygalacturonase* promoter to provide fruit-ripening specific expression of the cDNA.

The transformed plants displayed enhanced alcohol dehydrogenase (ADH) activities in the ripening fruit, which *influenced* the balance between some of the aldehydes and the *corresponding* alcohols associated with flavor perception. In particular, *hexanol* and Z-3-hexenol levels were increased in fruit with enhanced ADH activity. In a *preliminary* taste trial, the transgenic tomato fruit exhibited a more intense "ripe fruit" flavor.

A transgenic method for *producing* plant foodstuffs such as fruits (e.g., melons), vegetables, or seeds with a modified sweet component was patented by Tomes. A gene that encodes the sweet protein brazzein was linked to a *promoter* capable of directing the expression of brazzein in a favoured plant organ and thus enhancing the sweet component of the flavor.

S-Linalool synthase from *Clarkia breweri* (Onagraceae), an annual plant native to California, was the subject of another patent specification. By expressing the respective nucleic acid sequence in appropriate host plants, *enhancement* of their scent production has been attempted. 1-

Aminocyclopropane-l-carboxylic acid oxidase (ACO) is an enzyme involved in the *biosynthesis* of ethylene, a plant growth regulator initiating fruit ripening.

To improve the storage and handling characteristics of *cantaloupe* charentais melon (*Cucumis melo* var. *cantalupensis*, Naud. cv Vedrandais), a cantaloupe melon line was transformed with an ACO antisense gene. A strong reduction of ethylene synthesis and, as a consequence, delayed ripening were achieved.

The total quantity of volatiles detected in the antisense fruit was only 20 to 40% of that in the control fruit, indicating that biosynthesis of Flavours is strongly controlled by ethylene. Exogenous ethylene was able to restore a qualitative and *quantitative* aroma profile very similar to that of the control fruit without antisense ACO. Ultimately aiming at the modification of the essential oil composition of aromatic plants by genetic *transformation*, Faure et al. developed an efficient in vitro shoot *regeneration* method from spearmint (*Mentha spicata L.*) and peppermint (*Mentha X piperita*) leaf disks.

On the basis of these results, Diemer et al. established an *Agrobacteriwn tumefaciens*mediated transformation procedure for peppermint, spearmint, and cornmint (*Mentha arvensis L.*). The stable integration and *expression* of two reporter genes was confirmed by polymerase chain reaction (PCR), Southern blot *hybridization*, reverse transcription PCR (RT-PCR), and a histoenzymatic assay.

Plant Enzymes and Genomics

Although microbial enzymes are already widely applied in industrial flavor production, the failure in isolating and operating active and stable *multienzyme* complexes stable in vitro has still hampered broad *technical* implementation of plant enzymes.

Based on up-to-date RNA-DNA techniques, dissection of the complex developmental process of flavor genesis becomes feasible. The identification of flavor related-genes and their corresponding proteins as well as the growing *understanding* of molecular regulation of gene expression now adds new tools to flavor biotechnology and thus establishes a basis for profitable exploitation. The genes and peptides of an entire pathway toward the formation of volatile aliphatic and aromatic esters in strawberry fruit (*Fragaria* sp.) have been disclosed by Aharoni et al..

DNA sequences that encode strawberry fruit-specific *aminotransferase*, pyruvate decarboxylase, thiolase, alcohol *dehydrogenase*, or *acyltransferase* were cloned and characterized. Further acyltransferases and esterases involved in aroma genesis were isolated from apple (*Malus domestica* Borkh.), mango (*Magnifera indica L.*), and banana (*Musa sp.*).

These nucleic acid or protein sequences may be used in expression systems or to modify plants with the goal of producing natural or synthetic Flavours. In this context, a novel strawberry acyltransferase was identified by use of cDNA microarrays combined with *appropriate* statistical analyses. Such microarray assays allow *systematic* studies of the expression profiles of large subsets of genes in given tissues under specific *physiologic* and *environmental* conditions.

Another approach to isolate *ripeningrelated* genes from strawberry fruit utilized the differential screening of a high-quality cDNA library, whereby altogether 26 ripening-related cDNAs were identified. Complementary DNA clones encoding 4-coumarate-coenzymeA (CoA) ligase (4CL) (EC 6.2.1.12) and caffeic acid O-methyltransferase (EC 2.1.1.6), key enzymes of *phenylpropanoid* metabolism, were isolated from a cDNA library constructed from messenger RNA (mRNA) of a kinetin-treated cell suspension culture of vanilla (*Vanilla planifolia* Andr.). Based on studies using inhibitors of 4CL, it was concluded that down-regulation of this enzyme by the antisense technique would result in a redirection of the flow of *phenylpropanoid* precursors from lignin biosynthesis into flavor compounds.

These attempts hold much promise because vanillin not only is the impact compound of the world's most popular flavor, but also has antioxidant properties in food. The complex interrelations of phenylpropanoid biosynthesis were reviewed by Dixon et al., who presented examples of genetic engineering of, e.g., tobacco (*Nicotiana tabacum L*), alfalfa (*Medicago sativa L*), and soybean (*Glycine max* (*L*) Men.) plants and cell cultures to alter pathway flux.

Several plant enzymes involved in the early steps of terpenoid *biosynthesis* have been characterized, including acetoacetyl-CoA thiolase (EC 2.3.1.9), mevalonate kinase (EC 2.7.1.36), isopentenyl *diphosphate* isomerase (EC 5.3.3.2), and 3-hydroxy-3-methylglutaryl-CoA synthase (EC 4.1.3.5).

Cyclases convert linear isoprenoid diphosphates such as geranyl diphosphate, farnesyl *diphosphate*, and geranylgeranyl diphosphate into a variety of mono- and polycyclic hydrocarbons and alcohols. A number of terpene cyclases from plants, representing soluble, *magnesium-containing enzymes*, have been cloned and expressed in *Escherichia coli*.

Thus, there is now the potential to engineer plants to produce specific cyclic terpenes for use in the flavor and fragrance industries. Cloning and expression of the monoterpene synthases (-)-4-S-limonene synthase from spearmint, (+)-bornyl diphosphate synthase from sage (*Salvia officinalis L.*), and (-)-pinene synthase from grand fir (*Abies grandis*) in *E. coli* enabled Schwab et al. to gain insight into the mechanistic procedures of the reaction sequence toward cyclic monoterpenes.

An overview of the enzymology and regulation of essential oil biosynthesis with detailed description of the reaction mechanisms leading to the basic isoprenoid skeletons is given elsewhere in this chapter. Natural (Z)-3-hexenol (leaf alcohol), traditionally isolated from mint terpene fractions, is formed from linoleic and linolenic acid via the lipoxygenase pathway.

Lipoxygenases have been isolated, cloned, and *characterized* from various plant sources. The enzymatic genesis of the 13-hydroperoxy linoleic and linolenic acid is followed by the hydroperoxide lyase (HPO-lyase)-catalyzed cleavage to (Z)-3-hexenal, which is subsequently reduced to the corresponding alcohol. As in a *reconstituted* production system the activity of hydroperoxide lyase proved to be the rate-limiting factor, the gene coding for this enzyme was cloned from banana and heterologously expressed in yeast cells to yield a highly active lyase material.

Another plant HOP-lyase was purified 300-fold from tomatoes. Whereas only 13-hydroperoxides from linoleic acid and alinolenic acid were cleaved by the tomato enzyme, HOP-lyase from alfalfa (*Medicago sativa L.*) also accepted 9-hydroperoxides as substrates to form the respective volatile C9-aldehydes.

The specific activity for 9-hydroperoxy fatty acids was about 50% of the activity for the 13-isomers. The characteristic flavor of onion occurs when the enzyme alliinase (EC 4.4.1.4) hydrolyzes S-alk(en)yl-L-cysteine sulfoxides (ACSOs) to form pyruvate, ammonia, and sulfur-containing volatiles. Physical characterization of alliinase and molecular analysis of the respective cDNA revealed that two genes and thus two protein subunits were expressed in onion bulb tissue.

Although these genes for alliinase are highly homologous in their DNA sequence, there are differences in the proteins that they code for, probably due to varying degrees of glycosylation. Flavorless *glycosides* represent one accumulation form of aroma substances in fruit and in many other plant tissues.

In addition to developments in the analysis of these polar plant constituents, current attention is focused on biotechnological methods for flavor release and flavor *enhancement* through enzymatic *hydrolysis* of the glycosidically bound aroma precursors.

The liberation of the "bound" aroma portion offers a tool for the *production* of natural Flavours from otherwise waste materials such as peelings, skins, and stems. Because the practical application of endogenous and exogenous glycosidases is limited by their low activities at neutral pH values and strong inhibition by glucose, the *construction* of chimeric genes with improved hydrolytic properties and their *overexpression* in different hosts are the subjects of actual research.

An industrially relevant route for the production of a "natural" topnote flavor of concord grapes (*Vitis labrusca* "concord"), methylanthranilate (MA), is the peroxidase-catalyzed *N-demethylation* of methyl N-methylanthranilate (MNMA).

Comparison of different commercial peroxidase preparations showed soybean peroxidase to be the most effective biocatalyst for the N-demethylation of MNMA to MA. Upon complete conversion of MNMA, the yield of soybean peroxidase-catalyzed MA amounted to 82% within 10 minutes at 70°C and pH 4.

Current research is focused on the *improvement* of cacao plants (*Theobroma cacao L.*) for the food industry.

The efficiency of breeding programs could be increased if genetically based maps were available and markers associated with major quantitative trait loci for quality and productivity could be identified. Even though the target organism in this case is not genetically modified, genomics acts as an invaluable research tool.

PLANT CELL, TISSUE, AND ORGAN CULTURES

The term *tissue culture* is applied to any *nondifferentiated* cell culture grown on solid or, as suspension culture, in liquid medium. As the propagation of the cultures is strictly based on mitotic events, the entire genome and, thus, the full potential to form Flavours and fragrances are maintained in each cultured cell. However, organized cultures often exhibit an enhanced capacity to form volatile Flavours when compared with that of unorganized cell suspension cultures.

Commonly used are the hairy root cultures induced by the *transformation* of aseptic plantlets with *Agrobacterium rhizogenes*. Independent of the type of cell culture used, usually simultaneous application of different strategies for the improvement of yields is necessary to reach timedependent volumetric yields [mg product (L X day)$^{-1}$] sufficient for industrial commercialization.

These strategies include the selection of stable, high-yielding cell lines, variation of medium components and gas phase composition, precursor feeding, use of elicitors, in situ product removal, and *immobilization* techniques.

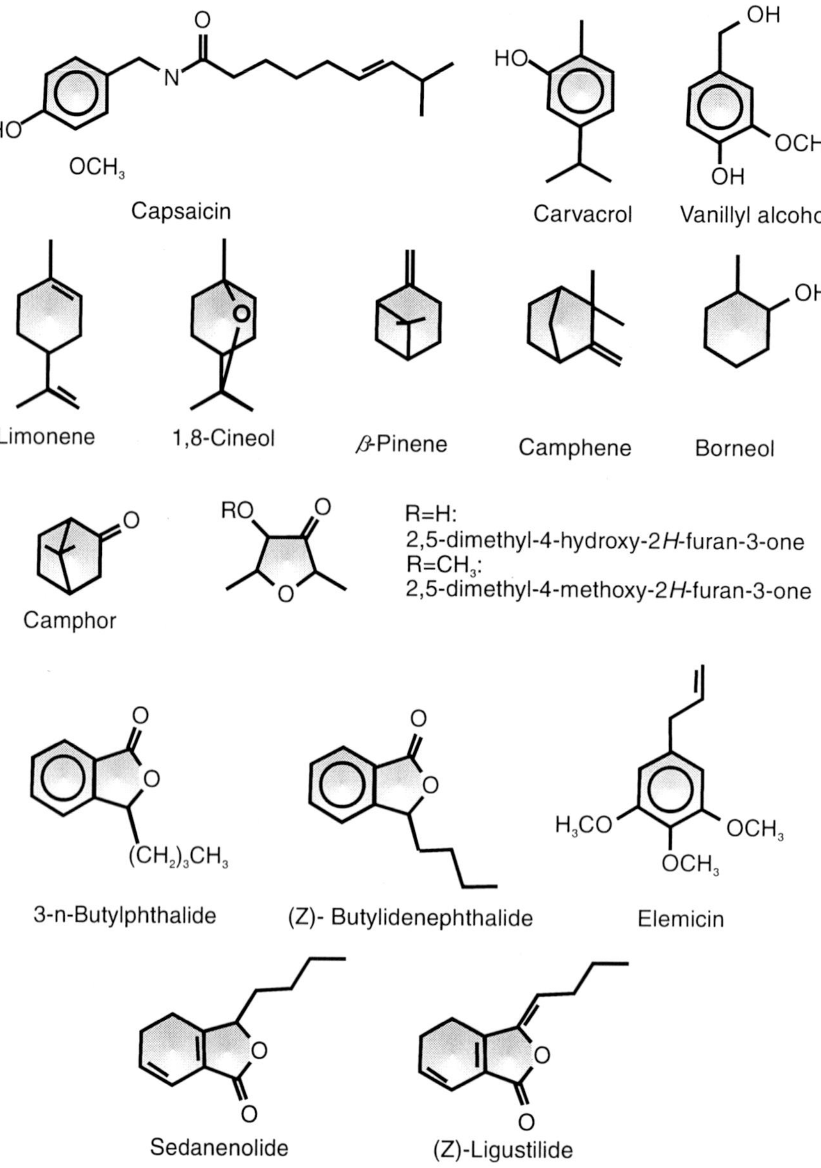

Figure 5.2: Flavours and fragrances from plant cell cultures.

Although individual strategies may result in enhanced secondary metabolite formation, often several strategies have to be combined to give a synergistic response. Numerous attempts to produce flavor and aroma compounds by plant cell, tissue, and organ cultures have been described. To avoid *recapitulations*, only references that were not cited in the preceding reviews were considered for the present section.

Tissue Cultures

Capsaicin, the major pungent principle of chilli pepper (*Capsicum frutescens L.*), may be extracted from callus cultures. By developing cell lines resistant to *p-fluorophenylalanine* (PFP), capsaicin yield could be increased up to 45% over normal cell lines (80 μg capsaicin/g fresh weight).

The activity profile of *phenylalanine* ammonia lyase, the *enzyme* responsible for conversion of phenylalanine to (E)-cinnamic acid, exhibited no correlation with the capsaicin content in both control and PFP-resistant cells. In the flavor and fragrance industry there is an enormous demand for essential oils, and many of the more than 3000 different essential oils have been *utilized* in the creation of fragrances.

Consequently, there has been extensive research on the production of essential oils by plant cell cultures. Only very low yields of volatile oil were achieved with callus cultures of pot *marjoram* (*Origanum vulgare L.*).

In contrast to the composition of essential oil from plants cultivated in the field, microdistillation of calli revealed only three major essential oil constituents, one of which was *identified* as carvacrol. In contrast to *expectations*, the source tissue of the *explant* may crucially affect the *production* of volatile compounds of the resulting tissue cultures.

Whereas embryogenic cell lines of sweet orange (*Citrus sinensis* (*L.*) Osbeck) emitted a sweet, fruity aroma, nonembryogenic cell lines derived from immature juice vesicles failed to form the characteristic flavor constituents of sweet orange. Seventeen aroma active *compounds* were identified from *embryogenic* cell lines, altogether amounting to 420 mg volatiles/ kg fresh weight tissue. A frequently underestimated aspect of culturing plant cells is the influence of the light regime.

For the callus cells of grapefruit (*Citrus paradisi* Macf.), lemon (*C. limon* (*L.*) Burm.), and lime (*C. aurantiifolia* (Christm. et Panz.) Swingle) a photomixotrophic state was indispensable for the generation of monoterpenes. The *chlorophyll* content and *accumulation* of isoprenoid-derived volatiles were positively correlated in each case.

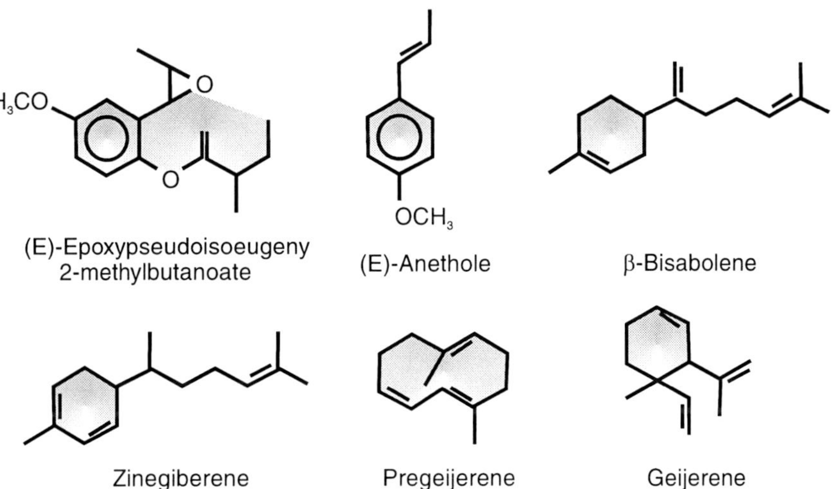

Figure 5.3: Flavours from hairy root cultures and fruits of anise.

Table 5.2: Possible Plant Sources of Flavor Components from Cell Cultures

Common name	Botanical name	Principal metabolites
Paprika	*Capsicum frutescens*	Capsaicin
Oregano	*Origanum vulgare*	Carvacrol
Sweet orange	*Citrus sinensis*	3-hydroxy-2-butanone/ethyl acetate/ acetaldehyde
Grapefruit	*Citrus paradisi*	Limonene/nootkatone/citronellal
White diosma	*Coleonema album*	Limonene/phellandrenes
Vanilla	*Vanilla planifolia*	Vanillin/vanillyl alcohol
Rosemary	*Rosmarinus officinalis*	β–Pinene/camphene/cineole/linalool/ camphor
Strawberry	*Fragaria x ananassa*	2,5-Dimethyl-4-hydroxy-2H-furan-3-one/ 2,5-dimethyl-4-methoxy-2H-furan-3one
Brazilian snapdragon	*Otacanthus coeruleus*	Menthone/valencene
Parsley	*Petroselinum crispum*	3-n-Butylphthalide/butylidenephthalide/ elemicinlsedanenolide/ligustilide
Anise	*Pimpinella anisum*	Epoxypseudoisoeugenyl 2-methlbutyrate/zingiberene/ β–bisabolene/geijerene/pregeijerene
Musk melon	*Cucumis melo*	(Z)-3-Hexenol/(E)-2-hexenal/1-nonanol/ (Z)-6-nonenol

After optimization of the growth medium's phytoeffector composition and the light regime, about 40 volatile mono- and *sesquiterpene hydrocarbons*, oxygenated terpenes, and aliphatic aldehydes could be recovered from grapefruit callus cultures.

The best yielding callus contained about 186 mg aroma active compounds per kg wet weight, representing about 5% of the volatiles found in peel tissue of the whole fruit. Similarly, the accumulation of chlorophyll and volatile *oligoisoprenoids* by white diosma (*Coleonema album* Thunb.) *photomixotrophic* cell cultures was favoured by high light intensities, an extended photoperiod, and elevated concentrations of phytoeffectors.

Total volatiles, including e.g. limonene and phellandrenes, accumulated to *approximately* 73 mg per kg wet weight. Few differences in the growth patterns were observed between darkand light-grown vanilla (*Vanilla planifolia*) cultures. However, the light conditions did affect the production of compounds associated with the vanillin pathway, particularly of 4-hydroxy-3-methoxybenzyl alcohol (vanillyl alcohol). Still a serious problem in *establishing* plant callus and suspension cultures is the risk of endogenous microbial infections, for which remedy can be found in the application of an appropriate antibiotic.

On the other hand, microbial infection may even contribute to flavor biosynthesis. Elicitors, components of biological origin involved in inter- or intraspecies interactions of plants, may be of significance for the formation of flavor constituents.

In cell cultures of rosemary (*Rosmarinus officinalis L.*) emanating cineole and β–pinene, persistent contamination with *Pseudomonas mallei* was reported. Unintended *elicitation* may be proposed to explain this observation. Two important character impact compounds of strawberry flavor, the furanones 2,5-dimethyl-4-hydroxy-2H-furan-3-one (DMHF) and 2,5-dimethyl-4-methoxy-2H-furan-3-one (mesifuran), were synthesized by strawberry tissue cultures (*Fragaria X ananassa*, cv. Elsanta) after they were treated with *Methylobacterium extorquens*.

Untreated (sterile) cell cultures and the bacteria alone were not capable of forming DMHF or mesifuran. A biosynthetic pathway in the strawberry *callus-Methylobacterium* system for the two furanones was proposed as follows: endogenous strawberry 1,2-propanediol is oxidized to 2-hydroxypropanal (lactaldehyde) by the *Methylobacterium* species.

The microbially derived lactaldehyde could be further condensed with dihydroxyacetone phosphate by the strawberry cells to form the furanone progenitor 6-deoXy-D-fructose-1 -phosphate. *Photomixotrophic* cell cultures of parsley (*Petroselinum crispum* (Mill.) Nym.) accumulated volatiles solely after treatment with the autoclaved homogenate of fungal cells.

Homogenates of the wood-destroying basidiomycetes *Polyporus umbellatus* and *Tyromyces sambuceus* induced a spicy, celery-like odor, triggered by elemicin (5-allyl-1,2,3-trimethoxybenzene), 3n-butylphthalide, (Z)- and (E)-butylidenephthalide, sedanenolide, and (Z)ligustilide. Considerable amounts of odorous mono- and sesquiterpenes have been recovered from in vitro callus cultures of Brazilian snapdragon (*Otacanthus coeruleus*) (*Scrophulariaceae*), an ornamental pot plant *originating* from east Brazil.

Interestingly, the amount of essential oil extracted from the nutrient media was often higher than the amount extracted from the cell cultures. High-sucrose treatments, especially from 40 g L^{-1} on, increased the oil quantities found in the medium, probably due to increased osmotic stress. Up to 0.34% total oil content was reached in cultures plus medium, which was more than in the respective plants.

With the aim of obtaining high levels of essential oils, cell cultures of two genotypes of rosemary were established. The compositions of the growth media for both callus formation and *regeneration* of plants crucially influenced the *monoterpenoid* profile.

Concentrations of calcium ions, sucrose, and plant growth regulators significantly affected the yields of camphene, 1,8-cineole, linalool, camphor, borneol, and bornyl acetate.

Organ Cultures

Hairy root cultures of anise (*Pimpinella anisum L.*) were grown in different nutrient media in darkness and under periodic light conditions. The composition of the essential oils obtained from hairy root cultures differed significantly from that of the fruits.

Whereas the major components of the essential oils from the hairy root cultures were the anethole precursor (E)epoxypseudoisoeugenyl 2-methylbutanoate, zingiberene, β–bisabolene, geijerene, and pregeijerene, the terpene spectrum of the fruits was dominated by (E)-anethole.

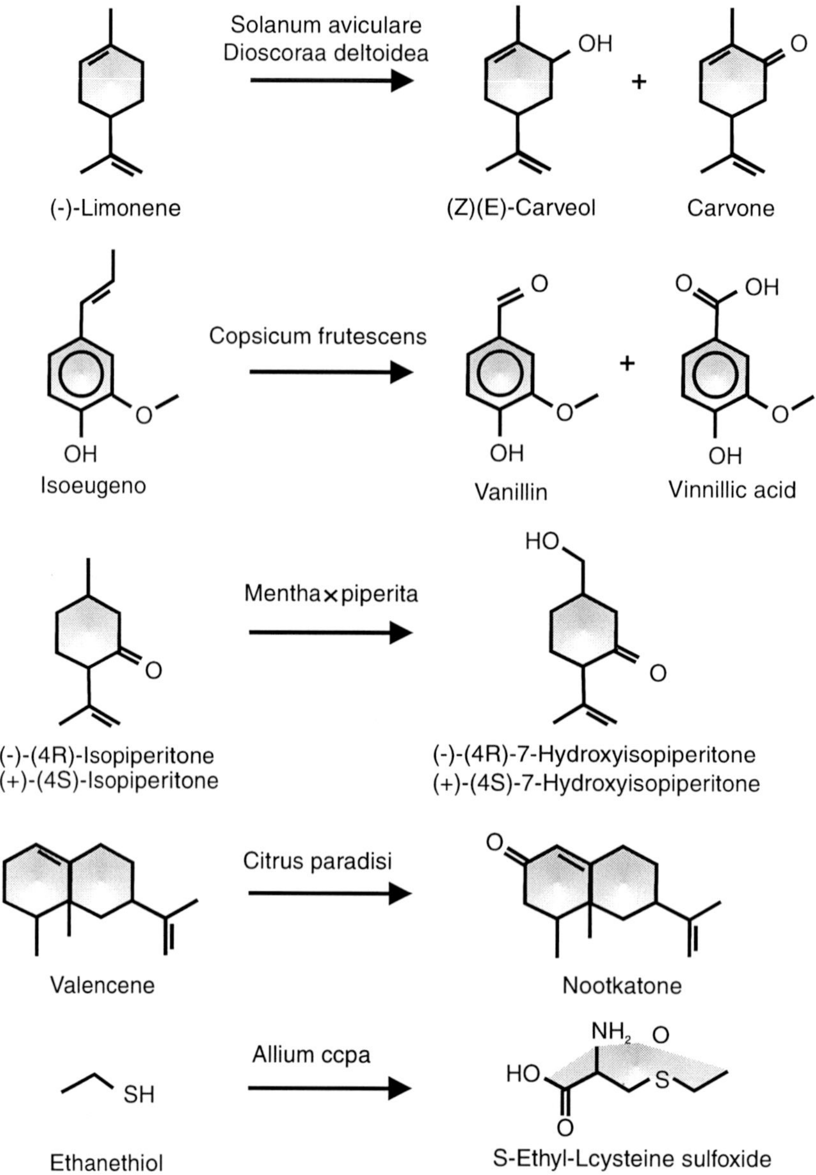

Figure 5.4: Bioconversion of exogenous substrates by plant cell cultures.

The highest essential oil yield obtained from hairy root cultures was 0.1%, which was comparable to that obtained from the roots of the parent plant and, when considering hairy roots on a dry weight basis, also that of the fruits.

With regard to potential biotechnological exploitation, the *morphological* stability of the "rooty" phenotype is of great importance. In one of four growth media tested, the hairy root cultures revealed high *morphological* stability with no dedifferentiation or greening even after more than 2 years of culture. Encouraged by these results,

Matsuda et al. produced mutant hairy roots of musk melon (*Cucumis melo L.*) with an altered metabolism of essential oils by means of T-DNA insertion mutagenesis. From more than 6500 clones, five fragrant hairy root clones were obtained and the clone emitting the strongest fruity flavor of ripe fresh melons was selected for further investigations.

Extraction of the volatile compounds and identification by means of gas-liquid *chromatography-mass spectrometry* (GLC-MS) revealed the presence of (Z)-3-hexenol, (E)-2-hexenal, l-nonanol, and (Z)-6-nonenol, which also shape the flavor of melon fruits. Aroma emanation was *successfully* maintained in the hairy roots when they were subcultured repeatedly for more than 3 years.

Preliminary scale-up experiments using a 4-L jar fermenter showed an overall profile of the extracted essential oils that was very similar to that of hairy roots cultured on a routine laboratory scale. When compared with that of the fresh ripe melon fruit, the yield of aroma compounds in this scale-up approach was *approximately* 6.5-fold higher, indicating possible biotechnological exploitation. Plant sources of flavor components from cell cultures are *summarized* in table elsewhere in this chapter.

Biotransformation by Plant Cell Cultures

As with microbial conversions, cultured plant cells can be employed as "cell factories" to conduct bioconversions of exogenous substrates. Looking at flavor effectiveness and availability, monoterpenes are of *outstanding* interest. A comprehensive overview of *biotransformations* of monoterpenoid alcohols, aldehydes, ketones, and oxides by plant and microbial cell cultures was given by Shin.

The conversion of monoterpenes, steroids, and indole alkaloids using numerous cell cultures was summarized by Hamada and Furuya. Special attention in these reviews was dedicated to the regiospecificity and stereospecificity of the biochemical reactions as well as to immobilization techniques for cells or enzymes. Immobilized and free cells of kangaroo apple (*Solanum aviculare*) and of a yam species (*Dioscorea deltoidea*) were utilized for the oxidation of (-)-limonene to (Z)- and (E)-carveol and to carvone. Depending on the immobilization medium, either carvone or (Z)- and (E)-carveol were formed predominantly. Suspended cells of chilli pepper (*Capsicum frutescens*) accumulated vanilla flavor metabolites such as vanillin, vanillic acid, and ferulic acid when fed with isoeugenol.

Increased biotransformation rates of isoeugenol could be achieved by *immobilizing* cells with sodium alginate and applying fungal elicitors. Product yields up to 23 Ag mL^{-1} were reached by the *simultaneous* addition of β–cyclodextrin and isoeugenol (2.5 mM). Further attempts to optimize the *biotechnological* production of vanilla flavor compounds have been reviewed.

The potential of peppermint (*Mentha X piperita*) cell suspension cultures to synthesize menthol has been investigated intensively. Studies showed that peppermint cells possess extensive hydroxylation activity toward terpenes.

After application of the biosynthetic precursors (-)-(4R)- and (+)-(4S)-isopiperitones to cell suspension cultures, metabolism yielded the corresponding 7-hydroxyisopiperitones, which were *concomitantly* converted into the respective *glucopyranosides*. The flavor synthesis of various *Allium* tissue cultures (onion, garlic, and chive) was less productive when compared with the respective plants.

This was attributed to the low aroma precursor concentrations inside the cells rather than to the C-S lyase activity. Based on the knowledge of the well-characterized biosynthetic pathways to the flavor precursors (+)-Salk(en)yl-L-cysteine sulfoxides (ACSOs) in *Allium* species, attempts were made to alter the flavor profile of onion root cultures by feeding of aroma precursors. Addition of cysteine, glutathione, and methionine increased the yields of methyl- and propenylcysteine sulfoxides, and the ratio of the propenyl to the methyl form was shifted significantly depending on the amount and type of the precursor used.

S-Ethyl-L-cysteine sulfoxide, which is not a naturally occurring compound, was produced by application of ethanethiol to the root cultures, indicating the possible use of such cultures for the production of novel *homologous* metabolites.

Incubation of suspended, stationary phase cells of grapefruit with *exogenous* valencene led to the intermediary formation of the 2-hydroxy derivative, followed by conversion to the 2-oxo compound, nootkatone. The transformation rate was 68% in 24 hours, and when the concentration of about 0.7 mg L^{-1} was reached, it was maintained for another 48 hours without noticeable change.

PROCESS DEVELOPMENTS

To increase *production* rates of secondary metabolites, different in situ extraction procedures have been applied to plant cell and tissue cultures. The extraction phases can either be water-immiscible liquids, such as n-hexadecane or Miglyol™, or solid adsorbents such as the hydrophobic polystyrene-divinylbenzene resins (e.g., Amberlite XAD). Zeolites have also been *successfully* applied for the specific accumulation of essential oil compounds from liquid fermentation media.

By provision of an external accumulation site, further metabolism and degradation of products in the medium as well as cytotoxic product concentrations may be impeded. Moreover, and especially for highly volatile Flavours, the danger of physicochemical losses of product is minimized by addition of an appropriate adsorbent.

In combination with further optimization attempts, such as *immobilization* or elicitation, the productivity of a cell culture process can be vitally enhanced. Superior production rates of cell culture systems compared with field-grown material are sought by numerous efforts to improve bioreactor design.

Current apparatus proposals for suspension cultures as well as for organized cultures were summarized by Scragg. Design equations for oxygen transfer rates in large-scale root culture reactors have been discussed by Tescione et al.. The tomato flavor enzyme system (*lipoxygenase* and *hydroperoxide lyase*) was harnessed as a crude enzyme preparation in a hollow-fiber reactor to produce hexanal from linoleic acid.

At exogenous substrate (linoleic acid) concentrations of 16 mmol L^{-1}, hexanal production rates of about 5 μg min^{-1} were achieved. The reactor system proved to be stable over an operation period of 5 days, indicating that flavor production with immobilized membrane-associated enzymes in a hollow-fiber reactor is a promising technique.

It allows retention of the enzyme system and substrate, with *concomitant* removal of the product. For the synthesis of extracellular metabolites the *immobilization* of intact plant cells provides several processing advantages, such as protecting cells from mechanical stress, enhanced productivity, high stability, and facilitated product recovery.

Several immobilization agents (polyurethane foam, carrageenan, alginate, pectate, polyphenyleneoxide) for cell cultures of *Solanum aviculare* and *Dioscorea deltoidea* did not affect the biotransformation course of (-)-limonene to (Z)- and (E)-carveol and to carvone but significantly changed product ratios.

CONCLUSIONS

The ever increasing consumer demand for "naturalness" of foodstuffs and cosmetics along with the enormous potential of plants in biosynthesis and bioconversion represents an attractive basis for plant aroma biotechnology.

The potential market for biotechnology-derived Flavours and fragrances is estimated to be 10% or more of the overall flavor market, which was expected to amount to $10 billion in 2000, tendency ascending. Indeed, up to now, the lion's share thereof accounts for microbially catalyzed processes. Contrary to the successful generation of high-value pharmaceuticals, plant cell cultures still need to be shown to be competitive with field plants or microorganisms in the production of flavor compounds on an industrial scale.

To reach this aim, the productivity of the cell culture systems will need to be improved significantly. Most promising starting points are given by recombinant DNA technologies. The genetic *information* responsible for fruit and herbal flavor formation can be isolated, characterized, and afterward either transferred into a suitable microbial *expression* system or used specifically to modify food plants.

A steadily increasing number of publications and patent applications on plant genes and transgenic plants indicates rapid scientific progress as well as industrial interest. After all, the short- and middle-term success of these technologies will, beyond *technological* and economic considerations, depend crucially on the acceptance of the novel products by the consumer.

Extensive evaluation and communication of scientific facts will be indispensable to deal with *widespread* concerns before achievements in basic science will turn into marketable Flavours and flavor-enriched products.

Chapter 6

FINE CHEMICALS FROM PLANTS

Plants have been used in traditional medicine for a long time. About 13,000 plant species have been used as drugs *throughout* the world, and *approximately* 25% of our current materia medica is derived from plants in form of teas, extracts, or pure substances.

Accordingly, plant secondary *metabolites* are an important source of various fine chemicals (phytochemicals) that are used directly or as *intermediates* for the *production* of *pharmaceuticals*. Additional applications are in the cosmetic industry and as food or drink additives. The plant kingdom provides an enormous portfolio of secondary metabolites of which currently about 100,000 compounds from plants are known and 4000 substances newly discovered every year.

The largest proportion of these compounds consists of terpenoids (more than 30%), followed by alkaloids (approximately 20%). The focus of this chapter is *predominantly* on alkaloids for *pharmaceutical* applications. In recent years, there has been a resurgence of interest in the discovery of new *compounds* from plants with the aim of finding novel activities against a variety of illnesses.

New technical developments in high-throughput screening techniques now allow the screening of substances at a rate not possible previously. In addition, the biological effects of minimal *concentrations* of secondary *metabolites* can now be measured due to the much improved sensitivity of the screening systems.

There are still many plant species that have not been examined with respect to their biological activities, and there is an expectation that tropical plants in particular will provide compounds with novel activities. Such compounds may be used as lead structures for the development of new drugs by chemical synthesis or, *alternatively*, may be used as drugs directly or as intermediates for chemical modification following *extraction* from the plant.

 PRODUCTION OF PHYTOCHEMICALS

The commercial production of plant secondary metabolites as fine chemicals can be done by either total *chemical* synthesis, extraction and purification from plant material, or partial chemical synthesis following extraction of *biosynthetic* precursors from plant material. The decision on which route is taken is made on economical grounds and/or depends on the *availability* of the plant material.

Chemical synthesis of plant-derived compounds is worthwhile only if few *synthesis* steps are needed and the source *chemicals* are available at low cost. Molecules of simple chemical structure with few steric centers thus lend themselves to total synthesis. Examples of such *compounds* are the piperidine alkaloids lobelin and arecoline.

In contrast, complex structures such as the cyclic diterpenoid taxol or alkaloids such as the tropane alkaloid scopolamine or the indole alkaloid *camptothecin* are either extracted from plant material or partially synthesized from extracted biosynthetic *precursors*. For example, taxol and its analogue taxotere are largely produced by acylation of their *biosynthetic* precursor 10-deacetylbaccatin III extracted from the needles of *Taxus*.

The anticancer therapeutic topotecan is obtained semisynthetically from the indol alkaloid camptothecin extracted from the leaves of *Camptotheca acuminata*. Several sources of plant material may be used for the purpose of secondary metabolite extraction. The *simplest* route is the extraction from plant material that has been harvested from wild plant resources.

However, wild plant resources may be limited and hence may not permit sustainable production of phytochemicals. In addition, *overexploitation* of wild plant resources is undesirable from an environmental point of view. An alternative preferred by producers of *phytochemicals* is the cultivation of medicinal plants by *conventional* farming.

Conventional farming permits the sustainable production of plant material in the amount required for phytochemical production, provides independence of commercial plant material suppliers, and allows *continuous* improvement of production levels and *economics* by breeding and selection of superior genotypes.

Disadvantages are the investments and the long lead times required for the establishment of plantations and for responding to changing market demands as well as *environmental* risks due to adverse weather *conditions*, pests, and diseases. Also, climatic and soil requirements of the plants to be cultivated have to be taken into account.

Examples of medicinal plants that are grown on farms for the purpose of phytochemical production are *Pilocarpus microphyllus* (pilocarpine), *Digitalis lanata* (digitalis cardiac glycosides), *Papaver somniferum* (codeine and morphine), and *Duboisia* interspecific hybrids (hyoscyamine and scopolamine). A great deal of progress has been made in the cultivation of plant cells under controlled conditions in *bioreactors* that can be operated at virtually any geographic location.

The low productivity of plant cell cultures regarding secondary *metabolites* that has often

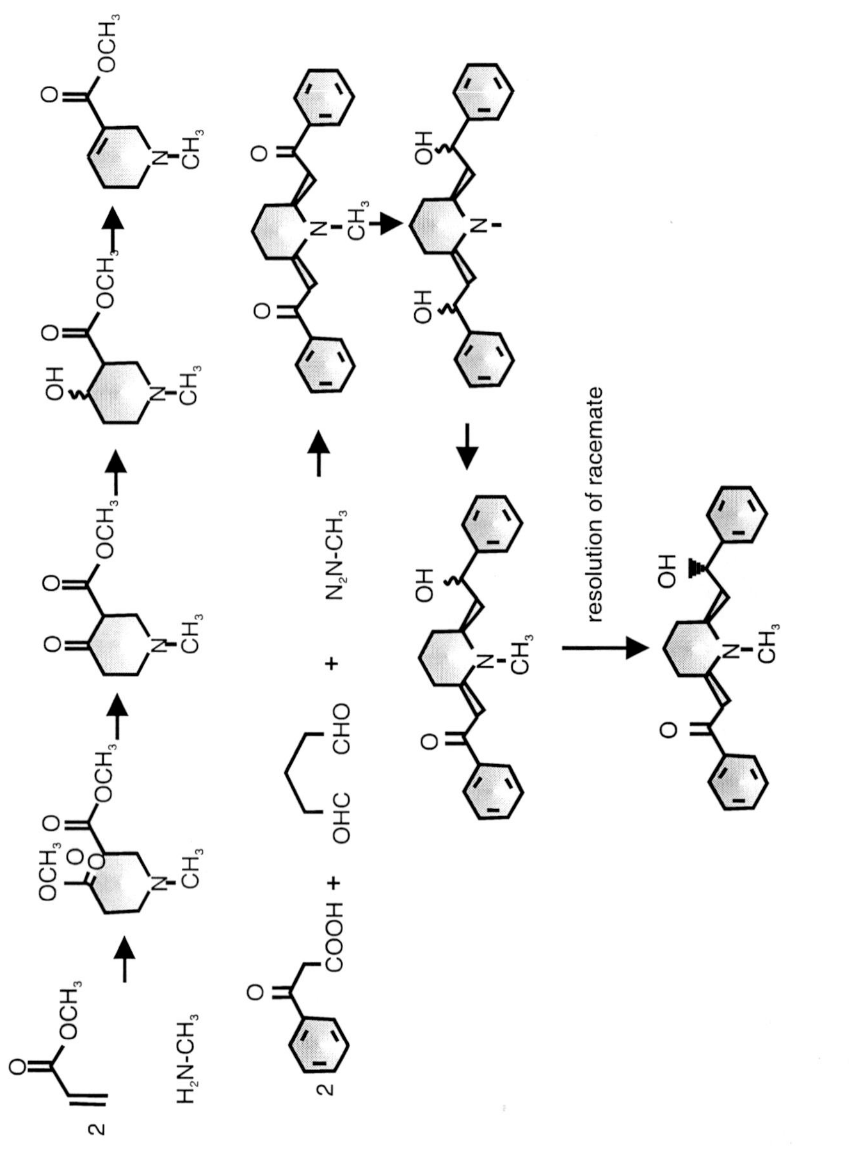

Figure 6.1: Chemical synthesis of the piperidine alkaloids lobelin (a) and arecolin (b).

been observed in many cases can be improved significantly by strain selection and elicitation. As an *alternative* to plant cell cultures, the use of organ cultures such as fast-growing hairy root cultures obtained after *transformation* using *Agrobacterium rhizogenes* has been proposed: the main location of secondary metabolite biosynthesis is often in the roots, which maintain secondary metabolite production in culture and are genetically stable for long periods of time, in contrast to what has been observed in many plant cell cultures.

However, the *cultivation* of organized structures such as hairy roots on a large scale in

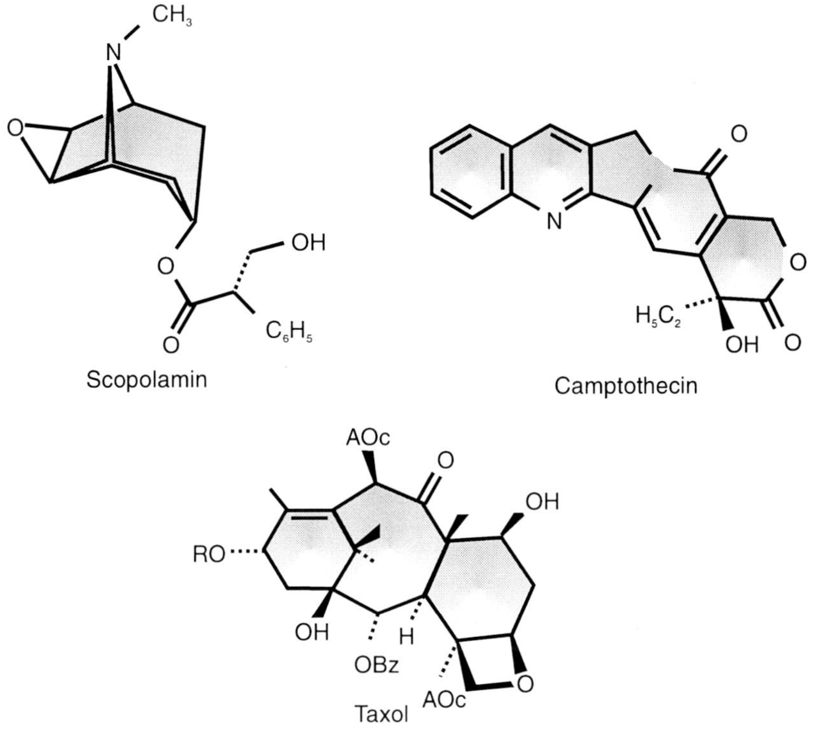

Scopolamin

Camptothecin

Taxol

Figure 6.2: Chemical structures of scopolamine, camptothecin, and taxol.

bioreactors is inherently more difficult than for cell cultures and, thus, has been demonstrated up to the 500 L scale only. In contrast, plant cells have been *successfully* cultivated up to the 60,000 L scale.

As the costs of large-scale production of *phytochemicals* using plant cell cultures are still prohibitively high, to date there have been only few *examples* of their commercial application.

METABOLIC ENGINEERING FOR IMPROVEMENT OF PRODUCTIVITY

With the advent of molecular biology and the possibility of genetically *transforming* plant cells and obtaining genetically modified (GM) or transgenic plants therefrom, there has been increased interest in improving the productivity and/or quality not only of arable crops but also-to a lesser extentof medicinal plant species. In addition, molecular biology provides the possibility to transfer single or multiple genes encoding biosynthetic enzymes into *microorganisms* with the purpose of *secondary* metabolite production. The general strategies for the biotechnological exploitation of alkaloid biosynthetic genes have been summarized by Kutchan, but they also apply for other secondary metabolites.

Plant secondary metabolite genes can be functionally expressed in microorganisms to produce either single *biotransformation* steps or short *biosynthetic* pathways. This approach requires that sufficient quantities of the secondary metabolite *precursors* needed for *biotransformation* are

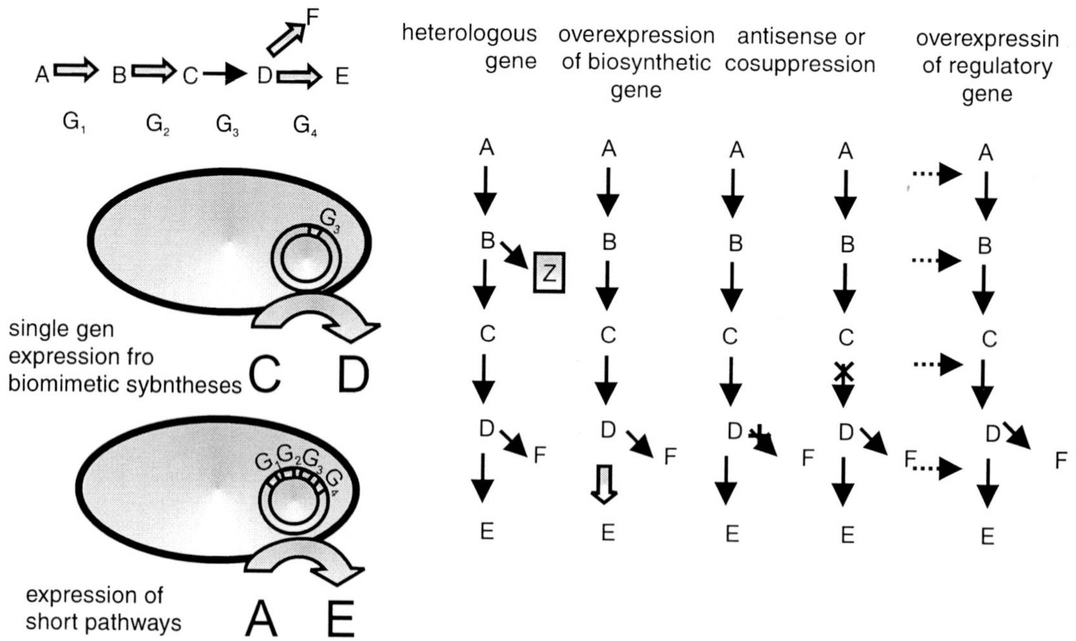

Figure 6.3: Potential biotechnological exploitation of secondary metabolite biosynthetic genes. Plant secondary metabolite genes can be functionally expressed in microorganisms to produce either single biotransformation steps or short biosynthetic pathways. Likewise, using overexpression or antisense or cosuppression technologies, medicinal plants can be tailored to produce important pharmaceutical secondary metabolites by introducing side pathways, elimitating side pathways, or accumulating biosynthetic intermediates. Furthermore, regulatory genes acting on one or more genes within a biosynthetic pathway may be used to up-regulate secondary metabolite biosynthesis and thus enhance product yield.

available at low cost. Promising results have been achieved in the laboratory of Verpoorte, who succeeded in the functional *expression* of the *biosynthetic* genes for strictosidine synthase and strictosidine glucosidase in transgenic yeast.

After addition of *tryptamin* to the transgenic yeast cultures growing in a medium containing a secologaninrich extract of snowberries, *strictosidine* and cathenamine, both precursors of the potent anticancer alkaloids vinblastine and vincristine, were obtained in high yield.

However, this *approach* is difficult or impossible if biosynthetic enzymes are involved that require plant-specific glycosylation for their activity. In this case, metabolic *engineering* will be restricted to plants or plant cells. As shown in Figure elsewhere in this chapter, *overexpression* of single *biosynthetic* genes in plants or plant cells may yield enhanced amounts of the desired secondary metabolites within a pathway or even novel secondary metabolites not normally produced by the plants.

Inhibition of the gene activity of biosynthetic enzymes by antisense or *cosuppression* technology may be utilized to knock out pathway side branches or catabolism of a particular *secondary* metabolite, thus enhancing product yield. Finally, *overexpression* of regulatory genes of biosynthetic pathways containing several rate-limiting steps might circumvent the necessitity to overexpress several pathway enzymes in order to increase the content of the desired secondary metabolite.

Table 6.1: Examples of Cloned Secondary Metabolite Biosynthetic Genes

Gene	*Biosynthetic pathway*	*Origin*	*Species in which gene has been studied using transgenic plants (P) or cell/ callus (C) or organ (O) cultures*
Berberine bridge enzyme	Benzyl isoquinoline alkaloids	*Eschscholtzia californica*	
Berbamunine synthase (CYP80)	Bisbenzyl isoquinoline alkaloids	*Berberis stolonifera*	
Tropinone reductase II	Calystegins	*Datura stramonium*	
Tryptophan decarboxylase	Indole alkaloids	*Catharanthus roseus*	*Catharanthus roseus* (C) *Peganum harmala* (O) *Cinchona officinalis* (O)
Strictosidine synthase	Indole alkaloids	*Catharanthus roseus* *Rauwolfia serpentina*	*Tobacco* (P) *C. roseus* (C) *Tabernae montana* (P) *Chinchona officinalis* (O)
Desacetoxyvindoline-4-hydroxylase	Indole alkaloids	*Catharanthus roseus*	
ORCA2	Indole alkaloids	*Catharanthus roseus*	*C. roseus* (C)
Acetyl-CoA:deacetyl vindoline-4-O acetyltransferase	Indole alkaloids	*Catharanthus roseus*	
O-Methyltransferases	Isoquinoline alkaloids Phenylpropanoids	*Thalictrum tuberosum*	
Tyrosine decarboxylase	Isoquinoline alkaloids	*Parsley*	
Cytochrome P450 reductase	Isoquinoline alkaloids	*Eschscholtzia californica*	
Norcoclaurine-6-O-methyltransferase	Isoquinoline alkaloids		
(S)-3-Hydroxy-N-methylcoclaurine-4-O methyltransferase	Isoquinoline alkaloids	*Berberis koetineana*	
Codeinone reductase	Morphine	*Papaver somniferum*	
Homospermidine synthase	Pyrrolizidine alkaloids	*Senecio vernalis*	
Taxadien synthase	Taxol	*Taxus brevifolia*	
Taxadien transacetylase	Taxol	*Taxus cuspidata*	
10-Deacetylbaccatin III-10-O-acetyltransferase	Taxol	*Taxus cuspidata*	

(Table Contd.)

Gene	Biosynthetic pathway	Origin	Species in which gene has been studied using transgenic plants (P) or cell/callus (C) or organ (O) cultures
Deoxy-xylulosephosphate synthase	Terpenes	*Mentha piperita*	
Deoxy-xylulosephosphate reductoisomerase	Terpenes	*Mentha piperita* Arabidopsis thaliana	
Isopentenyl mono-phosphate kinase	Terpenes	*Mentha piperita* *Escherichia coli*	
NADPH:cytochrome P450 reductase	Terpenes (coenzyme of geranyl-1 0 hydroxylase)		*Catharanthus roseus*
(S)-N-Methylcoclaurine 3'-hydroxylase (CYPBOB1)	Tetrahydrobenzyl isoquinoline alkaloids	*Eschscholtzia californica*	
HMG-CoA-reductase Sesquiterpenes	Triterpenes	*Camptotheca acuminata*	*Catharanthus roseus*
Hyoscyamine-6β–hydroxylase	Tropane alkaloids	*Hyoscyamus niger*	*Atropa belladonna* (P) *Nicotiana tabacum* (P) *Duboisia* (O) *Hyoscyamus muticus* (O)
Ornithine decarboxylase Nicotine	Tropane alkaloids	*Yeast*	*Nicotiana rustica* (O)
Arginine decarboxylase	Tropane alkaloids Nicotine	*Escherichia coli* *Tomato* *Avena* sativa	
Putrescine methyltransferase	Tropane alkaloids Nicotine	*Nicotiana tabacum*	
Tripinone reductase I	Tropane alkaloids	*Datura stramonium*	

The elucidation of the *biosynthetic* pathways of a number of plant *secondary* metabolites has advanced to great extent. One of the best known examples is the pathway for the biosynthesis of the *benzophenanthridine* alkaloid sanguinarine. The pathways of a number of other alkaloids and secondary metabolites of pharmaceutical interest, such as the anticancer diterpenoid taxol, have been characterized at least partially.

However, the *biosyntheses* of some alkaloids of *pharmaceutical* importance are still largely unknown. For example, not much is known about the biosynthesis of the jaborandi alkaloids, *specifically* pilocarpine. Also, the biosynthetic steps leading from the intermediate strictosamide to the anticancer indole alkaloid *camptothecin* still remain rather speculative.

The *sanguinarine* biosynthetic pathway is also a good example of the possible *complexity* of secondary metabolite biosynthesis: 15 enzymatic steps are required for the formation of *sanguinarine* from the amino acid precursor L-tyrosine. The *biosynthesis* of bisindole terpenoid indole alkaloids involves over 20 enzymatic steps, which take place in least three subcellular *compartments*. In addition to the potentially large number of biosynthetic steps that are involved in secondary metabolite biosynthesis, complexity can arise from biosynthetic networks as opposed to linear pathways. Furthermore, although many enzymes of secondary metabolite *biosynthesis* are highly substrate specific, there are a number of examples in which enzymes can utilize several substrates that may even belong to completely different metabolic pathways.

Metabolic *engineering* of such enzymes thus may have unwanted pleiotropic effects. Following the purification and *characterization* of secondary metabolite *biosynthetic* enzymes, the corresponding genes can be cloned using reverse genetics.

Genes of a large number of secondary metabolite biosynthetic enzymes have been cloned successfully; an extensive list of cloned genes involved in isoprenoid biosynthesis can be found elsewhere in this chapter.

Although the full *elucidation* of a pathway is not an absolute requirement for the purpose of gene cloning and metabolic engineering, *thorough* knowledge of the regulation and rate-limiting *enzymatic* steps in the whole pathway is advantageous for the selection of enzymatic steps to be engineered. Without this knowledge, *overexpression* of *biosynthetic* enzymes may not lead to enhanced production of the secondary metabolite of interest.

For example, overexpression of the enzymes phenylalanine lyase (PAL) and cinnamic acid 4-hydroxylase (C4H) in transgenic tobacco plants does not lead to increased production of lignin. This suggests the presence of downstream flux control points in the lignin biosynthetic pathway.

Similarly, the *overexpression* of the tryptophan decarboxylase gene in crown gall calli of *Catharanthus roseus* did not increase terpenoid alkaloid production despite increase tryptamine levels in the transgenic tissues, again *indicating* the presence of additional rate-limiting steps *downstream* in the pathway.

In this particular instance it is now known that the secoirodoid secologanin that together with tryptamine is required for the formation of strictosidine is rate limiting. The ever increasing number of genes of known function in DNA sequence databases now provides a fast gene cloning alternative to the reverse *genetics* approach mentioned before. Using reverse *transcription* - polymerase chain reaction (RT PCR) or *complementary* DNA (cDNA) libraries from tissues or cell-organ cultures specifically producing the secondary metabolite of interest, direct cloning of biosynthetic enzyme genes is possible using DNA primers targeted against consensus sequences within the genes of *particular* enzyme classes.

Using consensus sequences detected within the genes encoding various plant O-methyltransferases, direct cloning of novel *methyltransferases* common to isoquinoline alkaloid and *phenylpropanoid biosynthesis* has been achieved by Frick and Kutchan.

Results suggest that this approach should also be successful in the cloning of novel *acetyltransferase* genes and genes encoding cytochrome P-450 enzymes, cytochrome P-450 reductases, covalently flavinated oxidases, and 2-oxoglutarate-dependent *dioxygenases* involved in secondary metabolite biosynthesis. The *utilization* of regulatory genes for the up-regulation of alkaloid biosynthetic pathways in transgenic plants or plant cell cultures would be an elegant alternative to the overexpression of individual biosynthetic genes.

The transcription factor ORCA2 involved in the jasmonic acid- and elicitordependent regulation of the strictosidine synthase gene in *Catharanthus roseus* has been cloned. In *C. roseus*, the *expression* of terpene indole alkaloid biosynthetic genes is *coordinately* regulated in response to elicitor and jasmonates. Hence, *overexpression* of the ORCA2 gene in transgenic plants or plant cells could potentially increase terpene indole alkaloid content.

Of particular interest would be the effect on the alkaloids vinblastine and vincristine used in cancer treatment. In addition, it would be interesting to know whether ORCA2 is also involved in the regulation of the biosynthetic genes leading from strictosidine to the indole alkaloid camptothecin, which possesses potent anticancer activity.

TRANSFORMATION AND REGENERATION OF MEDICINAL PLANTS

Plant cells of virtually any plant species can now be transformed by one or more of the transformation technologies currently available. Of particular *importance* are the particle bombardment and *Agrobacterium-mediated* transformation technologies. At present, genetic *transformation* studies have been conducted with *approximately* 200 plant species. Of these, about 70 species belong to medicinal plants.

Metabolic engineering of medicinal plant cells with the aim of *overproducing* secondary metabolites of interest is regarded as a promising strategy to make the biotechnological production of phytochemicals in bioreactors economically feasible.

However, despite stable integration of the introduced genes, gene expression and hence secondary metabolite production are not necessarily maintained in the longer term, as has been shown for *transgenic* cell and hairy root lines of *C. roseus* containing the genes encoding tryptophan *decarboxylase* and strictosidine synthase.

In some cases, secondary metabolite production in transgenic cell lines declines over time despite continued *expression* of the introduced gene(s) at a high level. This seems to be associated with the well-known instability of plant cell cultures with respect to secondary metabolite *formation* that has been reported for numerous other cases. Of the various methods used for the *transformation* of medicinal plants, *Agrobacterium rhizogenes-mediated* gene transfer has been preferred by many researchers; many medicinal plant species are amenable to transformation by *A. rhizogenes*, yielding hairy roots that are typically more genetically and *physiologically* stable than cell culture lines.

This system has been used frequently to cointroduce with the *Agrobacterium* genes additional genes of interest. As mentioned earlier, the use of hairy roots for the *biotechnological* production of *phytochemicals* is currently not feasible on a large scale. However, for a number of plant species, regeneration of shoots from hairy roots has been observed, either *spontaneously* or after induction using phytohormones.

The shoots root easily and can be transferred to soil. Potentially, such hairy *rootderived* plants could be used in conventional farming for the production of phytochemicals. However, hairy root-derived plants usually show varying degrees of *morphological* abnormalities such as stunted growth, reduced apical *dominance, abnormal flower production,* and wrinkled leaves.

These symptoms are known as hairy root syndrome. The agronomical performance of such plants in comparison with conventional plants therefore remains to be tested. As with arable crops, successful commercial application of genetic modification technology will depend on naked DNA transformation methods or the use of nononcogenic *Agrobacterium* strains, which permit regeneration of phenotypically normal plants.

Here resides the main problem in the generation of genetically modified medicinal plants: many medicinal plants species are woody and of tropical origin. The development of regeneration protocols has been tedious or impossible in many cases, which is reflected by the preferred use of *A. rhizogenes* -mediated *transformation* methods, as mentioned before.

In some cases, transgenic tobacco plants have been used as a model system to study the expression of secondary metabolite *biosynthetic* genes. The obvious disadvantage is that the specific metabolic precursors are not normally present in a heterologous system. For research purposes, this problem may be alleviated to some extent by precursor feeding, but this *obviously* is no solution for production purposes.

A better alternative is the use of regenerable plant species that produce secondary metabolites the same as or similar to those of the target species that cannot be regenerated. This strategy has been used by Lopes Cardoso et al., who studied the expression of the strictosidine synthase gene in the Apocynaceous plant *Tabernaemontana pandacaqui* instead of *Catharanthus roseus* of the same family.

However, despite an efficient regeneration system for *T pandacaqui,* the authors could obtain only one transgenic plant, the data for which certainly cannot be generalized. Thus, to date the best example of metabolic engineering of a medicinal plant remains the heterologous expression of the hyoscyamine-6f3-hydroxylase gene of *Hyoscyamus niger* in transgenic *Atropa belladonna* plants.

In this study, the authors found *significantly* increased *scopolamine* levels in leaves of the transgenic *A. belladonna* plants, which normally do not contain appreciable amounts of this alkaloid in the leaves.

APPLICATION OF BIOTECHNOLOGY TO DUBOISLA FOR SCOPOLAMINE PRODUCTION

Boehringer Ingelheim is the major worldwide supplier of the tropane alkaloids hyoscyamine and scopolamine. Scopolamine, which is of higher value than *hyoscyamine,* is used as a *parasymphatolytic* and for the production of spasmolytic pharmaceuticals. Previously, the alkaloids were extracted from *Datura* and *Duboisia* plants, both belonging to the Solanaceae family.

Because of the low content of scopolamine in *Datura,* extraction of scopolamine from this plant was discontinued in the early 1990s. There are three known species of *Duboisia, D. hopwoodii, D. myoporoides,* and *D. leichhardtii,* all of which are indigenous to Australia. In a small area in Western Australia, interspecific hybrids between *D. myoporoides* and *D. leichhardtii* occur naturally.

Table 6.2: Size and Scopolamine Content of Field-Tested Plants Regenerated from A. rhizogenes-Transformed Hairy Roots of Duboisia.

Plant line	Number of plants tested	Average size (cm)	Average scopolamine content (% DW)	Total scopolamine yield (g)
Control	3	253.33— 5.77	0.94 ± 0.21	1.50
1	4	130.00 ± 4.76	0.79 ± 0.08	ND
7	4	149.50 ± 5.20	0.73 ± 0.09	ND
10A	3	75.33 ± 10.50	0.84 ± 0.15	ND
10B	3	93.33 ± 16.07	0.84 ± 0.11	ND
15	4	167.50 ± 11.73	0.84 ± 0.12	ND
22A	4	42.50 ± 2.89	1.31 ± 0.06	0.54
22B	4	53.75 ± 4.79	1.16 ± 0.14	0.89
26A	4	53.75 ± 11.09	1.22 ± 0.07	0.81
26B[b]	3	119.67 ± 25.70	0.63 ± 0.03	ND
200	4	167.25 ± 8.62	0.78 ± 0.06	0.83

These hybrids were found to have *particularly* high levels of scopolamine, with an average content of approximately 1% of leaf dry weight. Commercial cultivation of *Duboisia* hybrids began during the 1940s, the main area of cultivation being the South Burnett Region in Queensland, Australia. The *Duboisia* hybrids are cultivated in clonal plantations.

Conventional Breeding

To improve tropane alkaloid yield, Boehringer Ingelheim started an in-house *Duboisia* breeding program at Ingelheim during the mid-1970s, based on controlled crosses between superior *Duboisia* hybrid parents and recurrent selection on an annual basis.

During the time period between 1985 and 1991, the resulting *improvement* in scopolamine content translated into a 40% increase in total scopolamine production from virtually the same annual amount of *Duboisia* leaf extracted. Additional selection criteria have been tropane alkaloid *composition*, general growth, leaf density, rooting ability of cuttings, and nematode and insect tolerance.

However, insect and nematode damage remains a major problem that severely restricts the productive life of plantation-grown *Duboisia* plants.

Tissue Culture Applications

Micropropagation of *Duboisia* species is possible using nodal explants or shoot regeneration from various tissue explants. *Micropropagation* techniques can be used for mass propagation of plants and for plant transport purposes, *particularly* where local quarantine regulations restrict the import of conventional plants.

However, vegetative propagation of *Duboisia* clones using conventional cuttings is relatively straightforward and is done routinely to provide the plants needed for the ongoing planting program on Boehringer Ingelheim's farms. Hence, mass *propagation* of *Duboisia* clones in vitro is not a cost-effective alternative. In collaboration with the University of Barcelona in Spain, we also examined the potential of *Duboisia* hairy root cultures for *biotechnological* production of scopolamine.

Hairy roots were obtained after leaf disc infection with the *Agrobacterium rhizogenes* strain A4. Selected hairy root lines were able to produce up to 1.8 mg/L/day in a 4-L airlift bioreactor. This productivity of the bioreactor process using hairy roots is far too low to compete with the *conventional* farming approach. In addition, upscaling of the process to an 80-L bioreactor was found to be difficult. As a consequence, we did not pursue this *approach* further.

Agronomical Performance of Hairy Root-Derived Plants

As with other hairy root systems, *Duboisia* hairy root cultures may regenerate shoots spontaneously (see also earlier). Regenerated plants were transferred to soil and grown under greenhouse conditions. The plants displayed the typical symptoms of the hairy root syndrome to varying extents.

We wanted to know whether these plants could outperform conventional *Duboisia* plants and conducted a field trial to analyze growth and scopolamine content of these plants. Only the plants displaying the strongest hairy root syndrome symptoms had a *significantly* higher *scopolamine* content than control plants of the same clone.

However, because of their stunted growth, overall productivity was strongly reduced compared with the control plants: the control plants produced almost twice as much *scopolamine* as the best hairy root plants. Thus, our data suggest that hairy root-derived plants do not represent a viable alternative to the cultivation of *conventional* plants.

Genetic Transformation

Genetic transformation of *Duboisia* so far has been reported only for *Agrobacterium rhizogenes-mediated tranformation* methodologies. As mentioned before, the *disadvantage* of this system is that regenerated plants typically display the symptoms of the hairy root syndrome.

To supplement our conventional breeding program, we therefore started to develop genetic transformation protocols for *Duboisia* clones based on *Agrobacterium tumefaciens-mediated* transformation of leaf discs. The transformation efficiency was evaluated using different *A. tumefaciens* strains in combination with a binary vector system harboring an intron-containing β–glucuronidase (GUS) gene and the neomycinphosphotransferase II (*NPTII*) gene as a selectable marker.

Using our shoot regeneration protocol for leaf discs following *Agrobacterium* transformation, we were able to obtain transgenic *Duboisia* plants constitutively expressing the GUS gene. In contrast to the plants regenerated from hairy roots, no morphological difference could be detected between control plants and the plants obtained after *A. tumefa*ciens-mediated transformation, as expected. Of particular interest to the commercial application of genetic modification technology to *Duboisia* is the gene encoding hyoscyamine-6,β–hydroxylase (H6H).

Based on the published DNA sequence data, we cloned the gene from *Hyoscyamus niger* root culture RNA. Transgenic plants expressing the gene under the control of the cauliflower mosaic virus (CaMV) 35S promotor will be tested with respect to its effect on the levels of hyoscyamine, 6/C3-hydroxy-hyoscyamine, and *scopolamine*.

As *Duboisia* contains high amounts of scopolamine naturally, it will be interesting to see whether overexpression of the h6h gene will lead to a further *improvement* of the scopolamine content, similar to what has been observed in *Atropa belladonna* plants and *Hyoscyamus muticus* hairy roots.

Other Traits of Interest

Apart from modifiying secondary metabolite composition and content, the improvement of agronomic traits such as herbicide resistance, pest and disease resistance, and frost tolerance in *Duboisia* through genetic *modification* is also of interest.

The most widely used systems for herbicide tolerance are the Roundup Ready and Liberty Link technologies, providing tolerance to the herbicides glyphosate and glufosinate, respectively. *Bacillus thuringiensis* endotoxin genes have been used successfully for the improvement of resistance to various insect pests in transgenic crops.

There are also promising developments in the field of the genetic modification of nematode tolerance. Nematodes are very difficult to control chemically, and the nematocides currently available have highly undesirable *environmental* characteristics. Natural plant nematode tolerance genes such as the *Mi* gene from tomato or the *HS1* gene from sugar beet have been identified and cloned.

Other approaches rely on the use of proteinase inhibitor genes such as the oryzacystatin gene from rice or the BARNASEBARSTAR gene system. The improvement of frost tolerance via genetic modification is still in its infancy. The detection and subsequent isolation of plant "antifreeze" proteins, however, may open up a new route to the improvement of frost tolerance in transgenic plants.

Molecular Markers

Molecular markers can be used for genotype identification (genetic fingerprinting), estimation of the genetic diversity of natural populations or breeding stock, and marker-assisted selection of agronomic traits. We have established the random amplified polymorphic DNA (RAPD) marker technology for application in *Duboisia*.

Using this technology, we are now able to *discriminate* and identify our production clones *unambigously*. This ability may serve as a quality control tool during clonal propagation and as a deterrent against theft of our proprietary elite clones. Decisions on parent selection in the breeding program will be facilitated using the genetic data obtained by RAPD analysis.

CONCLUSIONS

Advances in the elucidation of secondary metabolite biosynthetic pathways and in the isolation of corresponding biosynthetic genes by reverse genetics or direct cloning make metabolic engineering of these pathways increasingly possible. Whether overexpression of rate-limiting enzymes will lead to enhanced yield of the desired secondary metabolites is a highly debated issue. All theoretical debate will not resolve this issue, and it will need to be addressed experimentally. If successful, metabolic engineering may make biotechnological production processes for phytochemicals using cell or organ cultures economically attractive.

This is particularly true if functional expression of biosynthetic gene arrays can be achieved in microorganisms. The application of metabolic engineering to whole plants will depend on the successful development of methods that allow the regeneration of phenotypically normal plants.

In addition, for transgenic medicinal plants to be grown in the field, the regulatory issues regarding the release of genetically modified organisms into the environment and public acceptance need to be taken into account. Public criticism regarding transgenic plants is directed largely against the introduction of such plants or parts therefrom into the human food chain but also against perceived *environmental* damage by transgenic plants.

As medicinal plants are usually highly toxic and thus not eaten by man, the former point should not be an issue; however, the latter point will certainly need to be addressed in a responsible and sensible manner. Apart from genetic modification of medicinal plants, other modern biotechnological approaches such as plant cell and tissue culture and molecular markers also have important applications in the field of medicinal plants.

Conventional methods of farming, plant propagation, and breeding will, however, remain the first method of choice in the cultivation and improvement of medicinal plants for the production of phytochemicals.

GENETIC ENGINEERING AND LIGNIFICATION

Over the last 35 years, the production of paper has more than tripled. To be competitive, to reduce the uncontrolled exploitation of wild forests, and to limit energy and *environmental* problems, the forest *products* industry must develop genetically improved woody materials. Until now, geneti improvement of trees was achieved using *conventional* breeding methods, which are particularly difficult to exploit for woody species because of long *generation* times and evaluation of specific characters at the adult stage.

Among the various facets of plant biotechnology, genetic engineering offers new op portunities and attractive perspectives for improving woody species. The first *transgenic* tree was obtained in 1987. Since that time, the development of genetic transformation techniques for several tree species and progress in the *characterization* of several important genes in woody plants have opened the door to wide *exploitation* of genetic engineering in forest *management*.

Genomic and genetic *transformations* are entering the field of plant biology at an extremely rapid pace, and their impact should enhance understanding of plant function and lead to the improvement of crops and forest products.

This may correspond to increases in productivity but also to optimization of the chemical composition to provide new products better suited to nutritional, pharmaceutical, or industrial purposes. As the composition of wood is very important for the pulp industry, lignin genetic engineering is a very active area of research that has been stimulated in recent years by the characterization of important genes controlling lignification.

A significant number of transformed plants exhibiting qualitative and *quantitative* changes in their lignins have already been obtained and, in a limited number of cases, preliminary data have *demonstrated* the industrial usefulness of the resulting products. Pulp and paper *production* requires the use of costly, *energy-consuming*, and often polluting treatments to separate lignins from cellulose, and it is clear that genetically engineered trees that produce modified lignins (in lower amounts or that can be more easily processed) would lead to *substantial* industrial and *environmental* benefits. The successful extension to clonal forestry of the efficient strategies defined on model systems has at least four *prerequisites*: convenient germ plasm, large-scale vegetative *propagation*, convenient transformation techniques, and long-term in-field confirmation of the effects observed in model plants.

Investigations are being actively conducted along these different lines and, in parallel, investigations are conducted on easy-to-transform model plants in order to define the best ways to engineer new cell wall compositions. This chapter will *critically* highlight recent results in this area, suggest new strategies for the future, and emphasize the long-term benefits that can be expected from manipulating lignin metabolic pathways.

RECENT ACHIEVEMENT IN THE FIELD OF LIGNIN GENETIC ENGINEERING

Among the polymers that contribute to the plant cell wall, little has been done with genetic *manipulation* of cellulose and hemicelluloses because of a lack of convenient regulatory genes. In contrast, over the last decade, it has become clear that genetic *engineering* can tackle lignin *composition* and content.

This is due to a reasonable knowledge of the *biosynthetic* pathways (and *corresponding* enzymes) leading to lignins even though recent results have revealed unexpected new pathways or new *regulatory* circuits. Figure elsewhere in this chapter *summarizes* our present knowledge of lignin biosynthetic pathways. It is clear that the synthesis of lignins from *phenylalanine* proceeds through three different sets of reactions.

1. The common *phenylpropanoid* pathway, which provides general intermediates (*cinnamoyl-CoAs*) for different phenolic syntheses
2. The monolignol specific pathway, which gives rise to the three building units of the lignin polymer, the coumaryl, coniferyl, and sinapyl alcohols
3. The *polymerization* of monolignols, for which *peroxidases* and laccases are candidates

Most of the genes encoding the enzymes along these pathways have now been characterized with the exception of the hydroxylase converting coumaroyl-coenzyme A (CoA) into caffeoyl-CoA. These genes have been exploited through antisense or *cosuppression* strategies in order to reduce the activity of the *corresponding enzymes* and alter the functioning of the lignin pathway. The modifications of lignin profiles that have been envisaged until now have dealt either with *reduction* in lignin content or with changes in the lignin monomeric *composition* because this parameter is important for lignin extractability.

However, it soon appeared that *experiments* aiming to decrease the lignin content indirectly altered the chemical composition of transgenic lignins. In the following sections significant results obtained through the down-regulation of different target genes will be *highlighted* irrespective of the initial objective.

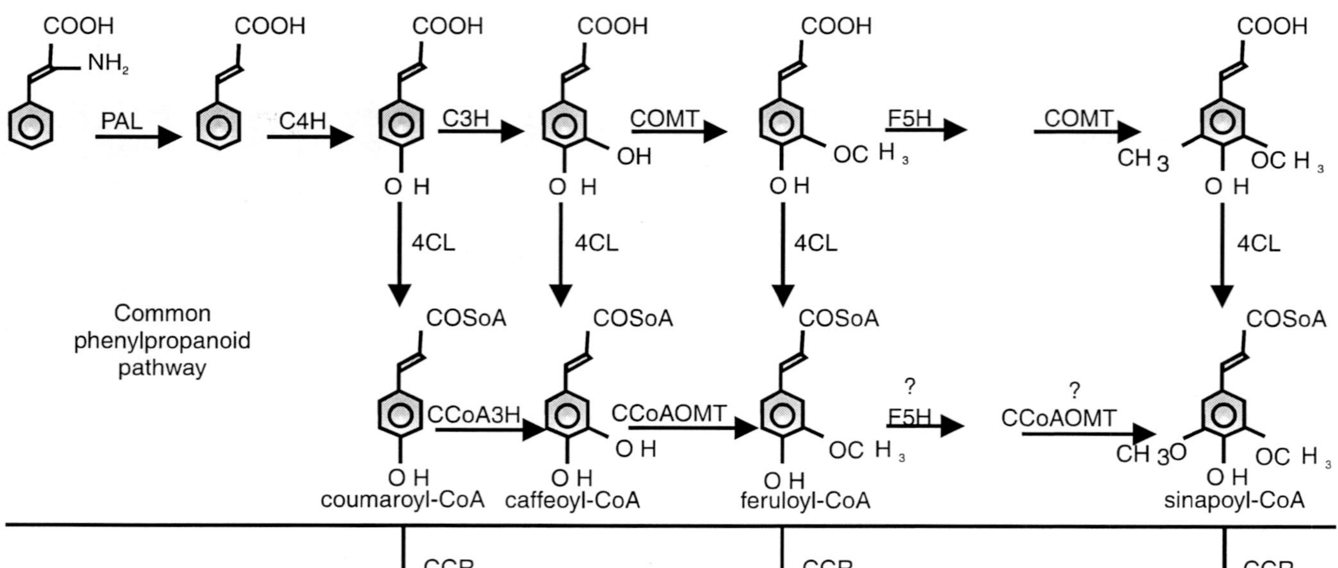

Figure 7.1: The lignin biosynthetic pathway. PAL, phenylalanine ammonia-lyase; C4H, cinnamate-4-hydroxylase; C3H, 4-coumarate-3-hydroxylase; COMT, caffeic acid 3-O-methyltransferase; CCoAOMT, caffeoyl-CoA 3-O-methyltransferase; F5H, ferulate-5-hydroxylase; 4CL, hydroxycinnamate-CoA-ligase; CCR, cinnamoyl-CoA-reductase; CAD, cinnamyl alcohol dehydrogenase. F5H may hydroxylate coniferyl aldehyde and coniferyl alcohol with better efficiency than ferulic acid. (Figure Contd.)

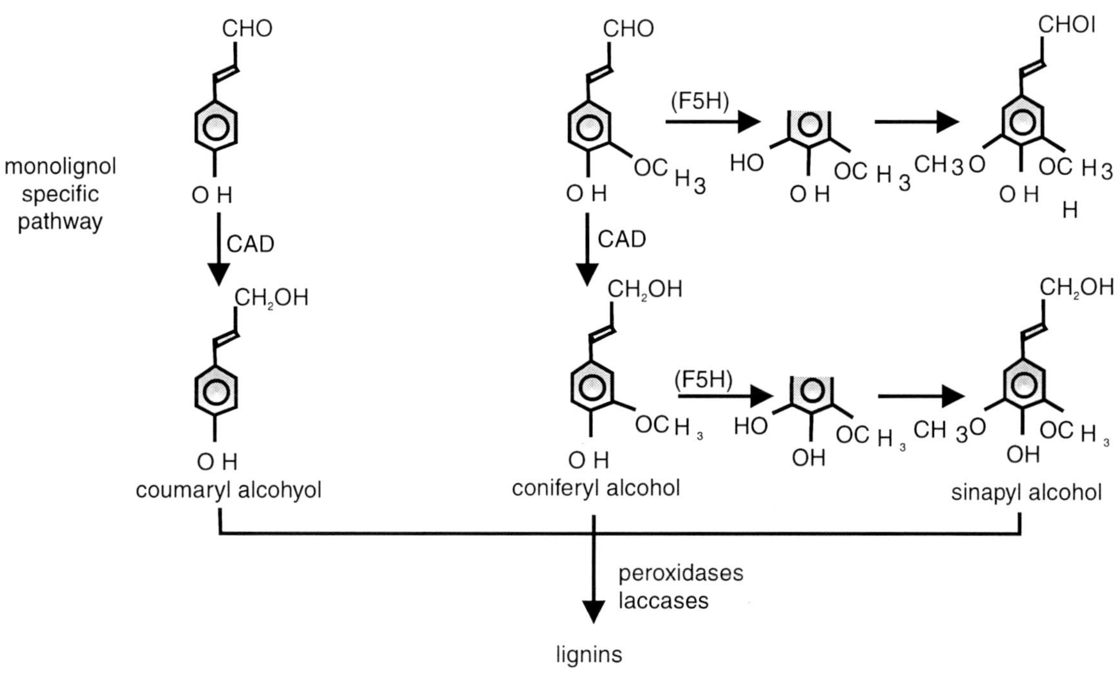

Figure 7.1: (Contd.)

Down-regulation of O-Methyltransferases

Higher plants contain at least three classes of O-methyltransferases that can control the degree of methylation of the *monolignols*. Genetic engineering *experiments* have confirmed that caffeic acid 3-O-methyltransferases (COMTs) give rise to sinapic acid from 5-hydroxyferulic acid and that caffeoyl-CoA 3-O-methyltransferases (CCoAOMTs) lead to feruloyl-CoA.

In addition, other *methyltransferases* can probably convert *hydroxyconiferaldehyde* and hydroxyconiferyl alcohol into sinapaldehyde and sinapyl alcohol, respectively. The down-regulation of COMT both in tobacco and in poplar through the antisense strategy did not decrease the lignin content, whereas the monomeric composition was dramatically modified.

Transgenic lignin has a decreased S content while the amounts of G units remained relatively unchanged. In addition, these *transformed* lines accumulated a novel 5-hydroxyguaiacyl unit in their lignins. Chemical and pulping experiments revealed that these lignins contain, as could be predicted, more condensed bonds (C-C) and are more difficult to extract from the cell wall (higher kappa number) than the control lignins.

These transformed plants are not particularly of interest to the pulp industry but may be of interest if the wood is used for fuel because the calorific value of condensed lignins should be improved.

Several groups have envisaged down-regulating another methyltransferase (CCoAOMT) considered to be particularly involved in the synthesis of coniferyl alcohol (M. Legrand, personal communication; W. Boerjan, personal communication). CCoAOMT has been shown to be encoded by multigene families in different plants including poplar and tobacco, and specific members of these multigene families have been used in antisense or *cosuppression* experiments. Reduction of CCoAOMT alone in transgenic tobacco plants resulted in a decreased lignin content but a simultaneous reduction in CCoAOMT and COMT activities induced a further reduction in lignin content, confirming that both enzymes are indeed involved in methylation reactions in lignin *biosynthesis.*

Surprisingly, although the transgenic plants showed a 40 to 60% reduction in lignin content, they appeared to grow normally under greenhouse conditions even though they exhibited a deformation of vessel elements.

These results have been partly confirmed by M. Legrand's group in Strasbourg (France) (personal communication) on the same material. However, in addition to a reduction in lignin content, CCoAOMT downregulation induced a decreased growth rate and a dramatic *disorganization* of vascular tissues (reduction of xylem *thickness, reduction* of vessel diameter).

These discrepancies concerning the growth of the plants have not yet been explained. W. Boerjan et al. (personal communication) obtained poplar lines cosuppressed for CCoAOMT that exhibit a slight reduction in lignin content. It thus appears that CCoAOMT alone or in combination with COMT is an interesting target for lignin genetic engineering, particularly if the developmental effects observed for some transgenic lines can be reduced.

From a qualitative point of view, G units were preferentially reduced in the β–O-4-linked *monomer* fraction of these transgenic plants, leading to an *interesting* increase in the S/G ratio of the lignins.

Down-regulation of 4-Coumarate CoA Ligase (4CL)

This enzyme governs a key step of the common phenylpropanoid pathway leading to hydroxycinnamoyl CoAs. A down-regulation of its activity should lead to pleiotropic effects, such as those observed when phenylalanine ammonia-lyase (PAL) and cinnamate-4-hydroxylase (C4H) are down-regulated, if the targeted enzymes (isoforms) are not strictly dedicated to monolignol biosynthesis. However, interesting results have been obtained *in Arabidopsis,* tobacco, and poplar 4CL down-regulated plants, suggesting that this enzymatic step is an interesting candidate for lignin genetic engineering. In both *Arabidopsis* and tobacco, a nearly total block in 4CL activity led to only a modest reduction in total lignin content and the plants were morphologically normal.

In contrast, transgenic aspen exhibited a substantial reduction in lignin quantity and a 15% relative increase in cellulose content. In addition, tree growth was substantially enhanced and phenolic profiles of the upper leaves and shoot apex were significantly altered in transgenic lines.

Even though their rationale is not understood at the moment, these secondary effects on plant growth and cellulose content are *particularly interesting* in the context of the pulp industry and these *investigations* merit further attention.

Cinnamoyl CoA Reductase (CCR) Down-regulation

As the first committed enzyme in monolignol biosynthesis, CCR channels phenylpropanoid metabolites into the biosynthesis of lignins. Significant down-regulation of CCR activity in tobacco was obtained by ectopic *expression* of the homologous tobacco antisense gene.

The CCR downregulated tobacco plants with a moderate decrease of CCR activity exhibited only a very slight reduction in lignin content and had a normal phenotype, whereas the most severely inhibited *transformant* showed a 50% reduction in lignin content and an abnormal, heritable phenotype (reduced growth, *abnormal* leaf *morphology*).

In these plants, the *hypolignified* xylem vessels were unable to withstand the compressive forces generated during transpiration and tended to collapse inward. In these *transformants*, the yield of thioacidolysis products was reduced, reflecting a lower proportion of β–0-4 bonds in lignin. However, this *uncondensed* lignin fraction was enriched in S units.

A substantial increase in G units containing free phenolic groups was also observed (C. Lapierre, personal communication). In addition, an increase of cell wall-linked phenolics released by mild alkaline hydrolysis occurred, the main enrichment *concerning* ferulic and sinapic acids and *acetosyringone*.

It was suggested that the *incorporation* of ferulic acid into the cell wall was responsible for the brown-orange colouration observed as a consequence of CCR silencing. Additional studies using ^{13}C nuclear magnetic resonance (NMR) revealed the presence of ferulate tyramine in cell walls of the CCR antisense line.

These different phenolic compounds could be an integral part of the lignin polymer because, at least in grasses, Jacquet et al. and Ralph et al. have shown that ferulate esters can be converted to phenoxy radicals that *copolymerize* with lignin polymers. It is clear that CCR silencing induces a marked reorientation of phenolic metabolism, resulting in a new *partitioning* of phenolic *precursors* into lignins and other related phenolic sinks.

Simulated pulping experiments performed on CCR down-regulated tobacco plants obtained in our laboratory or in collaboration with Zeneca revealed a significant decrease in kappa number with little *modification* of other *parameters* such as cellulose yield or cellulose degree of polymerization (DP). Taken together, these data suggest that CCR controls the entry of carbon flux into the lignin pathway.

However, the resulting *effects-reduction* in lignin, increase in cell wall-associated phenolics and in soluble phenolics, potential decrease in other monolignol-derived compounds such as lignans and/or dehydroconiferyl alcohol glucosides-may have an impact on plant development.

Whatever the molecular *mechanisms* involved, it is clear that these results illustrate the unexpected effects that can be associated with a dramatic decrease in lignin content (and associated responses). A compromise should thus be attained between a moderate reduction in lignin content and normal development.

Cinnamyl Alcohol Dehydrogenase (CAD) Down-regulation

CAD down-regulation was one of the most impressive successes of lignin genetic *engineering* research a few years ago. Since that time, the results initially obtained on tobacco have been confirmed by independent reports of CAD suppression in tobacco and have been extended to poplar.

The plants with a strong reduction of CAD activity have normal *development* and a novel red colour of the xylem at certain *developmental* stages. Their lignin content is not (tobacco) or slightly (poplar) altered but their lignins are enriched in coniferyl and *sinapaldehydes*, the aldehyde substrates of CAD. The newly formed lignins, which have been characterized in detail by NMR, are more easily extracted from antisense plant samples by sodium hydroxide or *thioglycolic* acid, suggesting that the structural changes in the antisense lignin make it more extractable.

Kraft pulping experiments have shown more extensive delignification of low-CAD tobacco and poplar plants when compared with control plants, *demonstrating* the benefit of this genetic *manipulation* for pulp and paper making, and field trials of these CAD down-regulated poplars are currently being performed in France and in the United Kingdom.

A confirmation of the effects of CAD down-regulation has been indirectly obtained from the study of a CAD-deficient *Pinus taeda* mutant that accumulates aldehyde components and substantial levels of dehydroconiferyl alcohol in its lignins.

Here again, the mutant plant stands normally and has a normal phenotype (except for the red colouration of xylem) and the resulting lignins are more easily extracted. These is no doubt that these CAD-deficient plants are *particularly* promising for the pulp industry.

Double Transformants

In order to combine the advantages of the down-regulation of individual genes and to yield new and useful lignins, several groups have envisaged producing double and triple *transformants* by crossing existing plants with single antisense genes or using *transgenes containing* multiple genes under the control of a single promoter. Our recent results on CCR/CAD down-regulated plants illustrate the potential interest of this approach.

By crossing homozygous tobacco lines down-regulated for CCR and for CAD, we have obtained hybrid lines *downregulated* for both enzymes. If the hybrid exhibits intermediate values between the two parents for some characteristics, its lignin content is *surprisingly* lower than for the CCR down-regulated homozygous line. However, in contrast to this parent line, its size and morphology are not affected.

This hybrid line with only 40% of residual lignin was processed in simulated kraft pulping experiments by the Centre Technique du Papier, Grenoble (France) (M. Petit-Conil, personal communication), and a 35% decrease in kappa number, a 24% increase in yield, and a 13% increase in cellulose DP were observed.

These interesting results, which have been confirmed several times on tobacco plants obtained in culture-room conditions, should now be extended to other species grown in natural conditions. They suggest that the CCR and CAD transgenes work in synergy in a still undefined way to give rise to new lignin profiles without altering plant *morphology*.

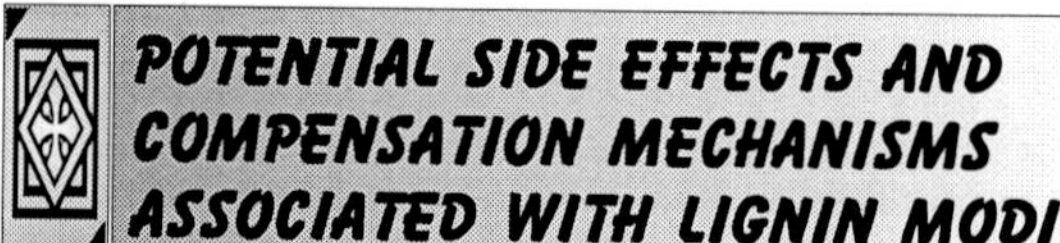

POTENTIAL SIDE EFFECTS AND COMPENSATION MECHANISMS ASSOCIATED WITH LIGNIN MODIFICATIONS

One envisaged drawback related to lignin manipulation in plants could be the potential attenuation of defense mechanisms against pathogens. Indeed, lignification is considered one of the adaptive plant responses to pathogen attacks.

Down-regulating lignin synthesis could reduce the ability of plants to protect themselves against pests. Such a hypothesis has not yet been substantiated using the transgenic plants already obtained, but the use of chemical inhibitors of lignification resulted in decreasing the *hypersensitive* response in wheat plants challenged by *Puccinia graminis. In* order to minimize the drop in these defense mechanisms, which usually occur at the surface of the tissues, the use of specific promoters to drive transgene *expression* has been envisaged.

Ideally, such a promoter should be xylem specific, avoiding a decrease in stress lignins produced on the plant surfaces. Another important aspect of lignin manipulation is the potential disturbance of plant development. Reduction or modification of the lignin content of plant cell walls may theoretically exert pleiotropic effects on plant functions through changes in the strength of plant organs, sap conduction through the xylem, or permeability of cell wall barriers (caspary band).

Changes in plant development have been observed for strongly depressed CCR tobacco lines even though it has not been clearly demonstrated whether the resulting phenotype (reduced growth) is due to changes in cell wall properties or to changes of soluble phenolic profiles. Such a reduction in size has also been demonstrated for CCoAOMT down-regulated tobacco plants.

Surprisingly, CCRICAD double *transformants* exhibit a strong decrease in lignin content but no changes in morphology (at least in culture room conditions). This last observation suggests that the decrease in lignin content per se is not directly responsible for the developmental changes observed but that other unknown metabolic changes are probably involved. It is worthwhile mentioning that in our hands the same tobacco transgenic line (CCR down-regulated) that exhibited normal growth in culture room conditions was developmentally altered when grown in field conditions.

It is possible that the outside habitat provides more adverse conditions (e.g., water stress, mechanical stress) and that the transgenic line adapts itself less easily to this natural context. It is clear that for applied purposes the *transformed* plants should behave as wild-type plants in terms of biomass production and agronomic performance.

This has been verified for 4-year-old CAD down-regulated poplars, which appear to be promising candidates for immediate application. The same evaluation procedures at the field level should be performed in the long term for each new transformed line. From the functional point of view, plants with altered lignin synthesis seem to adopt *compensatory* strategies for *maintaining* the integrity of their cell walls.

This is clearly illustrated in the case of CAD down-regulated plants that utilize cinnamaldehydes instead of cinnamyl alcohols as building blocks of their transgenic lignins. CCR down-regulated tobacco plants partially compensate for the lack of lignin in their cell walls by a striking increase in tyramine ferulate.

Additional reinforcement of the cell wall may also be provided in these transgenic lines by a very significant increase in wall-associated phenolic compounds. The question is still open whether these new *biochemical* phenolic decorations of the cell wall or of the cytosolic fraction have a positive or a negative impact on the pulping process.

A negative example is provided by *Eucalyptus camaldulensis* CAD down-regulated plants that overproduce tannins, interfering with the bleaching step during the pulping process (T. Ona, personal communication). In contrast, if the compensation strategy could concern useful components of the cell wall, the benefits would be obvious.

This situation is illustrated by the exciting results obtained by Chiang's group for 4CL down-regulated aspen, for which the down-regulation of lignin was accompanied by an increase in cellulose leading to a nearly doubled cellulose/lignin ratio. If the required defense, water transfer, and other properties survive, as they appear to in these particularly vigorous plants, the potential for improving plant utilization is enormous.

FUTURE TARGETS FOR ENGINEERING NEW LIGNINS

In addition to relatively well-defined strategies using, for example, CAD down-regulation, which can be of immediate utility, and other potential interesting target genes such as CCoAOMT, 4CL, or CCR whose interest has to be confirmed, other approaches and more diversified plant material will be exploited in the future for lignin genetic engineering. Some of the prerequisites for efficient targeted genetic *modification* of lignin profiles are

A new cell wall composition more adapted to specific agroindustrial purposes

A lack of secondary effects potentially inducing a reduction in plant *productivity* or in the efficiency of the pulping process

Easy adaptation to plant species of high economic interest

Different strategies aiming to fulfill the first two criteria are to be envisaged in the future. Among them are the use of new target genes downstream in the lignin pathway such as laccase/peroxidase genes potentially involved in the polymerization step of lignins and/or UDPG glucosyltransferase and coniferin β–glucosidase genes potentially involved in the transport, storage, and mobilization of monolignol precursors.

The exploitation of these new targets should reduce the pleiotropic effects due to a shortage in the production of monolignols. However, it is difficult to predict whether the down-regulation of these genes would avoid, through sequential feedback mechanisms, the accumulation of intermediates upstream in the pathway. Other strategies that have been particularly successful in the case of flavonoid metabolism *manipulation* deal with the use of transcription factor genes regulating a whole pathway.

Genes encoding transcription factors of the MYB family are good candidates because in many of the promoters of the genes encoding enzymes of the phenylpropanoid and lignin branch pathway, binding sites for these proteic factors have been *characterized.*

In addition, L. Tamagnone et al. have shown that ectopic expression of MYB genes in tobacco induced a reduction in lignin content. Interestingly, A. Kawaoka and H. Ebinuma have identified a new transcription factor that controls gene expression in the lignin *biosynthesis* pathway (Nt lim 1). Its deduced amino acid sequence is similar to that of the LIM protein family that contains a zinc finger motif.

Transgenic tobacco plants with antisense Nt lim 1 showed low expression levels of phenylalanine ammonia-lyase, 4coumarate CoA ligase, and cinnamyl alcohol dehydrogenase and a decrease in lignin content. This simultaneous down-regulation of several enzymes is particularly interesting because it can prevent the unwanted accumulation of phenolic intermediates along the phenylpropanoid and lignin pathways and facilitate the reorientation of carbon flux into primary metabolism. The production of multiple transformants down-regulated for several genes is also interesting to fine-tune lignin profiles.

This strategy is elegantly exploited by C. Halpin et al. through the use of multiple genes under the control of a single promoter, and in our hands it has already suggested the potential interest of CCR/CAD double transformants. In addition to down-regulation of specific genes, the *overexpression* or the combined down-regulation and overexpression of key genes along the pathway may be envisaged.

That is particularly illustrated by the overexpression of an angiosperm gene *F5H* in gymnosperms to increase their syringyl unit content and to make the lignin more readily extractable. Several groups are initiating research projects on this topic. Whatever the gene or the combination of genes used, the limitation of transgene expression to specific tissues or even to specific types of cells within the lignified tissues may be an important way to avoid *undesirable* effects.

Until now, promoters of *lignification* genes such as *CCR* or *CAD* were, at least in our hands, less efficient than the 35S CAMV promoter in driving *CAD* and *CCR* antisense expression. However, K. Meyer et al. have shown that the C4H promoter was more efficient than the 35S CAMV promoter in driving the expression of F5H in *Arabidopsis*. These results show the potential exploitation of specific promoters for limiting the expression of the transgenes.

More sophisticated approaches may be further envisaged through the use of promoters expressed in specific parts of the xylem such as fibers or vessels (W. Boerjan, personal communication) in order to alter fiber composition, for example, without disturbing the structure and function of the vessels.

A SOCIOECONOMIC PERSPECTIVE

World pulp production reached 198.2 million tons in 1997, and the European Union contributed 33.1 million tons to this total. It is expected that the success in lignin content reduction, in lignin solubility increase, or in lignin structure modification will have a very important impact on the pulp and paper industry.

There are a number of projects in progress around the world aiming to document the effect on trees of the modifications of lignification gene expression. One of the most advanced, partially funded by the European Union (EU), began in 1989 (OPLIGE) and gave rise to field tests of genetically engineered poplars that are under way in the United Kingdom and France.

Shell is developing an experiment with CAD down-regulated *Eucalyptus* trees in Uruguay. The trees were planted at the end of 1997 and have another year to go before they will be mature enough for felling and testing.

Advanced Technologies Cambridge (ATC) in collaboration with our laboratory is also involved in the transformation of *Eucalyptus camaldulensis* with different antisense constructs containing lignification genes. Other programs within the EU-supported project TIMBER aim to introduce such genes into spruce or into *E. globulus*, an important species for southern Europe.

Additional target species for which genetic transformation appears to be realistic are larch and the *Pinus* species *Pinus radiata* and *Pinus taeda*, for which efficient protocols using biolistic transformation of embryogenic tissues have been designed. One initiative that attracted a great deal of media attention was the $60 million joint venture between Fletcher Challenge Forest, International Paper, Westvaco, and Monsanto announced in April 1999.

Genesis Research and Development, Auckland, New Zealand is *providing* the genomic research. The experiment will concentrate initially on eucalyptus and poplar species, radiata pine, loblolly pine, and sweet gum. The genetic *improvements* aimed for include herbicide tolerance, higher growth rates, and improved fiber quality in order to meet the world's wood and fiber needs without increasing pressure on native forest.

In addition to the European investments illustrated by the EU OPLIGE and TIMBER projects, this new initiative demonstrates the worldwide interest in these new biotechnologies applied to trees. In the future, it would be crucial to combine the availability of convenient genes and the ability to transform important tree species easily.

Protection of intellectual property is an important aspect of these new strategies, and several companies are launching research programs in order to *characterize* new interesting genes to avoid sublicensing procedures. The European groups have already filed various patents protecting the exploitation of different key genes (*COMT, CCR, CAD*) and are well advanced in the transfer of the *technology* to species of economic interest.

In addition to previous studies on the poplar hybrid INRA 717 B4 *Populus tremula × P alba*, easy to transform but of limited economic interest, significant results have been obtained on the economically important poplar OGY cultivar (*Populus deltoides × P nigra*). One of the main concerns about genetically modified trees is their acceptance in public opinion. The fact that these transformed plants are nonfood products designed for industrial purposes should facilitate public acceptability. However, the recent destruction of *genetically* modified poplar trees at the Jealott's Hill experimental station of ZENECA near Bracknell Berkshire indicates the strong negative reactions of anti-GMO (genetically modified organisms) activists.

One of the main potential problems in addition to the unknown long-term effects is the risk of cross-pollination and the possible effect on biodiversity. In the ZENECA field trial, the trees were female and not able to produce pollen. But several approaches are being exploited worldwide for genetically *engineering* sterility at the same time as introducing the constructs of interest in order to avoid the release of pollen from *transgenic* lines.

Risk assessment for transgenic trees presents special challenges because of the space and time scale involved but also because of the complex interplay of ecological, genetic, agronomic, and social factors. Altering the lignin profiles of plants should not provide a *competitive* advantage to the transformed lines but could limit their resistance to different pests.

A careful examination of these new transgenic products is then absolutely necessary in order to evaluate the potential negative impacts, if any, that could outweigh the already identified advantages for the competitiveness of the pulp industry.

The process of genetically modifying trees is very much in its infancy, and the public perception of the new products is a critical aspect of its wide development.

 CONCLUDING REMARKS AND PROSPECTS

It is clear that the lignin content and composition of crops and woody species can be *manipulated* through genetic engineering. In addition to the application-orientated objectives that have triggered most of the research in this area, the impressive amount of data that have been accumulated in the last few years has generated new fundamental concepts about lignin biosynthesis pathways and lignin chemical *flexibility*. As with other metabolic *engineering* experiments, the results obtained have also revealed pleiotropic and unexpected effects beyond the targeted pathway.

Some of these could be explained through cross-talks between genes because it has been recently shown by G. Pincon et al. that COMT gene down-regulation has an impact on the expression of other genes of the *lignification* pathway.

Lignin genetic engineering is also a way to explore the subtle regulations occurring during the lignification process. The analysis of our CCR X CAD tobacco double *transformants* has shown that in addition to a strong reduction in lignin content, the simultaneous down-regulation of these two activities has a significant and specific impact on the nature of lignins synthesized and on the preferential cell *localization* of the residual lignins. In collaboration with K. Ruel and A.

Yoshinaga, it was demonstrated that the transgenic lignins were enriched in noncondensed units and that the reduction in lignin content was more important in the fibers than in the vessels. The new transformed plants may also help better identify the chemical characteristics of lignocelluloses, which are beneficial in wood processing.

Indeed, comparisons performed on wild-type and transgenic lines represent a new exploratory approach to reevaluate the criteria important for the efficiency of the pulping/bleaching process (in addition to the classical S/G ratio). Such chemical studies have been initiated by C. Lapierre (personal communication) using a range of sophisticated methods.

For example, lignins from CCR and CAD down-regulated plants are enriched in free phenolic groups, which improve their extractability. At the present stage of progress, and in addition to the evaluation of the stability of the traits in the long term, which has already been discussed, many tests still have to be performed on the existing *transgenic* material in order to evaluate its industrial usefulness.

Simulated pulping experiments have been performed by the CTP (Centre Technique du Papier, Grenoble, France) on tobacco stems and poplar branches and trunks of different transformants with decreased COMT, CCoAOMT, CCR, and CAD activities showing several interesting modifications in terms of kappa number, cellulose yield, and cellulose DP. The most interesting lignin *modifications* should now be integrated in the pulping/bleaching process taking into account the constraints and *limitations* associated with each technological stage.

Breeders and chemists involved in the pulp industry are usually looking for genetically engineered trees with the lowest lignin content possible but enough lignin (or the equivalent!) to enable them to withstand environmental hardships (winds, heavy rains, etc.).

At the same time, they want to process trees with lignin that would be easier to dissolve, thus requiring less chemicals, less heat, and less retention time in the digester. The resultant pulp should have equal or improved quality (attributes desired in the pulp and in the end-use product, paper) when compared with current bleached kraft market pulp. From the same biological resource, the quality of the pulp can be improved by modifying intermediate steps in the process and particularly in the cooking and the bleaching stages.

However, this improvement is usually associated with a decrease in yield and an increase in the amount of chemicals and energy required. Thus, it is clear that most of the time, a compromise has to be found between opposing objectives.

An optimized resource should increase the yield and the quality of the pulp and/or decrease the quantity of energy and chemicals used in the transformation process. Taking into account these potential limitations, the existing technology should now be rapidly extended to different woody species of economic interest in light of the progress observed in tree genetic *transformation*.

New avenues are also open to optimize and to extend the first results. They include, as partially described, the fine tuning of the lignin content or composition through the use of a combination of genes and the exploitation of *transcription* factors. Finally, progress in the characterization of the genes involved in the biosynthesis of the polysaccharides of the cell wall opens the way to targeted genetic manipulation of cellulose and *hemicelluloses* in plants.

A combined modification of polysaccharides and lignin profiles can also be envisaged. The resulting *transformants* should increase the natural variability of cell wall components in plants. They should then contribute directly or through *integration* in classical breeding programs to the improvement of the resource used for pulp and paper making.

8 Chapter

INCREASING TOLERANCE AGAINST VIRAL PATHOGENS

Compared with fungi and bacteria, plant viruses are the third important pathogens on cultured plants. They rely *completely* on host cells for replication and gene *expression*, and that is why numerous attempts to cure infected plants by chemical treatment have been *unsuccessful*.

Therefore, plant virologists have focused their research on quarantine measures (diagnosis, establishment of virus-free cultures), control of virus vectors (insects, fungi, and nematodes), and resistance breeding. Genetic traits of wild and cultivated plant species *introduced* by classical crossings have become the most sustainable *instruments* to protect plants from viruses.

These tools are now being augmented by gene *technological* engineering. Molecular biology has identified and characterized known resistance genes and created new resistance traits. Classical genetics and molecular biology have developed fruitful *interactions* and rely on each other for *long-lived* defense strategies. In contrast to animals, plants do not have a real immune system to combat invading viruses.

Whereas animals encounter viruses from the outside of the cell, plants receive viruses by wounding or direct injection into the cytoplasm. As a rule, plant viruses stay within symplastic tissues during further spread through plants without the need to cross membrane borders.

Exceptionally, those plant viruses have evolved *mechanisms* to bud out through membranes that multiply in their insect vectors. Natural as well as artificial resistance mechanisms have to *acknowlege* these *peculiarities* of plant viruses.

Definition of Terms

"Resistance" and "tolerance" have specific meanings in plant virology

in contrast to other areas of plant pathology. Unfortunately, the terms are often *intermingled* in the literature. It is, therefore, necessary to define the terms more precisely, at least to *understand* this review, following the principles of Matthews' classical textbook on plant virology.

Table 8.1: Definition of Terms Following the Principles of Matthews' Classical Textbook on Plant Virology

1.	*Nonhosts* (immune plants)	Viruses do not replicate in protoplasts, cells, or plants. After inoculation they might be disassembled but do not multiply, e.g., due to lack of essential host factors. (The term "immune" is frequently used in a general meaning and might be misunderstood; plants do not have a real immune system and the failure to multiply in nonhosts does not rely on an equivalent mechanism.)
2.	*Hosts* (infectible plants)	Viruses can infect and replicate in protoplasts.
2.1.	*Resistant* plants	Viruses remain confined to the primary infected cell(s). Further spread is suppressed either by lack of compatible host transport factors or by defense reactions (e.g., hypersensitive response).
2.2.	*Susceptible* plants	Viruses replicate and spread systemically through the plant.
2.2.1.	*Sensitive* plants	Plants react with more or less severe symptoms.
2.2.2.	*Tolerant* plants	Viruses do not induce obvious symptoms.
2.2.3.	*Recovery*	Some organs recover from infection either because they become accidentally virus free or because they develop a somaclonal resistance.

In spite of widespread misuse of terms in the literature, for practical applications it is crucial to assign the genetic traits accurately. In case of uncertainty, "protection" might be used instead of resistance, leaving open whether viral multiplication, spread, or symptoms are ameliorated.

DEFENSE RESPONSES OF PLANTS

Following inoculation, plants activate a broad spectrum of responses, either general ones after several types of stress, pathogens and wounding, or specific ones that require the *recognition* of a *particular* pathogen.

Both reaction types may be linked or act separately and determine whether the virus is *virulent* (the host susceptible) or *avirulent* (the host resistant). The resulting interaction is mostly the outcome of a race between virus *multiplication* and the velocity of defense.

General Responses

As with other pathogens, viruses encounter an oxidative burst early, followed by the transcriptional activation of pathogenesis-related (PR) proteins, accumulation of phytoalexins, and a systemic signal *mediated* by salicylic acid, leading to *systemically* acquired *resistance* (SAR) in *noninoculated* tissues or organs.

No evidence is available that PR proteins interact directly with plant viruses, and it is believed that the broad defense reaction is rationalized by the evolutionary experience that a virus seldom comes alone in nature.

A further general response has been attributed to ribosome-inactivating proteins (RIPs), which accumulate in certain plants to high levels in an inactive pre-form that is rendered active during wounding to destroy the *translational* machinery. Several *components* of the general response

Table 8.2: Examples of the Relation between Host Resistance (R Genes) and Virus (*avr* Genes)

Host species	*R gene*	*Virus*	*avr gene*
Arabidopsis thaliana	RCY1	Cucumber mosaic	Coat protein
A. thaliana	HRT	Turnip crinkle	Coat protein
Capsicum chinense	L3	Pepper mild mottle	Coat protein
Lycopersicon esculentum	Tm2	Tobacco mosaic L	ORF(30kDa) (movement protein)
L. esculentum	Tm2^2	Tomato mosaic	ORF(30kDa) (movement protein)
L. esculentum	Tm-1	Tobacco mosaic	Helicase-like domain in ORF 126/183 (replicase)
Nicandra physaloides	?	Potato A	6K2 and VPg (protein linked to the 5' end of genomic RNA)
Nicotiana clevelandii, N. edwardsonii	ccdl	Cauliflower mosaic	Gene VI (viroplasma protein, transactivator of translation)
N. glutinosa	N	Tobacco mosaic	Helicase-like domain in ORF (126/183kDa) (replicase)
N. sylvestris	N'	Tobacco mosaic	Coat protein
N. tabacum Samsun nn	?	Tomato aspermy	TAV2b (suppressor of PTGS)
Phaseolus vulgaris	?	Bean golden mosaic	BV1 (movement protein)
Solanum acaule	Rx	Potato X	Coat protein
Solanum stoloniferum	Ry	Potato Y	NIa proteinase (function?)
Vigna unguiculata	Cry	Cucumber mosaic	ORF 2a (replicase)

system have been *manipulated* in order to obtain *protection* against viruses but so far with only limited success.

Virus-Specific Responses

As Flor elaborated for fungi, genetic traits of a pathogen coevolve with the respective host resistance genes in a pairwise manner. This gene-forgene concept also holds true for plant viruses. Gene products of a virus are recognized by a host and lead to a defense response.

The viral genes are then said to be avirulence (*avr*) genes, although they fulfill different functions in the context of the viral life cycle. Almost all viral genes may function as *avr* genes by triggering a host response. Breaking resistance is most frequently caused by mutations in *avr* genes, and during classical breeding the main task has been to cope with this challenge by *introducing* new resistance genes into crop plants, *essentially* by crossing wild *predecessors* and cultivated plants.

The *avr* gene products elicit host responses on different levels. One example, *extreme resistance*, inhibits viral *multiplication* in the *inoculated* plant cells and in protoplasts. The fact that this genetic trait is *terminologically* considered resistance and not *immunity* is merely based on the observation that other strains of the same virus multiply readily in single cells. A second and

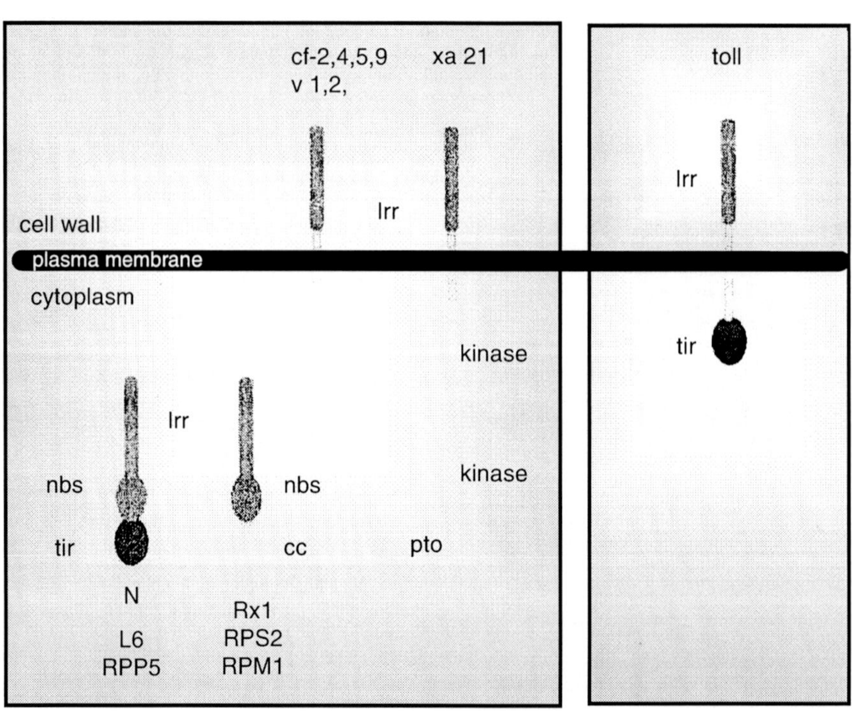

Figure 8.1: Similarity of plant resistance gene products and the signal receptor Toll of Drosophila. The proteins are composed of modular domains: leucinerich repeats (LRRs), kinase, Toll/interleukin-1 receptor (TIR), nucleotide-binding site (NBS), and coiled coil (CC) domain. The following resistance genes are compared: against Cladosporium fulvum (Cf), Verticillium dahliae (Ve), Xanthomonas oryzae (Xa), Pseudomonas syringae (RPS, RPM, Pto), Melamspora lini (L6), Peronospora parasitica (RPP), tobacco mosaic virus (N), and potato virus X (Rx).

most common example, the *hypersensitive reaction* (HR), allows *multiplication* in the inoculated cells and limited spread in the tissues, but then infected parts die and further infection is impaired.

It has been *questioned* whether resistance is solely due to this "suicide for survival", and at least in some cases *resistance* can be uncoupled from cell death. Extreme resistance and *hypersensitive* reactions are currently the best known barriers for viral infections; others are being investigated to elucidate additional *mechanisms* in the near future.

In particular, *apoptosis*, the *programmed* cell death of single cells thereby preventing necrosis of tissues, might be an interesting candidate. This mechanism has been *intensively* studied in animals and might also be responsible for resistance traits in plants.

Most virus-specific host responses rely on the general signal *transduction* cascades of *eukaryotic* cells, but for plants signal perception between virus and host takes place mostly inside the cell (in the symplast).

Recovery

The word "symptom" originates from the Greek *o-uµTrTwµa*, which means "chance, transient peculiarity". Correspondingly, symptoms may disappear during the infection process. Some shoots may escape from infection just by chance; others may develop virus-specific resistance that does not allow reinfection by the same virus, but unrelated viruses are *propagated* without problems.

This recovery *phenomenon* gave rise to intensive research and led to the discovery of virus-induced gene silencing, discussed later.

HOST RESISTANCE GENES

Numerous genes conferring resistance to viruses have been characterized by classical genetics and *localized* to certain chromosomes. The two best analyzed examples will be reported here in greater detail to exemplify current *experimental* strategies to transmit virus resistance from wild to domestic plants.

One of the most fascinating outcomes of this research was the discovery that resistance genes directed against *pathogens* as diverse as fungi, bacteria, and viruses produce effector proteins with similar molecular architectures.

N Gene

The N gene is the classical example of virus resistance associated with a hypersensitive reaction. It is specifically directed against *tobacco mosaic virus* (TMV). After its discovery in *Nicotiana glutinosa*, it was introgressed into the Samsun cultivar of *N. tabacum*. The "N" refers to necrosis on foliage leaves a few days post inoculation (dpi).

The development of local necrotic lesions restricts systemic spread of TMV in a *temperature-dependent* manner. Above 28°C, **HR** is suppressed and TMV can infect further tissues. Decreasing the temperature then again induces systemic necrosis in large areas, as far as TMV has spread. Exploiting this peculiar feature of the dominant *N* gene, it was possible to clone and sequence a virus resistance gene for the first time by a combination of *transposon* tagging and positional cloning. An isolated genomic clone *harboring* the *N* gene was *transferred* to the susceptible cultivar

N. tabacum cv. Petite Havana SRI and to *Lycopersicon esculentum*, proving that this clone was *necessary* and *sufficient* to establish TMV specific resistance. The *N* gene encodes a protein in which one of the domains shows high similarity to the *Drosophila Toll* gene and the interleukin-1 receptor of mammals (named the TIR domain), indicating that it might participate in the general signal *transduction* pathway of eukaryotic cells.

It contains further domains with a nucleotide binding site (NBS) and with leucinerich repeats (LRRs). Both signatures are *commonly* found in animal receptor proteins that perceive and transmit signals from outside the cell at the plasma membrane. In the case of the *N* gene product, however, no *transmembrane* anchor is present.

Therefore, it is suggested that the N gene protein recognizes TMV inside the cell. The *N* gene is composed of five exons and four introns, which are alternatively spliced. Interestingly, a larger transcript is *constitutively* expressed before and after TMV inoculation.

The alternative, shorter transcript is induced during infection. To provide resistance, both transcripts have to be expressed, leading to the assumption that two versions of N proteins cooperate in signal transduction.

Consequently, it is necessary to transfer the genomic clone rather than a complementary DNA (cDNA) clone to new species to obtain resistance. Using such transgenic plants as indicators, the avirulence gene of TMV, the helicase domain of the 126-kDa and 183-kDa protein, could be defined very precisely.

Rx Gene

The Rx gene of *Solanum acaule* is directed against *potato virus X* (*PVX*). It confers extreme resistance, which works at the single-cell level. The *corresponding avr* gene is the coat protein gene of PVX. For the molecular analysis, the Rx locus was defined by classical and bacterial artificial chromosome (BAC) mapping. Using *cobombardment* of BAC clones with reporter constructs of virulent or avirulent modified PVX strains, the *Rx* gene could be identified and transferred to susceptible potato and a heterologous plant species (*N. benthamiana*).

The two transformed plant species exhibited extreme resistance against *avr* PVX but not against a resistancebreaking strain. These results proved that the isolated gene was necessary and sufficient for the strain-specific resistance against PVX. The Rx gene with three exons and two introns encodes a protein of 937 amino acid residues (107.5 kDa), which revealed *surprising* similarities with HR-inducing receptor proteins of the NBS-LRR class.

Although an HR is not observed during normal infection of an *avr* PVX on an *Rx* plant, reinvestigation of this relation showed that if the coat protein of *avr* PVX was ectopically expressed under the control of 35S CaMV promoter in an *Rx* gene-containing plant, HR was *obviously* induced. Moreover, the avr coat protein of PVX was expressed from a TMV vector in NN tobacco also containing the *Rx* gene.

Extreme resistance was found in this interaction but no N-mediated HR, suggesting that *Rx* is epistatic to HR. The *Rx* prevents the multiplication of PVX inside the cell but has no influence on the transport of the virus. Double-grafting *experiments* showed that *avr* PVX moved from an infected wild-type rootstock through an *Rx* gene-containing scion to a second wild-type scion, inducing *symptoms* only in the latter.

These experiments indicate that the signal-inducing interaction between the *avr* and *R* gene does not occur in all cells of a plant. In summary, currently available *evidence* suggests that a continuum between extreme resistance, the micro-hypersensitive response, and the fully developed local or systemic HR exists in plants. The question is whether the defense reaction is triggered early or late in the infection process.

Avr Genes as Tools for Resistance Breeding

The discovery that even proteins responsible for extreme resistance can induce HR under certain conditions allowed the *development* of a versatile tool for the *identification* of unknown resistance genes as far as the viral *avr* genes of interest are delimited.

Using an *Agrobacterium-mediated* transient expression assay, further *Rx* loci were cloned and sequenced. The same assay was used to answer a reciprocal question, to identify an *avr* gene if the *resistance* gene is known. Ry provides extreme *resistance* in potato against *potato virus Y* (PVY). However, because no resistance-breaking strains of PVY are known, it was unclear which viral gene is the elicitor.

Agrobacterium-mediated transient expression assays assigned the NIa proteinase domain to the *avr* gene and provided evidence for the necessity of an intact catalytic center for HR induction. Although it cannot be completely ruled out that the structure of the center is responsible for virus recognition, the *experimental* results promote the intriguing hypothesis that the proteolytic function of this domain is essential.

PATHOGEN-DERIVED RESISTANCE

Classical Cross-Protection

In the early days of plant virology, a phenomenon was observed and called "cross-protection": Preinoculating a plant with a mild virus can protect it from a subsequently inoculated severe and related virus. Classically, such *experiments* were used to determine the relatedness of two viruses.

Although this phenomenon formally resembles that of *immunization*, it differs *significantly* in that the effect is obtained only if the mild virus continues to multiply. This circumstance implies that viruses are disseminated continuously when this strategy is used.

Because the term "mild" or "severe" does not define the virus proper but refers to a relationship between pathogen and host, the classical approach contains the possible impact of creating new diseases on other plants. In consequence, the application of such techniques has remained limited, although prominent success has been obtained against *Citrus tristeza virus* and *Papaya ringspot virus*.

The classical approaches using cross-protection and their respective risks have been reviewed in detail. A variation on this theme is the use of satellite viruses or satellite RNA as protective agents. These small entities need a helper virus for *multiplication*, and they gained special interest because they modulate symptom expression.

Dependent on the combination of helper virus, satellite, and host plant, symptoms may be increased or ameliorated. As with cross-protection, the effect of satellites depends on their multiplication and, in principle, involves the same risks. Nevertheless, the approach has been utilized with some success using *preinoculation* of a mild combination of helper virus and satellite. Envisioning the advantages as well as the safety impacts of this strategy, it was consequently a challenge to scrutinize whether the useful properties of a virus could be dissected from the harmful ones.

Pertinent questions were whether parts of the viral genomes are sufficient for the protection and whether viral protein or RNA is responsible for the effect. Starting in the 1980s, molecular biology has answered these questions unequivocally and opened new, unprecedented areas of resistance that have also revolutionized our understanding of basic gene regulation in eukaryotes on the level of epigenetics.

During this period it became obvious that cross-protection can be obtained on a variety of routes including viral proteins and RNA. In summary, cross-protection came out to be a more general term.

Protein-Mediated Protection

Several viral proteins can mediate cross-protection. Some provide protection only to the closest relatives, others to a broader community of related viruses. Among the strategies using expressed viral proteins, two have been predominantly proved successful: expression of functional coat proteins or of defective proteins from genes with dominant negative mutations.

Coat Proteins

One early idea to explain cross-protection focused on the assembly of virus particles. For TMV it has been shown that disassembly of invading particles starts by the interaction of virions and ribosomes. This cotranslational *disassembly* needs a partial free 5' end of the viral RNA for first recognition events, which is normally obtained by removal of five to seven coat protein molecules according to the thermodynamic equilibrium between viral particles and components inside the cytoplasm.

It should, therefore, be possible to shift the *equilibrium* to the formation of stable particles by increasing the amount of coat protein within the cells. The elevated level of coat protein could be produced by a preinoculated virus or, more *conveniently*, by ectopic expression of the coat protein in transgenic plants.

In fact, this concept proved to be successful not only for TMV as the first virus but also for a vast variety of viruses. In the light of the additionally found RNA-mediated protection (see later), it was questioned whether the effector in the case of coat protein expression was protein or RNA. The role of coat protein, however, has been confirmed by several lines of evidence.

1. The coat protein-mediated resistance can be overcome by inoculating naked viral RNA.
2. Mutations in the coat protein genes that affect assembly also abolish protection.
3. The protection occurs only for viruses with proteins that might coassemble to mixed-coat virions (phenotypic mixing).
4. Virus particles are stable for hours in protoplasts transgenic for coat proteins, whereas they are disassembled within a few seconds in wild-type protoplasts.

All these data have led to the conclusion that although RNA-mediated effects might overlap,

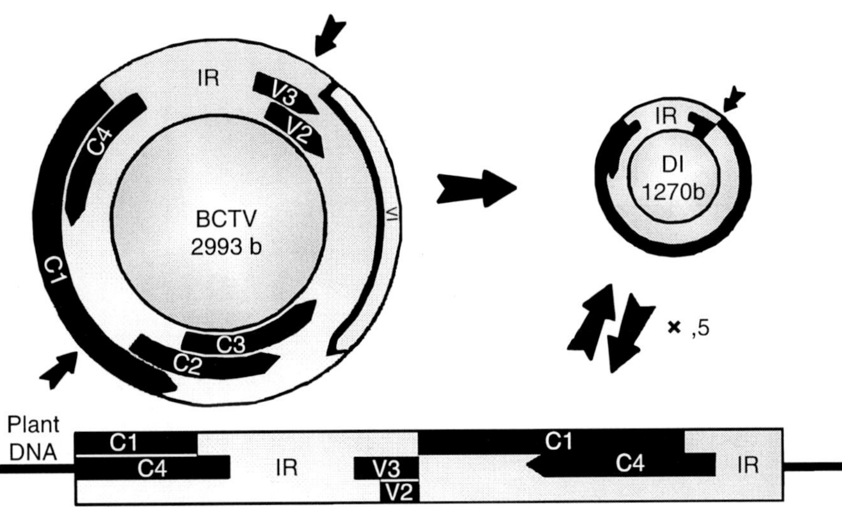

Figure 8.2: Defective-interfering (DI) DNA of beet curly top geminivirus (BCTV) to protect plants from virus infection. Open reading frames are named according to their complementary (C) or viral (V) orientation. IR assigns the intergenic region harboring viral promoters and the origin of replication. Bitmers (x1.5) were integrated into plant chromosomes, which are transreplicated upon infection with the cognate virus (BCTV).

particular cases are based on the presence of the correct coat protein. These cases are usually recognized by a correlation between the amount of expressed coat protein and the degree of protection. With one exception, this strategy was reliable for RNA- but not for DNA-containing viruses. Stimulated by plant virologists' work, it was also applied to animals.

Dominant Negative Mutations

A second idea has been raised by the perception that several viral proteins are *multifunctional* and are therefore composed of multiple domains. Such domains must cooperate, e.g., for RNA binding and RNA *polymerization* or for RNA binding and plasmodesmata gating.

It was predicted that if one of the functions of the domains was inactivated and the mutated protein still formed complexes with the RNA, the mutation might be dominant over the wild-type gene (dominant negative mutations).

Conceivably, most work *concentrated* on replicase-mediated protection because it was anticipated that the earliest defect during viral *multiplication* should be the most useful one.

Nevertheless, every viral protein might be prone to such an effective *modification*. The role of nonstructural viral proteins in protecting plants has been extensively reviewed, and it has been shown that RNA- as well as DNA-containing viruses may be impaired by this strategy.

In addition to the interaction of viral proteins with each other, in certain cases the binding of a viral with an unrelated protein was useful for protection.

Potyviruses need viral proteinases for the processing of their large preprotein. This function can be blocked in transgenic plants by ectopic expression of a cysteine proteinase inhibitor, providing broad resistance against distinct potyviruses.

RNA-Mediated Protection

During early work on protein-mediated cross-protection, some transgenic constructs behaved unexpectedly. While expressing low or no proteins, they nevertheless provided some degree of protection. In these cases no correlation between protein concentration and protective effect was observed, and sometimes, in control experiments, an *untranslatable* messenger RNA (mRNA) *serendipitously* appeared to be the effector molecule. This initial evidence founded the hypothesis that RNA by itself might mediate protection.

Antisense and Sense RNAs

An alternative idea finally led to a similar conclusion. To block translation of viral RNA by means of hybridization, antisense RNA was expressed in various plants. Surprisingly, in some cases not only antisense but also sense RNA, from a control construct, provided *protective* effects. The inhibition of viruses by sense constructs resembled a *simultaneously* discovered phenomenon perceived by plant molecular biologists and has been termed "cosuppression":

If several copies of the same gene or of the same promoter were artificially integrated into plant *chromosomes*, their expression was not increased but abolished. Antisense as well as sense RNA strategies have, *subsequently*, proved to be useful in certain cases but, even more important, have opened a new field of research that is now called "silencing" (see later), emphasizing the role of RNA in *protection* against viruses.

Interfering Replicons

During natural virus infections replicons may accumulate that are derived from the master virus but have a smaller size or are predominantly unrelated to the helper virus (satellites). Moreover, some replicons appeared to be *recombination* products of a helper virus nucleic acid and unrelated sequences. These additional replicons might enhance the effect of the virus, ameliorate the symptoms, or behave neutrally.

When they interfere with virus multiplication or symptom *development*, they are called defective interfering (DI) nucleic acids.

Defective Interfering (DI) Nucleic Acids

DI nucleic acids have been observed for RNA- and DNA-containing viruses. DI-DNA molecules of geminiviruses have attracted special interest. Geminiviruses encapsidate single-stranded circular DNA and replicate in nuclei.

Over the past three decades they raised worldwide devastating epidemics, *predominantly* in tropical and *subtropical* countries but also in the United States (*beet curly top virus*, BCTV) and around the Mediterranean sea (*tomato yellow leaf curl virus*, TYLCV). Their genomes consist of either one component (genera *Mastre-*, *Curto-*, and *Topocuvirus*) or two *components* (most of the genus *Begomovirus*), which are called DNA A and DNA B.

DI-DNA has been investigated in more detail for BCTV, with a set of half and smaller size DNA circles from a single genomic component, and for *African cassava mosaic begomovirus*, which *accumulates* smaller molecules derived from the DNA B component. All these DI molecules harbor the origin of replication and parts of predominantly the left halves of the genomic components.

They usually do not contain intact open reading frames with the exception of BCTV-DI, possessing the small ORF C4 influencing symptom expression. Integrating tandem copies of DI-DNA into plant chromosomes does not disturb the development of plants, and DI-DNA is not replicated because the viral replication initiator protein (AC 1 or C 1) is lacking.

Upon *challenge* by the cognate virus, DI-DNA replicates and *symptoms* are ameliorated, leading to a recovery after longer time periods of infection. During this process, DI-DNA accumulates and full-length viral DNA is reduced compared with infection of control plants.

It has been suggested that down-regulation of viral *multiplication* is caused by the competition of DIDNA with viral DNA for *replication* complexes, but it is not completely excluded that intact proteins (C4), defective proteins (SAC 1, ABC 1) as dominant-negative effectors, or RNA-mediated processes participate in the protection.

In this context it is interesting to note that smaller DI-DNA may replicate to even higher levels, but such an increase did not lead to enhanced inhibition. DI-DNA is packed into half-size particles and the amount of DI molecules is elevated after serial passages to further plants, rendering this strategy *especially* useful for field applications.

A limitation results from the necessity to recognize a specific origin of *replication* by the compatible replication-associated (Rep) protein of the cognate virus to induce DI-DNA multiplication. Therefore, DI-DNA can act only against closely related viruses that are able to transreplicate each other.

Satellites

Satellites are small, a few hundred nucleotides in size, RNA (satRNA) or DNA (satDNA) molecules that are transreplicated by a helper virus. Some of them, *encoding* their own coat protein for packaging their RNA, are called satellite viruses.

The other satellites might also contain small open reading frames (ORFs) of unknown function. Satellites modulate *symptom* expression of their helper virus, either increasing or decreasing severity. Their particular effects are governed by the triangular *interrelationship* between virus strain, satellite, and host genotype.

Expression of putative proteins from ORFs of satRNAs has been prevented by site-directed *mutagenesis* without abolishing *symptom* modulation. Therefore, it is believed that the secondary structure determines the effect rather than the coding capacity of the RNA. It was shown in model plants that satRNA expressed from transgenes can confer some protection against the helper virus effects.

For field application this approach was frequently questioned, especially because of the variability of possible effects upon coinfection with other viruses or because satRNA might be transferred to other nontarget hosts. Nevertheless, this strategy using either classical *coinoculation* techniques or transgenic means has been successfully applied in Asia, resulting in a considerable reduction of yield losses.

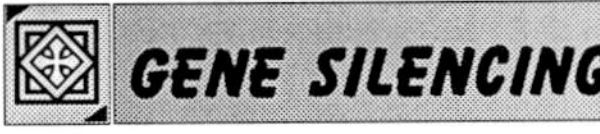

GENE SILENCING

Silencing of genes is a long known process providing programmed differential gene expression during the individual development of all organisms. It can occur at different levels, repressing genes in prokaryotic operons, combining sets of transcription factors in eukaryotic cells, or condensing chromatin structures. In addition to these regulatory means, it was already perceived in classical genetics that certain genes can be suppressed (phenocopied) and that such suppression can be inherited (paramutation, imprinting). It was proposed that this type of silencing might rely, at least for some examples, on the interaction of *homologous* sequences (ectopic pairing of homologous chromatin) followed by the inactivation of the particular gene, perhaps through *methylation*.

However, whether methylation, which is regularly seen in such genes, is the cause or the result of silencing remains to be shown. From a historical point of view, one of the most *fascinating* chapters of molecular biology was the perception during the past 10 years of how results of completely unrelated areas of research have converged to throw light on the puzzle of *silencing* mechanisms.

Phenomena called "cosuppression" for transgenic plants, "virus-induced gene silencing" for plant viruses, "RNA interference" for *Drosophila* and *Caenorhabditis*, and "quelling" for *Neurospora* turned out to rely on common molecular pathways. Summarizing the evidence, homology-dependent gene silencing (HDGS) may occur on two different levels: *transcriptional* gene silencing (TGS) based on promoter inactivation, *methylation*, and chromatin remodeling and posttranscriptional gene silencing (PTGS) caused by sequencespecific destruction of transcripts.

The removal of sequence-specific RNA in PTGS was shown to be based on the presence of homologous interfering double-stranded RNA (dsRNA). Some evidence suggests that a feedback loop of regulation from PTGS to TGS exists. Originally, these mechanisms were thought to control the copy number of genes to protect the genome from too many mobile genetic elements and viruses.

Currently, however, the possibility arises that similar *mechanisms* are also involved in the programmed *differential* gene activation during ontogeny.

Transcriptional Gene Silencing (TGS)

The TGS process is an unpredictable one in which multiple copies of a gene or a promoter influence each other, leading to the inactivation of a particular gene. In experiments it is recognized by a lack of steady-state transcripts and the absence of the particular transcript in nuclear run-on assays.

Frequently, it is associated with increased methylation of the promoter and the gene. TGS may be present in the whole plant or in sectors of various organs. The pattern of TGS may be inherited by the next generation (imprinting) and reverted to an active state of *transcription* under certain conditions.

Posttranscriptional Gene Silencing (PTGS)

The PTGS process relies on the multiplicity of genes; their inactivation is also *unpredictable*, as for TGS, but the effective homology must reside within the transcript. Experimentally, it is detected by reduced steady-state amounts of RNA as in TGS but the presence of nuclear run-on transcripts.

Moreover, the appearance of small RNA molecules (21-25 nt) of both polarities is diagnostic for PTGS. PTGS is not present throughout the whole life cycle of a plant but appears late during *development* in individual plants of silencing lines.

Virus-Induced Gene Silencing (VIGS)

The first evidence for VIGS came from the observation of recovery from symptoms after inoculating a potyvirus on transgenic plants containing a potyviral gene. The recovered shoots remained protected from a second infection with the same virus but were susceptible to others.

The interpretation of this observation became a heuristic idea, namely that effector molecules, presumably *complementary* RNA, had been generated to signal virusspecific inhibition. In a similar approach it was shown that viroids can also trigger gene silencing, *underscoring* that the effector molecule might be RNA. Interestingly, these peculiar experiments with viroids led to inactivation of its *homologous* transgene, associated with methylation of the DNA copy.

In other cases VIGS did not change the *transcription* but induced PTGS, which was best shown for PVX, a virus that replicates exclusively in the cytoplasm. Transgenes, e.g., glucuronidase (GUS), were silenced by PTGS if the plant was infected by a chimeric PVX containing the GUS gene, too. Conversely and surprisingly, a plant transgenic for GUS became resistant to this hybrid PVX.

Systemic Acquired Gene Silencing (SAS)

Once established at some site, the silencing signal may spread throughout the plant, which is most convincingly demonstrated by grafting experiments. A silenced rootstock can transfer the signal to an unsilenced scion.

This effect is maintained as long as the homologous gene is present in the recipient plant. Which molecules trigger SAS is still unclear. It has been suggested that the gene-specific small RNAs participate in the signal *transduction*, but recent grafting *experiments* have questioned this idea. Alternatively, longer dsRNA might induce SAS, but evidence for this *assumption* is still lacking.

Mechanistic Aspects of Posttranscriptional Gene Silencing

The mechanism of PTGS has been elucidated in different organisms, converging to a fundamental concept during the last few years. The trigger for PTGS is dsRNA (blunt end or with a few protruding 3'nucleotides) *homologous* to a target RNA.

Several genes are involved in this process in plants, animals, and fungi coding for a ribonuclease (RNase) III-type enzyme cutting dsRNA, an RNA-dependent RNA polymerase (RdRp), a helicase, and a protein with homology to a eukaryotic initiation factor (eIF2C).

These factors interact in (trans-)gene silencing, whereas for viruses a viral RdRp may replace or modulate the *analogous* host enzyme. One key enzyme is now called DICER because it chops small pieces of about 22 by (siRNA, for short interfering RNA) *proceeding* from the ends of dsRNA with a type III-like RNase activity.

The protein contains two RNase III domains, a putative helicase domain, and a PAZ domain, which is possibly responsible for protein-protein interaction with other factors. According to the currently discussed model, siRNA remains bound to DICER, is melted by a helicase, and *subsequently* guides the sequence-specific nuclease to homologous RNA of (+) or (–) orientation.

In this reaction, target RNA is cleaved in the middle of the recognized 22-nt sequence, leading to a periodicity in the digested RNA similar to that of siRNA but with a phase shift.

The advantage of the DICER reaction lies in the *amplification* of the signal because several siRNAs are generated from a single dsRNA molecule, each one ready to attack several new target RNAs. An even more efficient amplification of the signal for destruction would be obtained if target ssRNA, loaded with siRNA as a primer, was *complemented* by an RdRp to produce new dsRNA to be recognized by DICER again.

However, such a feedback cycle has yet to be shown *experimentally*. In any case, it would explain the functionality of host or viral RdRp genes in PTGS as inferred from genetic analysis. The *demonstrated* role of an inducible host RdRp in plant antiviral defense might be a further hint in the same direction.

Suppressors of PTGS

The PTGS process is thought to be a defense response against foreign genes, especially of viral origin. Therefore, it is not surprising that viruses have developed ways to combat such strategies. Consequently, certain viral genes were *discovered* to suppress PTGS.

Two of them, HC-Pro (helper component-proteinase) of potyviruses and ORF 2b of cucumoviruses, have been *intensively investigated* in this function. Although PVX was initially thought to lack such a capability, its p25 protein (part of the triple gene block with movement functions) inhibits PTGS under certain conditions.

These three examples, among several others, also represent *suppression* of PTGS at different steps in the course of the process. HC-Pro is able to switch off existing PTGS and leads to a decrease of siRNA levels. In contrast, CMV 2b has no influence on established PTGS but prevents its initiation, and PVX p25 abolishes the mobile signal of PTGS.

Whenever suppression of PTGS has occurred, it promotes not only parental but also unrelated viruses in *multiplication* and spread. Such synergistic effects were observed upon coinfection of two viruses as well as upon single-virus *inoculation* on transgenic plants harboring a viral PTGS-suppressor gene.

SUSTAINABILITY CONCERNS

Resistance breeding has always been a race between host response and viral evolution. Molecular techniques provide the breeder with new tools to accelerate transmission or selection of interesting host genes. Nevertheless, creating a new cultivar that is resistant to a particular virus and otherwise true to type for the market is still tedious work.

It is therefore necessary for *agriculture* and horticulture to choose sustainable strategies to be applied in practice. Most of the work discussed here has been performed with a few model plant species and laboratory strains of viruses.

The current challenge is to introduce resistance traits into *agronomically* relevant cultivars that have to encounter a variety of viral strains or viral species. For a growing number of virus problems, this aim has already been reached; for very important virus epidemics, e.g., geminiviruses, it is still a task.

To reduce the number of setbacks during this long-lasting process, a series of risk concerns have been evaluated by aimed experiments as well as field surveys. Most of them have been covered by a very *comprehensive* and detailed review, and therefore it is possible to summarize the most important topics here.

Tolerance

Contrary to real resistance, a tolerant variety, whether it is created by classical or molecular means, will accumulate virus populations that are as virulent as before on related plant species lacking a tolerance-inducing gene.

In geographically isolated field conditions such an approach might be helpful if no alternative is seen, but in the majority of *agronomically* relevant cases it might promote new epidemics of the same virus and/or accelerate the evolution of new virulent virus strains.

Resistance Breakage

In general, resistance based on multiple genes is less easily broken than a *monogenically* based resistance. Monogenic exceptions to this rule that were extremely durable (e.g., for the N gene) are obvious.

Again, the problem is similar irrespective of classical or molecular breeding. Pathogen-derived protein-mediated approaches tend to have a smaller spectrum of protective effects, whereas RNA-based strategies sometimes provide broader efficiency. In every case, there is no a priori indication of which trait will be broken soon and which will be long-lived. The probability has to be tested through case-by-case experiments and field trials.

Transcapsidation

Transcapsidation of two discrete but related viruses has been observed in classical field situations, where it may create an epidemic problem if changes in vector *transmissibility* are associated. Molecular studies have defined conditions for and frequencies of transcapsidation.

In the worst case, transcapsidation will create new virions that can be transmitted, e.g., from a transgenic crop plant to a next neighbor plant, but such a virion will not be harmful to a larger agricultural area because it is lost in the recipient plant. Nevertheless, a careful resistance strategy should aim to avoid any *pathogen-derived* sequence in the protective gene that contributes to vector transmission.

Recombination

Recombination between plant viruses is a well-established fact now. Some viruses use template switch as an obligatory step of replication (*pararetroviruses*) and are therefore prone to recombination. In other virus families, *recombination* is an accidental phenomenon.

Although it occurs at a low frequency, it is worth considering because of the huge numbers of viruses in plants. Mostly, recombinational effects are overlooked because wild-type viruses overgrow the recombinants. Consequently, evidence for recombination in field isolates of RNA plant viruses is limited.

In contrast to most RNA viruses, the DNA-containing *geminiviruses* show multiple footprints of recombination in their sequences, which has been associated with the evolution of resistancebreaking strains. Recently, a possible explanation for this tendency was found in that *geminiviruses* may replicate using a recombination-dependent pathway in addition to the classical rolling-circle replication. In summary, accepting that recombination occurs with different *frequencies* but always frequently enough to create new variants, the real critical question is whether new viral capabilities are selected that provide invasion of new plants or vectors.

This concern is equally relevant for natural coinfection of different viruses and for viruses infecting a cultivar containing viral transgenes because invading viruses have been shown to take up transgene sequences in different virus families.

In conclusion, viral sequences coding for vector *transmissibility*, tissue tropism, host range, or symptom expression should be identified and omitted from transgenic constructs.

Synergism

Suppression of silencing, as discussed earlier, is also a lesson for risk concerns using pathogen-derived resistance. It is necessary but not sufficient to analyze the manipulated trait by challenging with the target virus. In the field situation, unrelated viruses might be promoted rather than inhibited by the viral gene product.

The history of the discovery of PVX suppressor capabilities has shown that functions of these types are not always obvious but have to be elucidated by intelligent means. In conclusion, resistance traits to be released in the field have to be *challenged* in the respective crop plants by relevant unrelated viruses in addition to the usually tested cognate target virus. Moreover, because of the *uncertainties* of such tests, *surveillance* monitoring has to be carried out.

PERSPECTIVES

Pathogen-derived resistance (PDR) of the first generation had its merits as a step toward engineering virus resistance and, more important, in investigating the interaction of virus and host. However, it also has its limits and risks.

Now, the second generation of PDR in the form of gene silencing is superior in abandoning the necessity for functional viral genes, *providing* the *possibility* to silence the viral silencing suppressors, and extending the reservoir of effector molecules that might be directed against a broad spectrum of viruses. Possibly, this approach will gain the same role for plants as *immunization* for animals.

In addition to pathogen-derived resistance, the *overwhelming* progress in *deciphering* host responses and virus-specific recognition will change the main fields of research on resistance. Identifying receptor proteins and other components of the signal *transduction* pathway will lead to a profound understanding of host defense and open the *possibility* to *transfer* individual components of the resistance network to the crop plants of choice.

9 Chapter
INCREASING TOLERANCE AGAINST MICROBIAL PATHOGENS

Disease resistance in crop plants is a major challenge in plant breeding. Within *industrialized* agriculture, the need for efficient self-protection of *cultivated* plants is likely to increase in the future. To achieve this goal, diverse *strategies* will be necessary and compete.

Conventional breeding has made great progress in *incorporating* natural defense genes, but the limitations of this method are also obvious. The progress in plant molecular biology now allows the generation of transgenic plants, thereby *exploiting* the mechanisms nature has *developed* to control and to limit the infection of microbial *pathogens* on plants.

An additional benefit of transgenic plants is the possibility to validate the usefulness of *endogenous* plant genes in defense strategies. Changes in the expression or composition of a desired gene may still be achieved by *conventional* breeding assisted by the results from transgenic plants. The possibility to transform all major crop plants-although sometimes tedious and labor *intensive-opens* a new opportunity for novel *enhanced* plant tolerance toward microbial pathogens.

Over the last few decades many of the natural plant defense strategies were thoroughly investigated, and as a result numerous mechanisms are known by now. For example, the concept of *pathogenesis-related* proteins (PR-proteins) has *revealed* an inducible defense system that is thought to have antimicrobial properties. The constitutive expression of a single or a few genes of this group of defense genes was started in the late 1980s but with limited success.

This will be covered in the first section of this chapter. On the other hand, new strategies for enhanced pathogen *tolerance* try to use the plants' signaling network for defense activation. As a consequence, a

whole battery of diverse defense *reactions* is triggered (variable in different plant species), which seems to be more powerful than the overexpression of single *antimicrobial* proteins. These approaches acting on complex defense networks will be *described* in the second part.

SINGLE-GENE DEFENSE MECHANISMS

Pathogenesis-Related Proteins

About 40 years ago Ross performed *experiments* with tobacco Xanthi nc plants, which after viral inoculation exhibit a hypersensitive reaction in which a *limited* number of cells die and form a lesion. Plants that were inoculated with the tobacco mosaic virus showed much smaller lesions after a challenge infection 7 days later than newly *inoculated* leaves.

This phenomenon is now well known as systemic acquired resistance (SAR). Searching for the mechanisms underlying SAR, PR-proteins were discovered. Subsequently some of them were *biochemically identified* as hydrolases of fungal cell walls, namely β-1,3-glucanase and chitinase.

However, the biochemical properties and enzymatic function of other PR-proteins such as the well-characterized PR-1 remain puzzling. Transgenic tobacco plants *overexpressing* a chitinase gene from tobacco showed enhanced tolerance against fungal infection by *Cercospora nicotianae* indicating that high levels of plant hydrolyzing enzymes are a suitable strategy to increase *pathogen* tolerance.

By using a combination of a 8-1,3-glucanase and a chitinase gene, Broglie et al. demonstrated the *synergistic* effect of both enzymes, yielding a higher degree of resistance compared with the expression of each gene alone. A similar conclusion was drawn from a study in tobacco, in which a gene for a basic chitinase from rice and a gene for an acidic glucanase from alfalfa were *coexpressed* after appropriate crossing of individual transgenic plants.

The different gene *combinations* were compared, as was the level of expression of these hydrolytic enzymes in homozygous versus heterozygous plants. Based on the reduction of lesion size after *C. nicotianae* infection, it was shown that the combination of *glucanase* and chitinase *expression* even at a moderate level is more beneficial than the *expression* of either gene alone at a much higher level.

The concept of the constitutive expression of hydrolytic enzymes was later extended from tobacco to crop plants. The expression of chitinase in oilseed rape (*Brassica napus*) to obtain enhanced tolerance was tested in field trials after inoculation with three different fungal pathogens.

Although the overall protection of the transgenic plants in the field trials seems to be smaller than *previously* shown in experiments in a greenhouse, the *enhanced* tolerance in chitinase-expressing rape was effective against several fungi under natural field conditions.

Many other plant species were *transformed* with plant glucanases or chitinases, and most research groups were able to find at least one fungus that is sensitive to these hydrolytic enzymes. The reports on transgenic plants *overexpressiong* hydrolytic enzymes imply that this strategy might already be sufficient to combat most fungal pathogens.

However, this is obviously not the case. Quite often fungi were chosen for pathogenicity assays that are known to be sensitive to chitinases and/or glucanases, *Rhizoctonia solani* and *Trichoderma viride* being examples. In contrast, well-recognized plant pathogens are often not *significantly* inhibited in their pathogenicity. Thus, plant *hydrolases* are useful to limit the spread of some fungal *pathogens* and are likely to increase the basal tolerance of plants against fungal infections.

Whether the increased tolerance of transgenic plants with elevated levels of hydrolytic enzymes is the result of the direct inhibition of the fungal (tip) growth needs to be carefully analyzed in future work. Enzymatic cleavage of fungal cell walls liberating chitin or glucan oligomers will also activate diverse plant defense responses as these carbohydrate oligomers are potent elicitors in almost every plant.

The transcriptional activation of genes involved in lignin precursor *formation* or antimicrobial phytoalexins by elicitors is well known. The genes for PR-proteins of unknown biochemical function such as PR1 or PR5 were also *constitutively* expressed in tobacco plants. The PRla-overexpressing plants have a higher degree of resistance against a limited number of fungal *pathogens* from oomycetes.

However, no enhanced tolerance against other pathogenic fungi of tobacco or tobacco mosaic virus was achieved. It was later shown that PR1-proteins from *tobacco* and tomato inhibit the spore germination of *Phytophthora infestans* and reduce the lesion size of diseased tomato leafs.

Notably, the PRla isoform, used in the transgenic lines, was very inefficient and showed only 10% of the *biological* activity of the most potent antifungal isoform PRlg. The overexpression of a rice thaumatin-like gene of the PR5 family in rice plants gave *enhanced* tolerance against *Rhizoctonia solani*, the agent causing sheath blight disease.

The infected leaf area was reduced to one fifth in the best lines, *indicating* that the thaumatin-like gene is highly effective against *R. solani* infection. Expression of a similar osmotin-like gene in potato also enhanced tolerance against the late blight disease caused by *Phytophthora infestans*. One interesting point about PR-proteins in cereals is worth mentioning.

Wheat, for instance, expresses *hydrolytic* enzymes (β-1,3-glucance, chitinase) after pathogen infection. In contrast to this situation in *Arabidopsis* and tobacco, the status of a systemic acquired resistance in wheat is not correlated with the *constitutive* expression of these PR-genes. This raises the question of whether hydrolytic enzymes are an important part of the plant defense system at all.

Alternatively, other as yet unidentified genes (or mechanisms) are important players in plant tolerance to pathogens. Support for the latter view comes from experiments with *Arabidopsis* DNA microarrays in which many genes are *transcriptionally* induced in resistant plants.

The fact that 413 genes (out of -7000 genes *representing* 25% of the genome) were reported to show a consistently higher expression level in SAR or plant resistance indicates that there will be more than a thousand genes that are *significantly* induced in local resistance or SAR. This incredibly high number draws a far more complex picture of plant resistance than previously thought.

As well as being *frustrating* for researchers trying to dissect single-gene function in SAR, the high number of SAR-related genes is a huge challenge and opportunity for the plant molecular biologist to create novel transgenic lines with enhanced tolerance against a variety of microbial pathogens.

Defense Peptides

Plant and animals have developed an efficient mechanism to combat pathogens by using small antimicrobial peptides collectively termed defensins. These peptides are now divided into several families on the basis of sequence homology and structural properties.

They are usually relatively small (<60 amino acids) and in the case of plant defensins contain several cysteine residues that form one or more stable disulfide bridges. Defense peptides exhibit a broad spectrum of *antimicrobial* activity against bacteria, fungi, and even enveloped viruses.

In animal cells even parasites and tumor cells are inhibited. Most of the known defensin genes are from insects showing mainly antibacterial activity. The large diversity of these peptides (more than 500 varieties are known) provides a huge reservoir of genes that can be expressed in plants to enhance tolerance against pathogens, an approach that has just started to be exploited by plant molecular biologists. A plant defensin from radish (RsAFLP2) was *expressed* at high levels in tobacco plants.

Subsequent infection with the fungal pathogen *Alternaria longipes* revealed efficient protection of the transgenic plants resulting in more than 80% reduction of lesion sizes. Lipid transfer proteins were initially described as shuttle proteins, involved in the transfer of lipids between organelles.

Later, the antimicrobial activity of these peptides was discovered. Transgenic *Arabidopsis* plants overexpressing the lipid transfer protein LTP2 from barley showed a strong reduction in disease symptoms after infection with *Pseudomonas* syringae pv. tomato. Thionins are often found in quite high amounts in the endosperm of cereals and other plants.

They are toxic to plant pathogenic fungi but only at relatively high concentrations. Bohlmann et al. showed inhibition of the barley pathogen *Drechslera teres* at *concentrations* of 500 µM. Nevertheless, transgenic *Arabidopsis* plants expressing high thionin levels were shown to be more resistant to *Fusarium oxysporum* and *Plasmodiophora* brassicae. The *overexpression* of plant defense peptide genes to achieve higher tolerance against a broad range of pathogens was only partly successful.

A few pathogens (mainly bacteria) were restricted in their growth, but many other *pathogens* were not. This problem was overcome by the expression of chimeric defense peptides in potato plants. The synthetic peptides consist of two domains derived from cecropin (from the giant silk moth *Hyalaphora cecropia*) and melittin (the major component of bee venom). The Nterminus of the chimeric peptide had to be modified in order to be tolerated as *nontoxic* by the plant cells.

The transgenic potato plants were almost totally resistant against *Erwinia carotovora* even over a very long period of time (e.g., 6 months of tuber storage). This high degree of resistance was also observed after infection of potato plants with different fungi including *Phytophthora cactorum* and *Fusarium solani.*

As mentioned before, some defense peptides are also toxic to animals, implying the need for great care in the use of these defense molecules in edible plants. The transgenic potatoes containing the chimeric cecropin-melittin peptide were fed to mice for several weeks without any notable change in animal behaviour or body weight.

The large number of known potent defense peptides from insects combined with molecular biology tools will make it possible to exploit these natural defense *mechanisms* on a broad basis.

Ribosome-Inactivating Proteins

Ribosome-inactivating proteins (RIPs) are widely found in plants. They exhibit a specific RNA-N-glycosidase activity that selectively cleaves off an adenine residue from a conserved site of the 28S rRNA.

This prevents binding of the *elongation* factor 2 and consequently leads to an arrest in protein biosynthesis. RIPs do not inactivate the *ribosomes* of their own species but inactivate those of distantly related species.

Expression of the barley seed RIP in tobacco under the control of a wound-inducible promoter resulted in enhanced tolerance against fungal infections with *Rhizoctonia solani.*

However, attempts to express the barley RIP in wheat plants were *unsuccessful,* indicating that the constitutive *expression* of this protein is toxic for wheat to allow regeneration of transgenic lines.

RIPs are primarily antiviral proteins, and overexpression of RIPs often leads to resistance of the transgenic plant against a broad spectrum of plant viruses. However, an additional antifungal activity of RIP was observed when *overexpressing* pokeweed *antiviral* protein and mutant forms, which exhibit no N-glycosidase activity typical of the RIP function. The *advantage* of the mutant RIPs is their low toxicity compared with the original protein.

Plants with Elevated Levels of Antimicrobial Secondary Compounds

The efficient protection of many wild-type plants against microbial *pathogens* is thought to be mediated at least in part by toxic secondary metabolites from plants. Often these compounds require very complex *biosynthesis,* and many of the genes involved in their formation are not known or *characterized.*

These limitations usually make the formation of secondary metabolites with complex biosynthesis in transgenic plants very difficult. Therefore, today's strategies are based on the expression of a single gene (or a few genes) to equip a plant with a novel secondary metabolite.

A successful example is the expression of a stilbene synthase gene from grapevine (*Vitis vinifera*) in tobacco and crop plants under the control of its native pathogen-inducible promoter.

The enzyme requires only one *pcoumaroyl-coenzyme* A (CoA) (a lignin precursor) and three malonyl-CoA to form one molecule of the stilbene resveratrol, which has *antimicrobial* properties in plants. The novel phytoalexin accumulated after *Botrytis cinerea* infection to low millimolar levels within a few days, resulting in a reduction of diseased leaf area of roughly two thirds.

The same gene was later expressed in tomato, rice, and other crop plants. Again, a strong increase in basal pathogen tolerance was obtained. One drawback, however, is the *observation* that tomato plants producing *resveratrol* showed an increase in resistance against *Phytophthora infestans* (-*50%* reduction in diseased leaf area) but not against *Botrytis cinerea,* which was *efficiently* restricted on resveratrol-producing tobacco plants.

In retrospect, it is amazing to see that the grapevine stilbene synthase promoter is pathogen inducible in so many plants and that this inducibility is essential as the *constitutive* expression of the stilbene synthase gene results in detrimental effects such as male sterility in tobacco.

MULTIGENE DEFENSE MECHANISMS

Elevation of Endogenous Levels of Salicylic Acid

In the first section, strategies were applied that are based on the expression of a single gene (or a few genes) and a single target mechanism. From *epidemiological* studies it is evident that such strategies have a high chance of being overcome by pathogens, similar to resistance against chemical pesticides.

From this point of view, more complex defense strategies should be beneficial for enhanced long-term pathogen tolerance. One obvious strategy is to make use of the plant's own defense system, for instance, by lowering the *threshold* level above which a plant mounts an efficient set of defense reactions to combat microbial pathogens.

Verbene et al. described the *expression* of two bacterial genes in plant *chloroplasts* that lead to salicylic acid biosynthesis from chorismate. Transgenic tobacco plants have high levels (-100 μM) of salicylic acid glucoside (the plant's vacuolar storage form) and are resistant against the fungus *Oidium lycopersicon.*

Similarly, lesions after infection with tobacco mosaic virus were much smaller than those in wild-type plants, resembling the *establishment* of systemic acquired resistance (SAR). The constant production of salicylic acid in the transgenic plants turns on the immune system of plants. Although this strategy was so far tested only in tobacco, it seems to be very promising for many other plants.

Constitutive Systemic Acquired Resistance

Many laboratories have developed mutagenesis-based screens to look for plants with a defect in the plant immune system, simplified set equivalent to SAR. A single mutant was isolated independently by three groups. The gene is *synonymously* called *npr* (nonexpresser of PR-genes), *nim* (nonimmunity), or *sai* (salicylic acid insensitive).

Although the biochemical function of the NPR protein is not well understood, it seems to interact with transcription factors required for PR-gene expression in a salicylic aciddependent manner. One obvious experiment after the isolation of the *NPR* gene was to increase the expression level of this gene in transgenic plants. Luckily, the transgenic *Arabidopsis* lines showed strongly enhanced tolerance against infection by the biotrophic fungus *Peronospora parasitica.*

This was achieved by a threefold increase in the protein level of NPR, which turned out to be sufficient to activate the complex plant defense system constitutively, resulting in SAR and resistance against *P. parasitica.*

Hydrogen Peroxide

A surprisingly small and reactive molecule plays a key role in plant defense: hydrogen peroxide (H_2O_2). Previously, H_2O_2 was regarded as an unavoidable by-product of respiration and photosynthesis for which the plant cell has no use, and thus it is rapidly detoxified by means of, for instance, catalase or ascorbate *peroxidase.*

Over the past decade a totally different picture of the function of H_2O_2 and other reactive oxygen species has emerged from many studies. For instance, H_2O_2 drives the cross-linking of plant cell wall structural proteins. The local *toughening* of the cell wall is a barrier for *penetrating* fungi and is beneficial for the plant to mount a local defense to stop the ingression of the fungu. Cross-linked cell walls were shown to be much more resistant towards microbial cell wall cleaving hydrolyses.

Along the same line, the expression of a wheat germin protein in wheat leaves results in enhanced resistance against *Blumeria graminis* f.sp. *tritici*, the causal agent of wheat powdery mildew. It was shown that germin is oxidatively cross-linked in wheat cell walls at sites of attempted fungal penetration. From a biochemical point of view, it is also clear that other compounds can be polymerized in H_2O_2-dependent processes.

Many other phenolic secondary *compounds* are candidates for mixed *polyphenols* beside the lignin precursors. Thus, it is conceivable that part of the enhanced pathogen tolerance of stilbene-producing plants is mediated by the supply of the phenolic compound resveratrol for *polyphenol formation* rather than the direct antimicrobial activity of this phytoalexin alone. The plant-pathogen interaction that results in *programmed* cell death of the hypersensitive reaction (HR) exhibits an extra *oxidative* burst several hours after contact between plant and microbe.

This phenomenon is widespread and therefore seems to be important in plant resistance. The H_2O_2 from the oxidative burst was shown to be a signal that diffuses locally around the site of the infection and thereby transcriptionally induces genes in neighboring cells. Furthermore, H_2O_2 pulses (<10 minutes) induce cell death in soybean cell cultures several hours later.

Although the concentrations used for the H_2O_2 pulses were relatively high (2-5 mM), a similar result can be obtained by supplying a constant H_2O_2 concentration of 1050 μM for several hours using the *enzyme* glucose oxidase. Following these ideas, *transgenic* plants were generated in which a catalase gene was largely suppressed by an antisense strategy.

As a consequence, the steady-state levels of H_2O_2 are higher and these plants are more sensitive to microbial pathogen attack, resulting in enhanced tolerance. These observations resemble findings in transgenic potato plants that express a glucose *oxidase* gene from *Aspergillus* in their cell wall.

The slightly elevated levels of H_2O_2 in the potato plants have a strong impact on pathogen resistance. Why and how a small increase in H_2O_2 causes the greatly increased pathogen tolerance remain a mystery waiting to be solved in future studies.

As a final remark, the catalase antisense plants are more resistant to pathogens but they are also more sensitive to oxidative stress caused by photosynthesis under high light conditions. One should be cautious about the likely reduction in cold tolerance and drought stress, two unfavourable environmental conditions that put oxidative stress on the plants.

It seems that the concentration of H_2O_2 has to remain within a certain margin in order to avoid detrimental side effects on the plant's tolerance to unusual *environmental* conditions.

Cell Death as a Trigger of Plant Resistance

Mutants with Spontaneous Cell Death

The most potent plant defense against microbial pathogens is the hypersensitive reaction, a form of programmed cell death in plants. The principle of the HR is based on the early recognition of a pathogen, which then actively triggers a particular cell death program in the attacked cell.

Although it is easily conceivable that an attack of a biotrophic fungus can be stopped efficiently by killing the plant cell in contact with the pathogen, the molecular basis for the general success of the HR to stop pathogen ingression remains to be solved in detail.

The scientific problem comes down to the question of what else is turned on by the programmed cell death of the HR that is not activated by cell death per se (for instance, wounding). In general, an HR in one leaf will establish an immune response (SAR) in the whole plant that allows a more efficient HR in the next *infection* event, as mentioned before for the tobacco mosaic virus-inoculated tobacco plants.

A lesson from these and other studies is that the plant's endogenous cell death program is a valuable tool for plant resistance. Plant breeders have used programmed cell death in plants for decades to achieve resistance against pathogens. The barley *Mlo* gene is probably the best *understood* example. In rare cases, a mutation in *the Mlo locus* causes *programmed* cell death of single cells in leaves, a phenomenon termed lesion mimic. The important thing about lesion mimic is the discovery that this cell death causes plant *responses* very similar to those that HR of a few cells would cause after a primary infection.

Thus, lesion mimic is a physiological equivalent of an HR. The *Mlo* gene was identified by positional cloning and predicted to be a membrane protein that is a negative regulator (repressor) of cell death. About 10 years ago, several groups started to look for lesion mimic mutants in *Arabidopsis*.

Many mutants have been identified, and at least for some of them the molecular mechanism is known. In contrast to the hidden cell death in *Mlo* barley plants, the *Arabidopsis* lesion mimics often show drastic phenotypes *including* dwarfism.

Transgenic Plants with Induced Limited Cell Death

Meanwhile, several different approaches have been taken to induce cell death in plants. Often the cell death behaves like the cell death in the hypersensitive reaction after pathogen contact and subsequently triggers a whole battery of plant defenses, usually including elevated levels of salicylic acid (SA), *induction* of PR-genes, and *immunity* by the SAR process.

One example is the bacterial ribonuclease barnase, which is a very potent enzyme that kills eukaryotic cells when present at a few molecules per cell. This enzyme is effectively inhibited by the small protein barstar. Using a pathogen-inducible promoter of a glutathione-S-transferase gene from potato, *Strittmatter* et al. expressed the barnase gene in potato plants.

To avoid killing of the whole plant by the leaky promoter, it was necessary to coexpress the barstar inhibitor. Potato lines in which the strength of the pathogen-inducible promoter led to a surplus of free active barnase showed pathogen-dependent cell death after *Phytophthora infestans* inoculation.

Thus, a totally artificial cell death process was able to enhance plant tolerance toward fungal infection. The limited success of the study is most likely due to a *nonoptimal* choice of the promoters used, but nevertheless it demonstrates impressively the power of artificial cell death-inducing systems. Another cell death-inducing molecule is the fungal protein cryptogein, secreted by *Phytophthora cryptogea.*

It is one of many similar proteins of *Phytophthora* species, which are collectively termed elicitins. Expression of the gene encoding cryptogein under the control of the pathogen-inducible *hsr203J* promoter in tobacco resulted in enhanced tolerance of transgenic lines against *Phytophthora parasitica, Thielaviopsis basicola,* and *Erysiphe cichoracearum* infection.

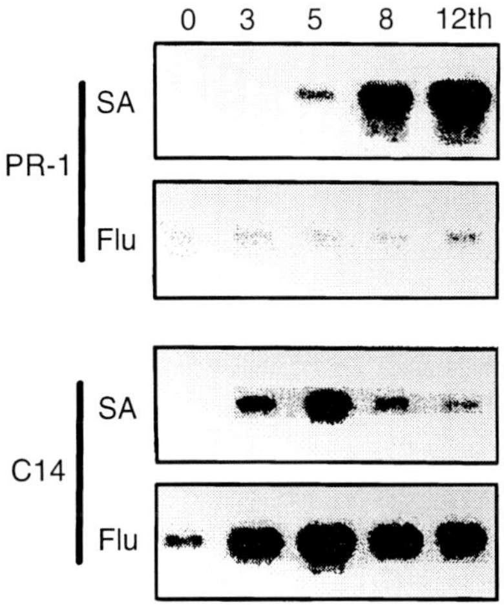

The mode of action seems to be the induction of a cell death program by the cryptogein protein, which then activates the general plant defense machinery. It is, however, currently anticipated that elicitins cause cell death only in tobacco species, thus *limiting* the use of this system in crop plants. A third example of induced cell death was published by Tang et al..

Figure 9.1: RNA blot with salicylic acid-regulated genes from tobacco. A BY- 2 tobacco cell culture was treated with 250 /uM salicylic acid (SA) or 25 /zM flufenamate (Flu) and samples were taken at designated time points. The upper set of samples was hybridized with a tobacco PR-la gene, showing the beginning of the induction of the PR-1 gene by salicylic acid whereas flufenamate is inactive in inducing the PR-1 gene. C14-1b is a tobacco gene of unknown function (88) that is only weakly induced by salicylic acid but strongly induced by flufenamate.

The researchers *constitutively* expressed the pto-kinase gene in tomato, which was identified some years ago and shown to be required for resistance against the bacterial pathogen *Pseudomonas syringae* pv. *tomato.* The constitutive expression of pto-kinase is already sufficient to induce programmed cell death in a limited number of cells in tomato leaves, subsequently activating the SAR response in tomato.

These transgenic plants exhibit broad spectrum pathogen tolerance as expected from the activated SAR response. Although the latter examples of engineered cell death are specific for particular plant species, a novel more generally *applicable* system for the induction of artificial cell death emerges from many studies of plant *resistance* and *microbial* avirulence genes.

As predicted from the early studies of Flor (1947), the interaction of a plant resistance gene product with a microbial avirulence gene product is the basis for the programmed cell death in the HR. Whereas the first *avr* genes were cloned from phytopathogenic bacteria in the early 1980s, the first plant resistance genes (*R* genes) were identified in 1994.

The rigorous test of whether the *avr* gene product by itself is sufficient to induce an HR was impressively answered and *confirmed* by studies in which the *avr* gene was *transiently* expressed in plant cells. Plant R genes seem to work functionally at least in closely related species.

For instance, the tomato *Cf-9* resistance gene was transformed into tobacco plants and the resulting transgenic lines still responded to the *corresponding* avr9 peptide from the tomato pathogenic fungus *Cladosporium fulvum.* When this tobacco line was crossed with a transgenic plant expressing the *avr9* avirulence gene, the siblings showed a whole-plant HR and died at the seedling stage, thus *confirming* the concept.

The expression of both *avr* and *R* genes in a strictly controlled pathogen-dependent manner

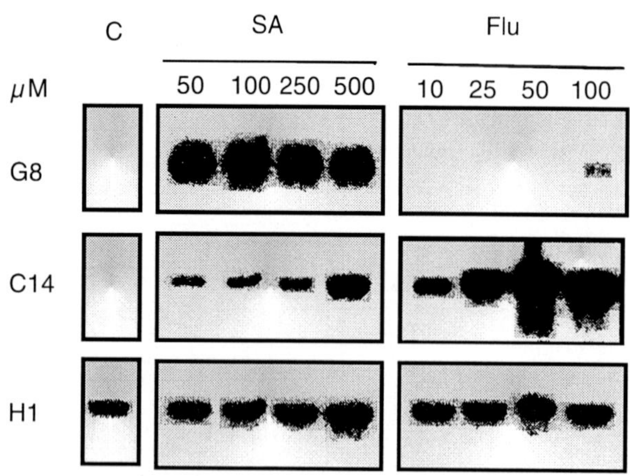

Figure 9.2: RNA blot with a dose-response experiment on salicylic acid-regulated genes in tobacco. A tobacco cell line (BY-2) was treated with different concentrations of salicylic acid (SA) or flufenamate (Flu) and collected for RNA isolation 5 hours later. The blot was hybridized with two tobacco genes (88) of unknown function, which exhibit different induction patterns. Whereas salicylic acid strongly induces the G8-1 gene, flufenamate is largely inactive in this response. In contrast, the C14-1b gene shows a reversed gene induction pattern with weak induction by salicylic acid and a strong increase in mRNA caused by flufenamate. The equal loading was verified by rehybridization of the blot with a gene for the tobacco histone 1 (H1).

is one of the most promising strategies for engineered cell death and subsequent activation of the plant's immune system. A great variety of suitable promoter elements for such experiments is currently under development.

The use of two different pathogen-inducible promoters for the resistance and the avirulence gene will help to minimize the detrimental effects of *unintentional* cell death. Thus, the regulation of cell death is an important issue and understanding it is necessary for further exploitation of *programmed* cell death as a novel mechanism for enhanced pathogen tolerance.

SALICYLIC ACID FUNCTION IN PROGRAMMED CELL DEATH

A central player in many but not all forms of programmed cell death in plants is salicylic acid. This was first demonstrated in transgenic tobacco and *Arabidopsis* plants expressing a salicylate hydroxylase gene from *Pseudomonas putida* called *nahG*.

These plants are still capable of synthesizing SA, but as soon as SA starts to accumulate it is converted into catechol by the enzyme salicylate hydroxylase. *Arabidopsis* plants of the Col-O ecotype, which as wild-type plants are genetically resistant to *Peronospora parasitica* infection, were totally *colonized* by the fungus in nahG-expressing plants.

This conversion of an incompatible to a compatible interaction could be reverted by spraying with high concentrations of salicylic acid or the synthetic analogue INA (2,6-dichloro-isonicotinic acid), indicating that SA is a key control molecule in plant resistance. Some of the dwarf lesion mimic mutants of *Arabidopsis* mentioned before could also be reverted to wild-type-like plants when crossed with *nahG* plants. Thus, the question arises of how SA controls *programmed* cell death in plants.

The discovery tour begins with a binding protein for SA, characterized from tobacco, that was shown to be a catalase, pointing to increased levels of H_2O, as the driving force of programmed cell death. This view was later extended by the finding that the other major H_2O_2-scavenging enzyme, ascorbate peroxidase, can also be *inhibited* in tobacco by SA. This model is attractive at first glance as H_2O_2 is an important signaling molecule in plant defense, as outlined earlier.

However, many other groups have tested the phenomenon in various plant species, and none of their studies has shown a significant inhibition of catalase or ascorbate peroxidase at *physiologically* relevant concentrations (<100 μM).

For example, in soybean SA (100 μM) neither inhibits both enzymes in vitro nor interferes with the capacity of soybean cell cultures to metabolize H_2O_2, which reflects the in vivo situation. In a model system for programmed cell death in plants, we investigate the HR in soybean cell cultures (cv. Williams 82) triggered by the avrA protein of the bacterial pathogen *Pseudomonas syringae pv. glycinea.*

The HR occurs according to the gene-for-gene hypothesis requiring the Rps2 resistance gene in soybean and the *avrA* avirulence gene in *Pseudoinonas.* The advantage of the cell culture system is its *flexibility* and the possibility to *manipulate* the system easily using inhibitors or activators.

The HR requires SA (~50 μM), which can be added to the cell culture medium to complete the cell death program. This phenotype in soybean resembles the studies with *nahG Arabidopsis* plants, in which the HR is also dependent on SA. The addition of SA to soybean cell cultures strongly *accelerates* the HR, finally leading to faster cell death.

By using the vital stain Evans Blue, we showed loss of *membrane* control as the final sign of cell death in the HR after about 8 hours in the SA-accelerated HR compared with about 14 hours in control inoculated cells without SA (similar to the time range of the HR in plants). Using this *acceleration* for a screenable test system, we identified several chemicals that can substitute for SA.

To our surprise, the chemicals were diverse in structure and thus made it initially difficult to come up with a model to explain their *biochemical* function. We have *collectively* termed these chemicals FASs (functional analogues of SA).

A rigorous check of the literature revealed an emerging function of FAS compounds in animal cells. Almost all of them are ligands of a transcription factor system in humans, the *peroxisome* proliferator-activated receptors (PPARs). The PPARs are a *subfamily* within the superfamily of nuclear hormone receptors, which are posttranslationally activated by binding their specific ligands.

One therapeutic aspect of PPARs in humans is their relevance in type II diabetes, which can be treated by the uptake of synthetic PPAR ligands (such as *troglitazone*) on a daily basis. This drug can also be used in soybean to complement and accelerate the HR, triggered by *Pseudomonas* bacteria, and by this criterion is an FAS compound.

The outlined model predicts that genes in plants are *transcriptionally* induced by SA or FAS compounds. We have described a novel putative lectin-encoding gene from soybean that is induced by both groups of compounds as predicted. Using *differential* display and subtractive suppression hybridization, we have identified a larger set of genes, which are transcriptionally induced by salicylic acid and FAS compounds (C Anstatt, N Auslander, A Ludwig, G Schwerdtfeger, M Hansen, R *Tenhaken, unpublished* results).

This set probably includes novel genes, which are required for the execution of programmed cell death in a salicylic acid-dependent manner. Chemicals such as INA or the *benzothiadiazole* Bion® are thought to mimic SA and are thus able to activate the *signaling* process leading to SAR.

This raises the question of whether FAS chemicals are similar to SAR inducers in their mode of action. *Arabidopsis* and tobacco treated with SA or Bion show a strong induction of the PR-1 messenger RNA (mRNA). In contrast, the FAS chemical *flufenamate* was unable to induce the same response in tobacco, pointing to different signal *transduction* pathways.

In the model plant tobacco, several SA-inducible genes were described besides the classical PR genes, for instance, in a study by Horvath and Chua. Whether theses genes are novel PR genes in the sense that they are induced in plant-pathogen interactions remains to be analyzed.

We have chosen the *C14-1b* gene as a probe to test whether FAS *compounds* will induce genes in tobacco as well as in soybean. The sensitive induction of the tobacco *C14-1b* gene by *flufenamate*, which occurs at a much lower *concentration* compared with SA, is an example. As also shown in Figure elsewhere in this chapter, another tobacco gene, *G8-1*, is strongly induced by salicylic acid but almost not induced by the FAS compound *flufenamate*.

These observations underline the different signal transduction pathways and mode of actions in which salicylic acid is involved in plants. The data can be *summarized* in a new model in which SA controls plant resistance by at least two independent processes. In the first place, high concentrations of SA are needed to execute the plant cell death program, and the predicted mode of action is the transcriptional activation of genes (which mostly remains to be identified in future studies).

This function of SA can be mimicked by FAS compounds as shown for soybean. The second major function of SA is the participation in the establishment of the plant immunity (SAR). This function of SA can be potently mimicked by INA or Bion. Our current goal is to identify an SA/FAS-regulated *transcription* factor that is involved in programmed cell death in plants.

By functional analysis of the promoter, we identified *a cis* element in an FAS-responsive gene that is also specifically bound by nuclear protein extracts in gel *retardation* assays. Controlled *activation* or repression of this factor will probably be a valuable tool to modify *programmed* cell death in plants.

We anticipate a novel mode of enhanced plant tolerance toward microbial pathogens by engineering the execution of a natural cell death program and making use of the powerful natural broadspectrum resistance that plants have developed during evolutionary history.

CONCLUSIONS AND FUTURE PERSPECTIVES

The dream of transgenic plants resistant to viruses, bacteria, fungi, and insects is still (and is likely to be forever) a fantasy. What has been achieved in the last 15 years in creating transgenic plants with *enhanced* tolerance against *pathogens* is, however, very remarkable.

The rapid success took advantage of decades of biochemical work of plant pathologists and has now opened a wide field of approaches for novel resistance principles in plants as a defense against *microbial* pathogens. Clearly, from today's point of view, the *approaches* that activate the host's defense machinery will be successful.

Artificial cell death triggered under the strict control of *pathogeninducible* promoters is my personal favourite. Although we can already use the plant's innate immune system, we basically understand very little of how it works. Detailed knowledge of single or network-like mechanisms will be a *prerequisite* for a next generation of *engineered* plants that specifically activate certain parts of the complex immune response required in particular for *individual* pathogens.

10 Chapter INCREASING TOLERANCE AGAINST INSECT PESTS

Control of insect pests represents one of the major input costs of world *agricultural* production and consumes billions of dollars annually, *predominantly* in chemical pesticides and lost *production*. Insect control with pesticides is, however, *becoming* more problematic in both developed and third world countries. Farmers and consumers are increasingly aware of the environmental and ecological impacts of excessive pesticide use.

As the target insects are repeatedly exposed to the same pesticide chemistries, they often develop heritable *resistance* to those pesticides and require the use of *higher* and higher doses or more toxic insecticide blends to achieve economic levels of pest control.

Plant breeders, seed companies, and farmers are now turning to biotechnological solutions to these important pest problems in agriculture because of the *environmental* and economic advantages of *deploying* inbuilt insect control strategies as opposed to external *applications*.

Over the past 10 years, transgenic crops protected against insects have been generated in some of the *important* broadacre crops, including cotton and corn, as well as in *horticultural* crops such as potato, and have been released *commercially*.

BACILLUS THURINGIENSIS CRY GENES AS A SOURCE OF INSECTICIDAL GENES FOR CROPS

The bacterium *Bacillus thuringiensis* has had a long history of use as a sprayable microbial biopesticide. It has been used predominantly in horticulture and to a smaller extent in broadacre crops, especially those grown organically.

During *sporulation*, the bacterium produces a series of insecticidal proteins assembled into a parasporal crystal. A mixture of the dried spores and crystals is *reconstituted* with water and sprayed on plants. On ingestion by the target insects, the *crystals* are *solubilized* and activated by *digestive* proteases to form highly potent and specific toxins that bind to *particular* gut receptors.

The toxins are thought to aggregate and form *ionpermeable* pores that lead to gut dysfunction, lysis of gut epithelial cells, and the eventual death of the insect. Individual crystals in the *bacterium* may be a complex mixture of toxins each with its own range of insect specificities.

The individual proteins within the crystals are encoded by both plasmid and *chromosomal* Cry genes that were identified as early targets for *incorporation* into crop plants to protect them from insects. There are now hundreds of identified *Cry* genes, and there is a standard nomenclature to describe them based on sequence similarities. Initial attempts to express Cry genes in *transgenic* plants were not *particularly* successful, and this was attributed to the bacterial origins of these genes and especially their high AT content, which resulted in low levels of insecticidal protein.

Resynthesis of the *Cry* genes removing cryptic plant polyadenylation signals, putative *messenger* RNA (mRNA) *destabilization* signals, improving the codon usage bias, and increasing the GC content were strategies that increased *expression* to a useful level (0.2-0.3% of total soluble protein) in *transgenic* plants.

Modified and unmodified, full-length and truncated Cry genes have so far been *expressed* in an array of plant species (from trees such as poplar, larch, and eucalypt; cereals like wheat, maize, and rice; legumes like chickpeas, soybeans, and peanuts; *vegetables* such as potato, tomato, cabbage, broccoli, and sweet potato; and fruits like apples and strawberries), but *intellectual* property ownership has restricted *commercialization* to a few high-value *agricultural* species, such as cotton and corn and to a lesser extent potato.

COMMERCIALIZED BACILLUS THURINGIENSIS (BT) CROPS

Bt-Corn

The United States is the largest corn-producing country in the world. One of the *significant* pests of U.S. and Canadian corn is the European corn borer (ECB) (*Ostrinia nubilalis*), a lepidopteran insect, whose larvae are difficult to control as they bore into the corn stalk, where they are protected from applied *pesticides*. Only a few percent of the total acreage of corn is sprayed for control of ECB, so economic losses from this insect can be high.

Btcorn varieties targeted at ECB control were first released in the United States in 1996 and were so rapidly adopted by farmers that over a quarter of all the corn sown by 1999 was Bt-corn. Five different types of Bt-corn are *currently* registered by the U.S. *Environmental* Protection Agency (EPA), each with either *different Cry* genes (*CrylAb, CrylAc, or Cry9C*) or different levels or patterns of expression.

The Monsanto and Syngenta Yieldgard corns express truncated codon-modified *CrylAb* genes derived from *B. thuringiensis* subsp. *kurstaki*. The Syngenta corn line has been backcrossed into both field and sweet corn varieties and, as with the Monsanto line, the *CrylAb* gene is expressed *throughout* the plant, *including* the silks and kernels, but is particularly high in leaves.

Bt-corns called KnockOut (Novartis) or NatureGard (Mycogen) also express *CrylAb* but use a novel two-gene strategy to target expression to ECB-susceptible tissues. One *CrylAb* is controlled by the corn *phosphoenolpyruvate* carboxylase (PEPC) gene directing *expression* in green *photosynthetically* active tissues. A pollen-specific promoter from the maize *calcium-dependent* protein kinase (CDPK) gene controls the second.

The combination of PEPC and pollen promoters provides high *CrylAb* gene expression in leaves and pollen, where it is highly effective in controlling European corn borer. Changes in business structures have resulted in the phaseout of KnockOut and NatureGard corns, and their registration will not be renewed. All existing stocks of these events can now be used only until the 2003 corn-growing season. A Dekalb Bt-corn called Bt-Xtra contains three genes, the *CrylAc* gene from *B. thuringiensis* subsp. *kurstaki*, the *bar* gene from *Streptomyces hygroscopicus*, and the potato proteinase inhibitor *pinll.*

While proteinase inhibitor genes expressed at high levels can inhibit insect digestive proteases and confer insecticidal properties to transgenic plants, the *pinll* gene in BtXtra corn was truncated during integration into the corn genome and no protein expression is detectable. CrylAc is very similar to CrylAb but has a slightly different insecticidal activity spectrum.

Since the purchase of Dekalb by Monsanto, the Bt-Xtra corn has been phased out in favour of Yieldgard. Finally, StarLink is a Bt-corn *expressing* a completely different type of *Cry* gene, the *Cry9C* from *B. thuringiensis* subsp. *tolworthi.* The Cry9C protein is active against ECB and some other lepidopteran pests of corn, including black cutworm (*Agrotis ipsilon*), but not the corn earworm (*Helicoverpa zea*). StarLink corn was registered only for animal feed and nonfood industrial use as there were some questions raised at registration *concerning* its potential allergenicity in humans.

Subsequently, *Cry9C* was detected in corn chips and other corn food products, in violation of the original animal feed use registration. StarLink was voluntarily withdrawn from registration in 2000, and there is now an *extensive* program in place to track and remove remnants of StarLink corn from the human food chain.

At the time of its withdrawal, it had been sown on less than 1% of the corn area in the United States. Thus, only two of the five original transgenic Btcorn lines will be available commercially in the next few years. Bt-corn varieties have been shown to be very effectively protected against ECB, but levels of infestation vary from year to year and region to region.

It has been estimated that in 10 of the last 13 years growers would have received an economic benefit had they been growing Bt-corn when ECB pest pressures were high. Since their release, modest reductions (1.5%) in pesticide usage have been realized, but given that *insecticides* are rarely effective for ECB control and hence seldom used, this is still significant.

Indirect benefits are also likely as the reduced ECB damage to Bt-corn is also likely to reduce sites for entry of pathogens, particularly those that produce *mycotoxins* that are health hazards to humans and farm animals eating the corn.

The Cry]-expressing Bt-corn varieties have clearly allowed farmers to better control a very difficult agricultural pest (ECB), for which effective and affordable pest control options were unavailable. Yield losses from this insect have reached as much as 300 million bushels of corn in a single year. Such losses could be virtually *eliminated* using Bt-corn. New additions to the current suite of Bt-corn varieties are likely in the next few years; the first, a CrylF-expressing corn (lepidopteran active), received *conditional* registration in 2001.

Of particular interest will be the first Bt-corn targeted at beetle pests, especially the corn rootworm (*Diabrotica sp.*). Corn rootworm is really a complex of three or four different species of *Diabrotica* that are serious pests in the United States, with estimated costs of over U.S. $1 billion in chemical control and lost production.

The larvae of these beetles attack the roots, and so control is *primarily* with soil insecticides, crop rotations, and foliar insecticide applications to kill the adult beetles and prevent further egg laying. Monsanto have developed a new transgenic corn (MaxGard) expressing the beetle-active *Cry3Bb* gene that appears to be very effective in *controlling* the larval *stages* of corn rootworm.

The gene construct is believed to be a codon-modified synthetic *Cry3Bb* with a leader region from the wheat chlorophyll alb binding protein gene, an intron from the rice actin gene, and a terminator from the wheat *hspl7* gene. Monsanto applied for full registration of a number of events of its MaxGard corn in late 1999. The petition for *nonregulated* status was *withdrawn* in 2001, but Monsanto continues to do largescale trials all over the U.S. corn belt.

The transgenic corn will have to compete with other nontransgenic corn rootworm-resistant varieties. These nontransgenic varieties may be more acceptable to *consumers* who are *concerned* about GM corn products.

Bt-Cotton

Cotton is a major world crop grown primarily for its fiber but also for its oil and seed meal. Cotton is a *demanding* crop requiring *significant* inputs of both water and agricultural chemicals (*insecticides, herbicides, fungicides, defoliants,* and *fertilizers*).

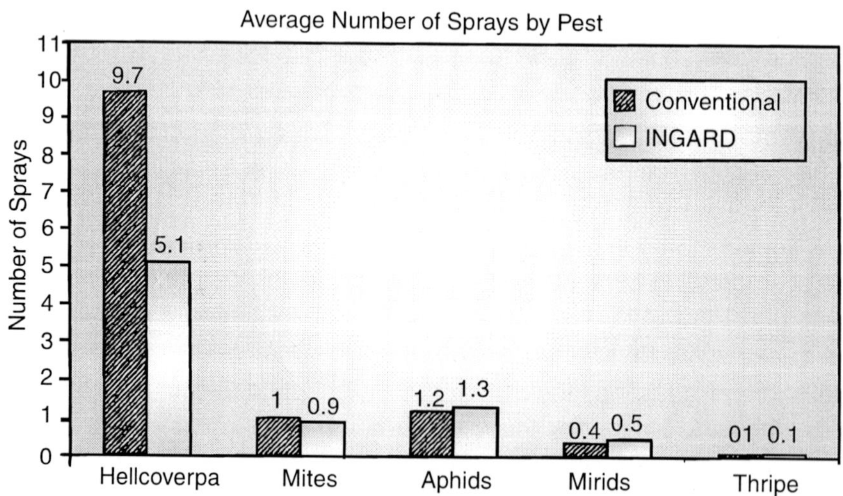

Figure 10.1: INGARD cotton under commercial production required significantly fewer pesticide sprays for caterpillar pests than similar conventional varieties in the 1999-2000 season. An area of 191,000 ha of cotton was surveyed, of which 28% was INGARD cotton. Pesticide applications to INGARD were 47% less than on conventional fields, and there were no major differences in pesticides applied for other pests.

High inputs and high returns have made cotton one of the leading crops for the application of biotechnology, and by 1999-2000 about 12% of the world cotton area was sown with genetically modified varieties. In 2000 over 70% of the U.S. crop was sown with insectand/or herbicide-tolerant GM cotton varieties: about 60% were herbicidetolerant varieties and 40% were Bt varieties (about three *quarters* of the latter were *stacked* with a herbicide tolerance trait).

The Bt varieties (Bollgard) were first released in the United States in 1996 primarily for the control of *Heliothis virescens* (tobacco budworm, TBW) but also for other pests such as *Helicoverpa zea* (cotton bollworm, CBW, or corn earworm) and *Pectinophora gossypiella* (pink bollworm). Bollgard cotton varieties contain a single insertion of a codon-modified hybrid *CrylAb/CrylAc* gene from *B. thuringiensis* subsp. *kurstaki.* Three lines of Bt-cotton, 531, 757, and 1076, were initially deregulated, but only one, 531 (Bollgard), was released commercially in the United States.

Initial sowings of Bollgard cotton in 1996 were about 1 million hectares (about 12% of the U.S. cotton area). This was a difficult year for a commercial launch because there were unusually high levels of CBW rather than the more usual cotton pest, TBW (CBW is less susceptible to *CrylAb/c* than TBW). Many thousands of hectares of Btcotton in the U.S. southeast became infested with CBW and had to be sprayed with pesticides.

This poor performance was blamed on the increased corn area that year (which increased populations of CBW) and the hot dry weather that *appeared* to decrease *expression* of the *CrylAb/c* gene, particularly later in the season. Subsequent years proved less difficult for growers, and the performance of Bt varieties has improved as growers have adjusted their adoption and management of Bt-cotton to suit their particular pest problems and *economics*. The benefits of Bt-cotton varieties in the United States have been difficult to quantify despite extensive surveys since their *introduction*.

Attributing effects on yield, pesticide usage, and profits due to Bt is a statistical challenge as many other factors can influence yield and pesticide usage even on a single farm. However, a number of analyses have indicated that there are at least three benefits to growers of Bt-cotton. First, there have been statistically significant reductions in yield losses due to the target pests in many areas.

Pesticide usage has also declined in many areas, but again statistical analyses suggest that this decrease is small and mainly for the pesticides other than major organophosphates and synthetic pyrethrins. These increases in yields and decreases in pesticide usage translate to higher net returns to growers who adopt Bt-cotton technology. Australia saw the first release of Bt-cotton in 1996, as INGARD varieties (Bollgard was already registered as a proprietary name for a different technology), on a relatively small area (30,000 ha or about 10% of total cotton area).

In Australia, the main insect pests of cotton, as in the United States, are also the larvae of heliothine moths, in this case *Helicoverpa armigera* and *H. punctigera.* Infestations are normally extreme by comparison with that in the United States, and it is not unusual to spray 12-14 times per season to control these pests (compared with 2-3 in the United States).

The total crop in 2000 occupied about 500,000 ha (about 180,000 of it INGARD) and insect control costs on conventional cotton often exceed AUS$100 million annually, for a crop worth about AUS$1.6 billion. Both *H. armigera* and *H. punctigera* are naturally less susceptible (by about 10-fold) to the CrylAb/c protein expressed in INGARD (or Bollgard) cotton and are much more abundant in cotton-producing areas than the similar pests in the United States. Early research trials indicated that although INGARD cotton controlled *H. armigera* well, particularly during the early part of the season, efficacy declined late in the season when fruit was being set. Annual surveys of the usage of *pesticides* and economic returns to growers using Bt-cotton have been carried out in Australia since 1996.

Because INGARD cotton can be only a proportion of the cotton on any one farm, detailed paired *comparisons* between the performance of INGARD and corresponding conventional varieties were possible. Pest control costs represent a significant proportion of the annual variable costs of cotton *production* in Australia, so the impact of INGARD on pesticide use appears to be much more apparent than in the United States. In all 4 years there was a significant reduction in overall use of pesticides (across all pesticide groups) and particularly those used against the *Helicoverpa* caterpillars.

In 1999-2000, for example, there was a 40% decrease in pesticides targeted at all pests (down from 10.3 sprays in conventional cotton to 6.2 in Btcotton) or 47% reduction in pesticides targeted specifically at *Helicoverpa* species (from 9.7 down to 5.1 sprays on Bt-cotton).

There was a 75% reduction in endosulfan use (a pesticide under threat in Australia because of its high toxicity to fish and the very low tolerance set for endosulfan contamination in rivers) and a 43% reduction in pyrethrins. This should reduce the pressure on synthetic pyrethroids that have selected a high incidence of resistance among cotton pests. The main concern to growers has been the high variability of lepidopteran control in Bt-cotton crops.

The number of effective days of *Helicoverpa* control (time from planting to first foliar spray of insecticide) varies from as little as 20 days up to 140 days with considerable differences in the performances of different transgenic varieties. Reduced control has been correlated with a decrease in both Cry IAb/c protein and mRNA and possibly increases in secondary metabolites that decrease the efficacy of Bttoxins.

Most of the benefit of Bt-cotton is realized in the first half of the season, when little insecticide now has to be used to control both major *lepidopteran* pest species. Careful crop *monitoring* and spraying when pests reach their economic thresholds (new thresholds were established specifically for INGARD varieties) has *stabilized* the performance of INGARD cotton.

There is a strong tendency to sow INGARD cotton in *environmentally* sensitive areas (fields close to waterways and towns as Australia has very strong pollution control laws in relation to pesticide *contamination* of rivers *etc.*) *to* capture the *significant environmental* benefits of reduced pesticide applications.

The economic benefit to the grower has been variable, in line with the variability in successful insect control. Of the paired comparisons carried out, 54% recorded some economic benefit and the rest were about break-even. The Bt technology clearly has benefits, but some *limitations* have emerged in Australia (and *presumably* in Asia, where *H. armigera* is a major pest of cotton).

In response to the poorer efficacy of Bt-cotton in Australia (and to enhanced *H. zea* control and better resistance *management* in the United States), a double gene product is being developed that contains two different Bt-toxin genes, the *CryIAb/c* gene (in INGARD and Bollgard) and *a Cry2Ab* gene also from *Bacillus thuringiensis.*

These two gene cottons (Bollgard II) are still in the breeding stage, but initial field studies have indicated much better *H. armigera* control. Bt-cotton is now approved for food use in Argentina, Australia, Canada, China, Japan, Mexico, and South Africa, as well as the United States.

Bt-cotton was grown on about 0.5 million hectares in *mainland* China in 2000-much of it Bollgard, but also some Bt-cotton developed in China, e.g., with outcomes very similar to that observed in Australia, where the lepidopteran pests are similar.

A number of Asian, European, and Latin American countries have *experimental* crops of both Bt-cotton and Btcorn for precommercial evaluation.

Bt-Potatoes

In 1996 about 1% of the total U.S. potato acreage was planted to Bt-potatoes, and this rose to about 3% in 2000. The target pest for Bt-potatoes was the Colorado potato beetle (CPB) (*Leptinotarsa decemlineata*), whose adults and larvae defoliate potatoes, reducing tuber yields to the extent that potato production has had to cease in some areas. Although nonchemical methods of control are available, none are as cost-effective or practical as chemical pesticides.

CPB easily develops resistance to chemical insecticides, and many *populations* are now resistant to a broad array of chemical types. Microbial biopesticides containing Cry3A Bt-toxins are *effective* in killing the young larvae but, in practice, are not very effective against the most *damaging* life stages, the third and fourth instar larvae and adults.

Expressing the *Cry3A* gene in the plant has considerable advantages in targeting the most vulnerable stage of the insect's life cycle, neonates, but also, if the expression levels are high enough, in controlling larger larvae and adults. Several different transgenic cultivars of potato (sold as NewLeaf varieties) express the *Cry3A* gene from *B. thuringiensis* subsp. *tenebrionis.*

Because potato is a vegetatively propagated plant, with low or no fertility, each cultivar or variety must be separately *transformed*, whereas with Bt-corn or Bt-cotton a single event can be backcrossed into several different elite cultivars or hybrids.

NewLeaf potatoes expressing Cry3A proteins were the first to be released, and control of CPB was very effective together with over 40% reduction in insecticide applications to the NewLeaf variety.

In most potato-growing areas, aphids are also a *significant* pest, not only for the damage they can do to the plant but also because they transmit harmful plant viruses such as potato leaf roll virus (PLRV) and potato virus Y (PVY).

The introduction of NewLeafPlus and NewLeafY potato varieties that have a built-in transgene protection against PLRV and PVY, respectively, as well as the Bt gene, might have made an even bigger impact on the use of Btpotatoes in areas where these diseases are prevalent.

However, large buyers of potato products have refused to buy GM potatoes and processors have followed suit, reducing the market for NewLeaf varieties despite good evidence that they provide considerable economic benefit to the farmer.

After the poor economic performance of its NewLeaf potatoes, Monsanto appears to be reluctantly *withdrawing* completely from the *transgenic* potato market to concentrate on its other more successful biotech crops.

Resistance Management and Bt Crops

One of the key concerns with deploying single *Cry* genes into crop plants is that the increased exposure will select for resistance in the target insects. This could destroy the potential for long-term control using this technology and affect other users of microbial pesticides.

Unfortunately, field resistance to microbial Bt *formulations* has already occurred in both the Indian meal worm (*Plodia interpunctella*) in stored grains and the *diamondback* moth (*Plutella xylostella*) in a number of geographically isolated insect populations attacking vegetable crops. Laboratory-selected resistance has also been *observed* in a number of species that attack Bt-crops, including *H. virescens* and more recently *H. armigera* and *P. gossypiella.*

These relatively isolated *occurrences* of resistant insects have, however, provided models for how to manage the development of resistance to Bt-crops in an agricultural setting. The *provision* of non-Bt plants or refugia nearby to generate sufficient numbers of susceptible adults is the most commonly used resistance *management* strategy. This *ensures* that any rare homozygous resistant insects selected on the Bt crop will find only fully susceptible mates, thereby *continually* diluting the resistance genes in the target insects.

For Bt-cotton, the refugia can be unsprayed or sprayed cotton or other crops that are hosts for the pest species and generate adult insects at the same time as those that might emerge on Bt-cotton. The area and location of these refugia relative to the Bt crop are critical and in Australia, at least, have been *determined* empirically for Bt-cotton from the numbers of pupae of *H. armigera* generated by crops treated in different ways.

The requirements for refugia and other resistance management procedures are legislated into the registration label for INGARD cotton. The IPM approach adopted in Australia has been *summarized.* At present, refugia *requirements* are easily achieved as the total Bt area for any one farm can only be 30% of the total cotton planted.

This area limit is likely to be lifted only when cotton with two Bt genes becomes available around 2003 or 2004. Similar refuges for Bt-cotton and Bt-corn have been *strongly* recommended by U.S. regulators in response to scientific concerns that the technology was at risk from overuse.

The effectiveness of refuge strategies is dependent on many factors *including* the biology and population dynamics of the pest species, the frequency and mechanism of resistance, the placement and *management* of the crop and *neighboring* crops, and the expression level of the transgenes.

Nontarget Effects of Bt Crops

A second concern with Bt crops, or any other insecticidal transgenic plant, is that when released on a large scale they may have unintended, or even unnoticed, effects on other organisms in agricultural or neighboring ecosystems. Because Bt-corn is thought to exude Bt-toxins into the soil, where they can persist for relatively long periods bound to soil particles, and Bt-containing biomass is regularly returned to the soil during *agricultural* production, impacts on soil insects and microbes must also be considered. Two instances of possible nontarget effects have been described.

First, Btcorn has been reported to have unexpected effects on a beneficial insect, the green lacewings that feed on the European corn borer (ECB). Green lacewings fed ECB that had eaten Bt-corn had a higher death rate and delayed development compared with the controls, and this was attributed to the poor *nutritional* quality of ECB larvae exposed to the Bt toxin.

This study has not been extended to an agricultural setting. In a second case of possible nontarget impacts of insecticidal crops, Bt-corn was believed to accelerate the demise of the *endangered* monarch butterfly (*Danaus plexippus*) in the United States.

Monarch caterpillars feed on milkweed plants that often grow near cornfields. In a laboratory simulation, milkweed leaves were dusted with Bt-corn pollen and these leaves were fed to monarch larvae. After 4 days, only 56% of the larvae survived relative to larvae fed on plants dusted with non-Bt pollen or no pollen at all. Surviving larvae were also smaller than the controls.

This laboratory study raised *questions* about the validity of the regulatory *assessment* of the environmental impacts of transgenic plants and prompted new field studies that did not confirm the *laboratory* results. The field study showed that Bt-corn would not have any adverse effects on nontarget lepidoptera such as monarch butterflies and demonstrated that the potential exposure of larvae to Bt-corn pollen was, in fact, very low.

The risks to monarch butterflies from Bt crops must be considered small compared with the risks posed by habitat destruction and must be weighed against the effects of chemical pesticides on all *environments* adjacent to cropping areas. This incident *highlights* the need for field-based *confirmation* of any laboratory study that makes a claim for benefits or risks associated with any new biotech product.

OTHER SOURCES OF INSECTICIDAL GENES FOR CROP PROTECTION

Bacillus thuringiensis and its close relatives have proved to be a valuable source of insecticidal genes. Nevertheless, after the screening of many thousands of isolates, new types of insecticidal Bt genes have been difficult to find. The commercial and *environmental* successes of Bt-crops have provided the impetus for a *widespread* search for other potent *insecticidal* genes from *microbes*, insects, plants, and even animals.

These new insecticidal genes could be used instead of Cry-toxins or used to augment Cry-toxins to strengthen resistance *management* programs for the current *generation* of transgenic crops that rely on a single insecticidal activity.

The main *requirements* for these new genes are that the insecticidal agents must be orally active and preferably encoded by relatively few genes as *transformation* technologies can still handle only a couple of genes at a time. Novel insecticidal genes have been found using mass screening or the rational approach of seeking specific inhibitors of an insect's digestive or neural physiology.

Several potential new technologies have emerged, but none of these has yet had the *commercial* impact of the Cry genes.

New Oral Toxins

Different Cry genes have been *isolated*, covering a spectrum of *insecticidal* activities, but many important pests still cannot be controlled by Cry proteins. Most mass screening efforts to identify novel *Bacillus* strains have concentrated on the *identification* of new crystal proteins and hence have been carried out with *sporulating* cultures.

B. thuringiensis isolates with high activity against corn rootworms (*Diabrotica sp.*), for example, have been found only recently, but a novel screening approach has been used to discover a rootworm-active insecticidal complex *produced* during the vegetative growth phase of *B. cereus.* One *non-crystal-forming* isolate, AB78, contained a proteinaceous insecticidal activity produced during log phase growth that was absent at sporulation.

This was traced to the presence of two proteins designated Vip1A and Vip2A (vegetative insecticidal protein) that, together, appear to have activity against corn rootworms. The corresponding *Vip* genes were cloned and were found to be widespread in *Bacillus* species. Vip2 has been *crystallized* and has been shown to be an ADPribosylating toxin.

During the vegetative phase screening, a strain of *B. thuringiensis*, AB88, was also identified. This strain had high activity against many lepidopteran pests but no activity against coleopterans, and from this strain a third type of vegetative insecticidal protein, Vip3A, has been isolated. *Vip3* has no *homology* to the *Cry* genes or any other protein in the sequence databases and thus *represents* a totally new class of *insecticidal* genes.

Vip3 expressed in transgenic tobacco achieved partial protection against *Spodoptera litura*, but no extensive analyses of transgenic plants expressing this or other *Vip* genes have yet been published. The existence of the *Vip* genes will encourage a new round of screening of the existing *Bacillus* strain collections. The venom of many insect predators such as spiders and scorpions contains potent *neurotoxins*, many of which are insect specific.

These have been used to enhance the speed of kill of insect viruses but seem unlikely candidates for expression in plants because of the food safety concerns, real or *imagined*, that they would arouse in *consumers*.

Inhibitors of Digestion

The insect gut is the obvious target for orally acting *insecticidal* agents to be *expressed* in plants. The *membranes* lining the gut appear to be the target for the Cry toxins and probably the Vips, through their poreforming or lytic activities. The insect's digestive *biochemistry* is another target.

Disruption should reduce nutrient intake, resulting in mortality or at least in slowing the growth of larvae to such an extent that they are subject to a greater degree of parasitism and predation in the field. Different *components* of the digestive system can be targeted depending on whether the food source is rich in protein or carbohydrate.

Plants already appear to have adopted this as a defense strategy, as many *accumulate* high levels of proteinaceous inhibitors of digestive enzymes in their storage organs, such as seeds, fruits, tubers, and corms. A number of plants contain wound-inducible inhibitors of insect digestive *enzymes* that are switched on during herbivory.

Protease Inhibitors

To utilize the proteins present in their diets, insects rely *predominantly* on the serine proteases trypsin, chymotrypsin, and elastase. Trypsin is the dominant protease type in lepidopteran larvae. Plants *accumulate* high levels of trypsin *inhibitors* in their seed.

These are thought to act as insect antifeedants as well as nitrogenous seed reserves. A number of genes for *trypsin-chymotrypsin* inhibitors have been cloned and expressed in plants. These transgenic plants *demonstrated* antifeedant activity against a number of lepidopteran larvae.

Larval growth rates were reduced, and in some cases mortality was markedly increased. Levels of the *inhibitors* had to be over 1% of leaf soluble protein in order to afford any protection. Similar results have been reported in transgenic rice, wheat, tobacco, Lucerne, and poplar plants with a variety of serine and cysteine protease *inhibitors* from both plants and insects. For example, a gene for a trypsin-chymotrypsin inhibitor from the giant taro plant, *Alocasia mycrorrhiza*, was expressed in transgenic tobacco. This inhibitor retarded the growth of *Helicoverpa armigera*, but the larvae rapidly altered their digestive physiology to *compensate* for the presence of the inhibitor in their diet.

Although very active against *mammalian chymotrypsin*, the giant taro inhibitor turned out to be active only against *H. armigera* trypsin; its chymotrypsin inhibitor domain proved to be inactive in the insect. Insects fed on transgenic plants containing the giant taro inhibitor (or *artificial* diets *containing purified inhibitor*) adapted by elevating the levels of chymotrypsin and elastase in the midgut to counter the reduction in trypsin activity.

Similar responses have been noted for other protease inhibitors, although the *mechanisms* of adaptation can differ. This process of adaptation may be responsible for the failure of any transgenic plants *containing* protease inhibitors to reach the marketplace, although there are a couple of reports of field tolerance, e.g., to stem borers in rice expressing the cowpea trypsin inhibitor genes.

It will be important to include multiple protease *inhibitors* with differing specificities in order to develop robust insect tolerance in plants. For example, the stigmaspecific protease inhibitor from *Nicotiana alata* (ornamental tobacco) is produced as a single polyprotein that is subsequently processed into six different trypsin and chymotrypsin inhibitors and the gene confers tolerance to *H. punctigera* and *H. armigera* when expressed in transgenic plants.

Alpha Amylase Inhibitors

Some insects have diets rich in starch and utilize the enzyme α–amylase to digest the starch to simple sugars. α–Amylase inhibitors (aAls) are produced in the seeds of many plants and may confer some insect tolerance. Seeds of many domesticated crops have been selected for reduced levels of their inhibitors of digestion, as they are *antinutritional* components for human or animal *consumption*.

This has made some grain crops more vulnerable to attack, *particularly* in storage. Field peas are widely grown across southern Australia for both human and animal feed, but the green pods are prone to attack by the bruchid beetle, pea weevil (*Bruchus pisorum*).

Some legumes are highly tolerant to attack by beetles and produce high levels of aAl, among other *antinutritional* compounds in their seeds. A gene for aAl from the common bean *Phaseolus vulgaris* was linked to a strong seedspecific promoter and used to generate transgenic field peas expressing levels of αAI as high as those in bean seeds. The inhibitor was stably expressed through to at least the T5 generation and the pea seeds were resistant to damage by pea weevil, both in the glasshouse and in the field, as well as to a number of pests of stored grain (cowpea weevil, *Callosobruchus maculatus* and azuki bean weevil, *C. chinensis*).

The seeds were shown to have no detectable antinutritional effects in animal feeding trials. The same construct in transgenic azuki beans confers resistance to three stored grain pests, *C. chinensis*, *C. maculatus*, and *C. analis*, but not to the South American bruchid *Zabrotes subfasciatus*. This technology therefore holds promise for *protecting* grain legumes against certain coleopteran pests.

Lectins and Assorted Insecticidal Proteins

Few insecticidal proteins have been found that are active against sap-sucking insects such as plant hoppers, leafhoppers, and aphids, yet these insects represent a significant *component* of the pest problem in many crops.

Frequently, they are vectors for serious viral diseases *devastating* world agriculture. Sugar binding proteins, or lectins, have been purified from many plants, and a number of lectins have been reported to have toxic effects on sap-sucking insects that derive most of their energy reserves from the sugars being transported in the phloem.

The mannose binding lectin from the bulb of snowdrop (*Galanthus nivalis*) *is* toxic to the peach-potato aphid (*Myzus persicae*), the glasshouse potato aphid (*Aulacorthum solani*), and the rice brown planthopper (*Nilaparvata lugens*). When the snowdrop gene is expressed in *transgenic* tobacco from either a constitutive or a phloem-specific promoter, the lectin has been shown to be ingested by the aphids, as it can be detected in their honeydew.

The gene confers some tolerance to aphids in whole plant bioassays. Wang and Guo have expressed both the gene for the Cry lAb Bt toxin and the gene for snowdrop lectin in transgenic tobacco and have generated plants showing high insecticidal activity to both *H. armigera* and *M. persicae*, suggesting that it may be possible to stack genes active against both lepidopteran and sucking pests. When three genes (*CrylAc*, *Cry2A*, and the gene for snowdrop lectin) were stacked in transgenic rice, protection against three important pests (a leaf folder, a stem borer, and a plant hopper) was achieved.

Similarly, a pea lectin in transgenic tobacco was thought to have an additive effect with protease inhibitors in conferring tolerance to *lepidopteran* larvae, again *highlighting* the importance of multiple components of the *defensive* system.

Snowdrop lectin in transgenic plants was also reported to have antinutritional effects on some lepidopterans, as was wheat germ agglutinin and jacalin. Many of these lectins are generally toxic, and experiments with transgenic potatoes containing the snowdrop lectin have been implicated in downstream effects on predators of the target sucking insect pests.

Subsequent analyses, however, indicate that this is due not to the toxicity of the lectin to the insect predator but to the lowered nutritional value of the affected aphids. No effects were reported for the development of a wasp parasitoid fed on *Lacanobia oleracea* larvae raised on GNA–expressing potatoes, and there was a significant reduction in plant damage, at least in the glasshouse, using the combination of transgenic plant and parasitic wasp.

However, as yet, no lectin-expressing transgenic plant has reached the marketplace. The biotin binding proteins avidin and streptavidin have also been shown to have strong insecticidal activity and have been expressed at high levels in the kernels of maize.

Although originally produced for the commercial production of these proteins, the plants show good levels of resistance to a number of stored grain pests of corn. A thorough analysis of the human food safety issues associated with avidin and streptavidin corn will be necessary before the grain can enter the food chain. Cholesterol oxidase from a *Streptomyces* species is a potent oral inhibitor of the cotton boll weevil (*Anthonomonas grandis grandis* Boheman) and has reduced activity against a number of lepidopteran species.

It is thought to act through the oxidation of cholesterol in the membranes of the midgut brush border, and low concentrations cause mortality in larvae and reduced fertility in adults. The reason for the *specificity* of the protein is unclear as both susceptible and tolerant insect species have similar cholesterol levels. Gut pH may be involved, as the pH optimum of the enzyme does not favour its activity in the high pH found in the *midguts* of *lepidopteran* larvae.

The gene for cholesterol oxidase has been cloned and expressed as enzymatically active protein in plant cells. The specificity of cholesterol oxidase makes it an attractive target for *expression* in transgenic cotton to enhance the current *conventional* approaches to boll weevil control.

However, the success of the current boll weevil *eradication* program in the United States, which relies on conventional technology, may be a contributing factor in the lack of *commercial* incentive to progress the cholesterol oxidase gene as an insect control option in cotton. Other enzymes, chitinase and *lipoxygenase*, have also been reported to confer some insecticidal activity, but this has not been demonstrated in transgenic plants.

Secondary Metabolites

Plants produce an abundance of secondary chemicals that serve as a defense against insects. In some cases, they act as olfactory or oral cues to both beneficial and pest species. Some of the defensive chemicals are being evaluated with the aim of *manipulating* the genes for their biosynthesis in transgenic plants to enhance the host plant resistance or for the biological production of *commercial* pesticides.

Thomas et al. created transgenic tobacco plants expressing the *Catharanthus roseus* gene for tryptophan decarboxylase (TDC), which converts tryptophan to the insecticidal indole alkaloid tryptamine. Sweet potato whiteflies (*Bemisia tabaci*) fed on these plants showed a dramatic decrease in fertility. However, others have reported undesirable plant phenotypes as well as elevated tryptamine levels. Alterations in metabolite profiles brought about by overexpressing key branch point enzymes, such as TDC, can have both desirable and undesirable pleiotrophic effects, as has been reported in transgenic potatoes and canola.

In potato, overexpression of TDC resulted in an altered balance of key substrates in the shikimate and *phenypropanoid* pathways, leading to reduced levels of *phenolics* and other defense compounds. These plants were more susceptible to fungal pathogens.

In canola, reductions in the available tryptophan pool resulted in reductions in the levels of tryptophan-derived indole glucosinolates as well as increased tryptamine. Complex regulation of secondary metabolic *pathways* may also have allowed Smigocki et al. to *inadvertently* elevate secondary metabolites in transgenic tobacco plants expressing the cytokinin-producing ipt gene from Agrobacterium tumefaciens driven by a wound-inducible promoter, either through the activation of cytokinin-regulated biosynthetic genes or through changes in pools of core metabolites shared between secondary metabolism and cytokinin biosynthesis.

Their plants showed a *considerably* enhanced tolerance to tobacco hornworm (Manduca sexta) and the green peach aphid (*Myzus persicae*). Transgenic plants with altered disease tolerance were generated by Hain et al. when they introduced into tobacco two genes from grapevine encoding the enzyme stilbene synthase that converts 4-coumaroyl CoA and malonyl CoA into the toxic phytoalexin resveratrol.

Plants that produced resveratrol constitutively showed enhanced tolerance to the fungal pathogen Botrytis cinerea, but this was associated with altered flower colour and male sterility, *highlighting* the importance of regulating the production of toxic defense chemicals.

Using the native grapevine genes, however, with their own highly regulated pathogen and wound-inducible promoters has allowed the production of transgenic tomatoes without the deleterious side effects.

These plants were protected from infection by the fungus Phytophthora infestans, but not by B. cinerea and Alternaria solani, even though these pathogens induced the accumulation of resveratrol. Before we can routinely engineer pest and pathogen tolerance by manipulating secondary metabolism in plants, we must develop a better understanding of the complex interactions between different metabolic pathways and their regulation.

CONCLUSIONS

Insect control through biotechnology is an *outstanding* example of the use of gene technology to enhance the efficiency and sustainability of production of broadacre crops. It is not without its risks, such as the development of resistance by the target insects and potential nontarget impacts in the environment.

There must be a concerted effort to develop new insect tolerance genes to ensure that the existing technologies are not lost by overuse in the short term. However, finding highly potent insecticidal genes that are as effective as the first generation of genes based on delta endotoxins from Bacillus *thuringiensis* is not a simple matter.

The new class of vegetative insecticidal genes from Bacillus species holds the most promise for the control of difficult *lepidopteran* and coleopteran pests, but they have yet to be expressed effectively in transgenic plants. Inhibitors of digestion used against lepidopterans and/or sucking pests have received a great deal of publicity but are yet to prove themselves commercially and will be challenged by the great adaptability of insects and the problems of antinutritional activity against humans and animals if they are used in food or fodder crops.

They are most likely to be at their best with highly *specialized* insects that are very host specific, such as some of the stored grain pests, and do not possess well-developed adaptive mechanisms to cope with a wide array of digestive inhibitors in their diets.

The next decade will be an exciting time for biotechnologists and *entomologists* as they explore the full-scale *commercial* production of transgenic insect-protected crops.

IMPROVING MEDICINAL PLANTS

Medicinal plants have been the subject of man's curiosity and purpose since time immemorial. The importance of medicinal plants in the treatment of chronic diseases needs no elaboration. In fact, even with the *tremendous* advancement in the field of synthetic chemistry, almost 50% of the commercial drugs available in the market remain of plant origin. The herbal system was, however, pushed to the background with the advent of allopathic system.

It is now back with a venegence and the age-old system of herbal medicine is being revived due to its long lasting curative effect, easy availability, natural way of *healing* and rare or no reported side effects. Due to growing world population, increased anthropogenic activities, rapidly eroding natural ecosystem etc., the natural habitat for a great number of plants are *dwindling* and many of them are facing extinction.

The inevitable ruthless exploitation of herbs leading to their rapid *depletion* from the wild is a cause for concern. In fact, the pace of depletion has outpaced the pace of conservation. New strategies are being therefore *formulated* for rapid *multiplication* and conservation of medicinal plants. Besides the *conventional* methods, biotechnology has proved useful in the improvement of herbs that yield drugs.

In this resurgent era of herbal drugs it is very difficult to make an accurate assessment of the volume and value of herbal trade in India. Consequently, it varies widely. According to estimates by the Ayurvedic Drug *Manufacturers* Association (ADMA), the current value of trade in Indian System of Medicine (chiefly Ayurveda, Siddha and Unani) and Homeopathy is around Rs. 4205 crores, *roughly* close to US$ 1 billion.

Therefore, the value of medicinal plants is also reflected in the economics of global market which was estimated to be 60 billion US dollars in 2000. The Asian region rich in biological wealth and genetic diversity also has a *substantial* share in herb trade.

It is surmountable that medicinal plant biotechnology has grown from cell technology, specifically plant tissue culture. Regeneration of plants has been achieved with cells and tissues excised from various *medicinal* herbs. The powerful *techniques* of plant cell and tissue culture, and recombinant DNA and bioprocessing technologies etc., coupled with sophisticated analytical tools such as NMR, HPLC, GC-MS, LC-MS etc., have offered mankind a great opportunity to exploit the totipotent, biosynthetic and biotransformation capabilities of plant cells under *in vitro* conditions.

The scope for *in vitro* germplasm preservation and large-scale production of plant secondary metabolites has brightened.

Advantages of extracting *secondary* metabolites using plant tissue culture are:

1. The source of these metabolites, i.e., most of higher plants have *specific* agroclimatic requirements. Hence specific *metabolites* can be produced in cultures all through the year even in places where these crops are not grown.
2. The already limited supply of these raw materials can not be *exhausted* considering the future needs.
3. If not in all, at least in remarkable number of cases cells under culture tend to produce greater amounts of these *metabolites* than that is *accumulated* in nature.

In addition, *in vitro* technology also facilitates: (i) conservation of genetic diversity and germplasm of medicinal plants through cryopreservation, and (ii) gene *transfer* through recombinant DNA technology and the *molecular* markers in the form of AFLP and RAPD.

In this article, emphasis has been laid on the fact that protection and preservation of *germplasm* of medicinal plants is *indispensible*, without which the knowledge of herbal medicines will remain futile. Also, various ways of enhancing the yield of active *components* are reviewed.

MATERIALS AND METHODS

Micropropagation

Juvenile Explants

Seeds of the desired plant species are washed with 0.5–2.0% cetrimide followed by treatment with 0.1% mercuric chloride and dipped in 70% alcohol, thereafter washed with sterile distilled water. Such *sterilized* seeds are implanted on basal medium for *germination*. Various seedling *explants* such as hypocotyl, epicotyl, cotyledon and radicle are incoulated on suitable media with growth regulators.

Mature Explants

Explants such as stem segment, shoot apex, axillary buds, leaf, root, anther, etc., from field grown plants are surface sterilized with 1–2% cetrimide followed by treatment with streptomycin sulphate and bavistin solution. They may then be treated with 0.1% mercuric chloride, 70% alcohol and finally washed with sterile distilled water.

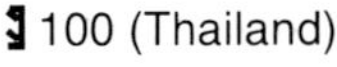

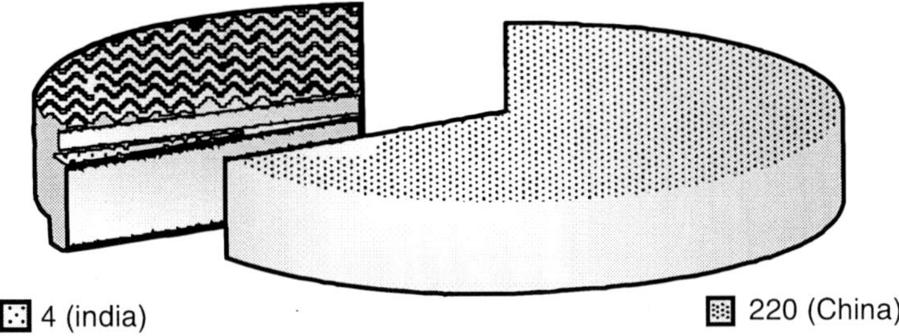

Figure 11.1: The market value of natural health products in 2000 was already worth US $ 500 billion of which 220 was projected for China, 100 for Thailand and only 4 billion for India.

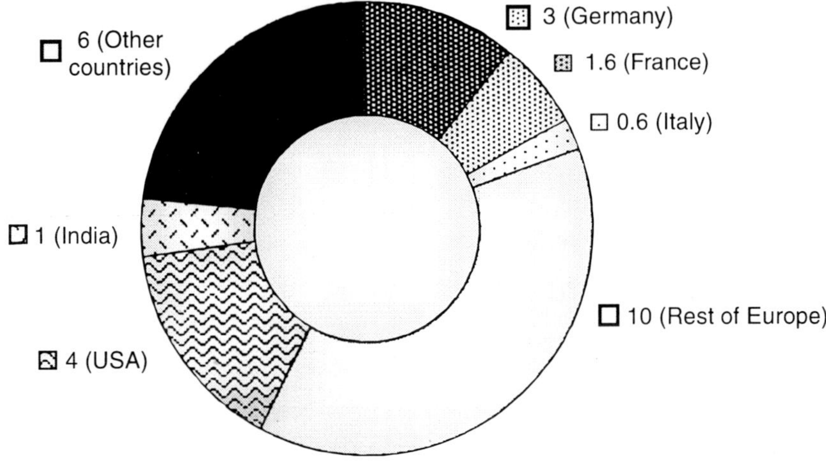

Figure 11.2: In 2000, country-wise share of herbal medicine was US $ 60 billions with India's share of only 1 billion. The predicted annual growth rate was 7% for this sector.

After sequential sterilization, explants are implanted on media with auxin and cytokinin in appropriate combination and concentration. Most of the cultures are maintained in a culture room at 25 ± 2°C with 55 ± 5% relative humidity and 10–14 hr light/dark period with irradiance of 60–100 µmol m–2s^{-1} provided by white cool flourescent tubes.

The cultures are monitored at regular intervals and the regenerants are maintained on the best suited medium. The rooted plantlets are hardened and then transplanted to pots and finally transferred to field.

Secondary Metabolite Analysis

Cultures harvested during different stages of growth and *differentiation* are analysed for the presence of secondary metabolites (alkaloids, steroids, flavonoids, glycosides, *furanocoumarins*, etc.). Quantification of isolated *compounds* is made either through spectrophotometry, High *Performance* Liquid *Chromatography* (HPLC) or Gas Liquid Chromatography (GLC).

Stage showing highest yield of the active principle is selected as the harvesting stage for that particular culture. As they are present in low amounts in plants, attempts can be made to enhance the yield by *supplementing* the medium with elicitors, *precursors* or *manipulating* the hormonal *combination* of the medium or *subjecting* biotic/abiotic stress to the cultures.

Cryopreservation of Cultures

Various explants have been used for cryopreservation of medicinally *important* plants. The general protocol involves treating the cultures with *appropriate cryoprotectant* such as DMSO, glycerol, sucrose or proline, etc. and then plunging in liquid nitrogen (–196°C). After freezestorage, the cultures are thawed at 35–40°C, washed and recultured. Complete plantlets can be *regenerated* from such frozen cultures.

Synthetic Seeds

This technology involves the *encapsulation* of propagules (somatic embryos/axillary buds/ shoot apices, etc.) which *functionally* mimic seeds and can develop into *plantlets* under suitable conditions. For *encapsulation*, the propagules may be embedded in a matrix that serves as endosperm, containing carbon source, nutrients, growth *regulators* and *antimicrobial* agents.

Sodium alginate is commonly used. However, there are several other agents including guargum, calcium alginate, gelrite, sodium alginate with gelatin, potassium alginate, sodium pectate, etc. In addition, polyethylene oxide homopolymers, synthetic sodium-magnesium-lithium silicate, sodium crylate, etc. have been tried as coating agents.

After mixing in the encapsulation matrix, the propagules are picked up by pipette and then dropped into a solution of calcium chloride. Thereafter, they are kept undisturbed for surface complexing to obtain encapsulated beads. The beads are kept in a solution of 2.5% $CaCl_2$ for 40 min on a shaker.

After the completion of incubation period, the beads are recovered by decanting the $CaCl_2$ solution and washed 3–4 times with basal medium. Such encapsulated propagules cultured on nutrient medium or different substrates like filter paper, soilrite, etc. can develop into plants.

Transformation

In recent years, *Agrobacterium-mediated transformation* has emerged as an efficient method for genetic manipulation of plants. Although direct DNA transfer methods, particularly particle bombardment, are also being employed, other gene *transfer* methods include electroporation and electrophoresis, laser microbeam technique, microinjection, liposome fusion and injection.

Agrobacterium-mediated transformation, however, has major advantages over these systems. After establishing a reliable protocol for micropropagation the explants can be incubated with *Agrobacterium* suspension, blotted dry on whatman filter paper and transferred to regeneration medium for co-cultivation.

The co-cultivated explants are then transferred to the selection medium. After selection, the explants are allowed to grow on regeneration medium + Cefotaxime. The putative transgenics can be rooted and after hardening transferred to field.

The transgenic nature of regenerated plants can be confirmed by *polymerase* chain reaction (PCR) and southern blot analysis.

Table 11.1: Examples of micropropagation of some medicinal plants.

Plant	*Therapeutic use*	*Cultured explant*	*Medium*	*Response*
Abrus precatorius	Abortifacient	Epicotyl segments	MS + NAA (0.1) + BAP (0.5)	Plantlets
			MS + NAA (0.1) + Kn (0.5)	Plantlets
Ammi majus	Leucoderma	Nodal segments + CH (1000)	MS + IAA (0.5) + Kn (2.0)	Multiple shoots
Isolated shoots			MS + IAA (0.5) + Kn (5.0) + CH (500) + Ad (40)	*In vitro* flowering and fruiting
			MS + IBA (0.2) + Glu (100)	Plantlets
Artemisia annua	Antimalarial, anti-HIV	Cotyledonary leaves	MS + (in μM) NAA (0.5) + BAP (13.0) + GA_3 (0.3) + Glu(700) +	Multiple shoots
		Stem segments	Asp (300) + Arg (300) + Cyst HC1(30)	
		Hypocotyl segments	MS + (in tM) NAA (1.0) + BAP (13) + CM (2 %)	
		Immature inflorescence segments	MS + (in μM) NAA (0.5) + BAP (13.0)	Multiple shoots
Allium wallichii	Tuberculosis, nerve defects, cold, cough	Seedlings (without the root portion)	MS + Zt (20 NM)	Multiple shoots
Arnica montana	Anti-inflammatory	Nodal segments	MS + (in μM) NAA (5.3) + 2iP (5.0) + Phloroglucinol (0.6 mM) + Ad (0.2 mM)	Plantlets
Atropa acuminata	Antispasmodic, narcotic, analgesic, antiasthamatic	Shoot tips, nodal segments	MS + BAP (1.0) + IBA (1.0)	Shoot buds
		Isolated shoots	RT + IAA (1.0)	Elongated shoots
RT + IBA (1.0)	Plantlets			
Bacopa monniera	Memory vitalizer	Nodal segments	MS + NAA (0.2) + BAP (5.0) + CH (500)	Callus, multiple shoots
			MS + NAA (0.1) + BAP (0.5) + CH (500)	Plantlets
Catharanthus roseus	Antileukaemic	Juvenile explants	MS + NAA (2.0) + BAP (5.0) +	Callus

(Table Contd.)

Plant	Therapeutic use	Cultured explant	Medium	Response
		and mature stem segments	Asp (100) + CH (1000)	
		Callus	MS + NAA (0.1) + BAP (5.0) + Zt (1.0) + Asp (100) + Glu (100)	Multiple shoots
Clerodendrum inerme	Substitute for quinine	Leaf segments	MS + BAP (2.0) + NAA (0.5)	Callus, multiple shoots
			MS + IAA (2.0)	Plantlets
Coleus Jbrskohlii	Anti-inflammatory	Shoot tips	MS + (in NM) IAA (0.57) + Kn (0.46)	Plantlets
Datura innoxia	Anticholinergic	Anthers	WB + NAA (1.0) + BAP (2.0) + CH (500)	Multiple shoots
			WB + IBA (0.1)	Plantlets
Dioscorea bulbifera	Antifertility	Nodal segments	MS + IAA (0.1) + Kn (5.0) + CH (500) + Charcoal (2000)	Plantlets
Holarrhena antidysentrica	Dysentry, colic pain	Node with axillary buds	MS + BAP (15 l.IM)	Multiple shoots
			MS + IBA (35 NM)	Plantlets
Isoplexis canariensis	Source of cardiac glycosides	Seedling explants	MS + BAP (5.0 l.IM)	Multiple shoots
			MS + (in tM) BAP (2.25) + IAA (0.17)	
		Isolated shoots	MS + (in μM) BAP (0.22) + IAA (0.17)	Plantlets
Nothapodytes Jbetida	Antitumor	Leaf segments	MS +TDZ (1.36 l.IM)	Multiple shoots
			MS (1/2)) + (in μM) BAP (2.22) + IBA (0.49)	Plantlets
Peganum harmala	Abortifacient	Cotyledonary node with shoot tip	MS + (in NM) NAA (0.1) + BAP (5.0)	Multiple shoots
			MS + IBA (8.0 NM)	Plantlets
Phyllanthus caroliniensis	Antidiabetic and used against hepatitis B virus	Nodal segments	MS + (in μM) BAP (5.0) + Kn (1.25-5.0)	Multiple shoots
		Isolated shoots	MS	Plantlets
Plantago ovata	Laxative	Shoot buds	MS + (in μM) 2,4-D (4.5) + Kn (2.3)	Callus
		Callus	MS + (in μM) BAP (4.4) + NAA (2.7)	Somatic

(Table Contd.)

Plant	Therapeutic use	Cultured explant	Medium	Response
			+ CM (10 %)	embryogenesis
Plumbago rosea	Anticancerous	Nodal segments	MS + IAA or IBA (0.1) + BAP (1.5) + Ad (50)	Multiple shoots
			MS (1/2) + IBA (0.25)	Plantlets
P zeylanica	Leprosy, skin diseases	Nodal segments	MS + (in μM) Ad (27.2) + IBA (2.46)	Multiple shoots
			MS + IBA (4.92 μM)	Plantlets
Psoralea corylilblia	Psoriasis	Nodal segments	MS + BAP (0.5)	Multiple shoots
			MS + IAA (5.7)	Plantlets
Rauwolfia serpentina	Cardiovascular diseases, sedative or tranquillizer	Shoot apices	MS + BAP (2.0)	Multiple shoots
		Nodal segments	MS + BAP (1.0) + NAA (0.1)	Multiple shoots
			MS + NAA (2.0) + BAP (1.5)	Plantlets
Sterculia foetida	Abortifacient, diuretic	Cotyledonary nodes	MS + BAP (4.0)	Multiple shoots
			MS + IAA (2.0)	Plantlets
Stevia rebaudiana	Antidiabetic	Nodal segments	MS + (in μM) BAP (8.87) + IAA (5.71)	Multiple shoots
			MS (1/2) + IBA (4.90 μM)	Plantlets
Silybum marianum	Antihepatotoxic	Nodal segments	MS + IAA (0.1) + Kn (5.0)	Multiple shoots
			MS + NAA (0.1) + Zt (0.5)	Plantlets
Solanum khasianum	Steroidal drugs	Leaf segments	MS + 2,4-D (3.0) + Kn (1.0)	Callus
		Callus	MS + BAP (3.0)	Multiple shoots
		Shoots	MS + NAA (2.0)	Plantlets
Tylophora indica	Asthma, bronchitis anti-tumorous	Leaf segments	MS + (in μM) 2,4-D (9.04) + Kn (0.05)	Callus
		Callus	MS + 2iP (9.84 μM)	Somatic embryos
		Somatic embryos	MS	Plantlets
Typhonium flagellifbrme	Anticancerous	Shoot buds (from rhizome)	MS + (in μM) IBA (2.46) + BAP (1.33)	Plantlets
Valeriana jatamansi	Tranquillizer	Shoots buds	MS + BAP (4.44 μM)	Multiple shoots
			MS + (in μM) NAA (4.03) + BAP (4.44)	Plantlets

(Table Contd.)

Plant	Therapeutic use	Cultured explant	Medium	Response
Vitex negundo	Anticancerous	Nodal segments	MS + NAA (0.1) + BAP (2.0)	Multiple shoots and flowering
		Shoots with immature flowers	MS + NAA (0.5) + BAP (0.1)	Flower maturation, plantlets
Withania somnifera	Antistress, antitumor, anti-inflammatory	Leaf segments	MS + BAP (1.0)	Multiple shoots
			MS + IBA (10.0)	Plantlets

MS = Murashige and Skoog medium, WB = Wood and Braun medium, RT = Revised Tobacco medium (Khanna and Staba, 1968)
Ad = Adenine, Arg = Arginine, Asp = Asparagine, BAP = Benzylamino purine, CH = Casein hydrolysate, CM = Coconut milk, 2,4-D = 2,4-dichlorophenoxyacetic acid, Glu = Glutamine, IAA = Indole-3-acetic acid, IBA = Indole-3-butyric acid, 2iP = 2 iso-pentenyladenine, Kn = Kinetin, NAA = α-naphthaleneacetic acid, TDZ = Thidiazuron, Zt = Zeatin.
*Concentration of growth hormones are in mgl^{-1} unless mentioned otherwise.

Molecular Markers for Ascertaining Clonal Fidelity

DNA-based markers provide an efficient tool for screening tissue culture raised plants because these markers are not affected by *environmental* factors and present more reliable results. PCR-based markers such as RAPD have been used for detecting off-types from micropropagated plants.

AFLP, and SNPs are now preferred as it combines the reliability of RFLP with RAPD. For AFLP analysis, total genomic DNA can be isolated from desired plant parts by using a suitable method. It can then be restricted with *restriction* enzymes followed by ligation with specific adapters. Pre-amplification of the adapter-ligated DNA can be done by using selective nucleotides.

The samples are electrophoresed on acrylamide gel and *autoradiographed.* AFLP amplification products are scored for their presence and absence across the individuals tested. Genetic *similarity* between pairs is estimated by Jaccard's coefficient. The phenetic dendrogram can be constructed by UPGMA (unweighed pair group method of *arithmetic* averages) in order to group *individuals* into discrete clusters.

RESULTS AND DISCUSSION

Micropropagation of Medicinal Plants and Yield of Secondary Metabolites

In vitro cultured cells and tissues can be induced to *differentiate* into plants through *organogenesis* or somatic embryogenesis. The response of any tissue *in vitro* is attributed to the composition of the medium besides other factors including a balance between growth regulators. MS medium *originally* developed for rapid growth of tobacco tissue culture is the most *frequently* used for majority of the species.

Already there are credible reports of *in vitro propagation* of medicinal plants by using various explants, such as leaf, stem, shoot buds anthers, roots, shoot tips, nodal segments, and seedlings. The earliest detailed reference of plant cell cultures as an *industrial* route to natural product synthesis dates back to 1956. Despite the success and the related surge in *information,* the expected progress during the following decades remained slow.

After 1973, a turning point in cell culture technology *demonstrated* reasonable yield of desired secondary metabolites. Earlier it was believed that enhancement in the yield of *secondary* metabolites was dependent on prolonged tissue cultures or *organogenesis.*

Subsequently, it has been revealed that the ability of product *biosynthesis* continues throughout during the culture regime and can be detected at various stages of growth and differentiation. Yield of *secondary* metabolites can be *enhanced* by modifying the chemical milieu and culture conditions. Zenk et al. observed that the *composition* of culture medium not only affects growth and *production* of metabolites but also plays a critical role in initiation of *morphogenic* events in the culture.

Consequently, almost all the major components of the growth medium have been tested for their varied effects on different types of differentiated and *undifferentiated* cultures. The most commonly used carbon source for tissue culture media is sucrose. The other carbon sources

Table 2. Effect of stage of culture and conditions on the yield of some secondary metabolites.

Plant	Active constituent	Culture conditions and yield of secon]dary metabolite
Agaveamaniensis	Sapogenin steroid	Absence of calcium ions in media increased the sapogenin steriod content, while relatively high concentration of Mg, Co and Cu showed inhibitory effects
Ammi majus	Xanthotoxin	Xanthotoxin content monitored during different stage of growth and differentiation revealed highest content at plantlet differentiation stage bearing immature green fruits (*in vitro*)
Artemisia annua	Artemisinin	Enhanced artemisinin content was found *in vitro*
Beta vulgaris	Betalains	B5 medium supplemented with Co^{2+} (5 μM) increased the betalains production
Catharanthus roseus	Catharanthine and vindoline	Multiple shoot cultures raised directly from sterile seedlings inoculated on MS medium containing BA (4 μM) produced mainly catharanthine and vindoline in amounts higher than in the parent plant
	Indole alkaloids (ajmalicine, serpentine) Vinblastine	Zt or BA were more active than Kn in increasing the content of alkaloids. But all the three cytokinins enhanced the production of indole alkaloids High degree of differentiation was correlative to the increased vinblastine production
Cinchona ledgeriana	Quinine	Shoot cultures contained much higher levels of quinine and related alkaloids than the cell suspensions
Datura stramonium	Hyoscyamine and scopolamine	Maximum contents were found in the stem and leaves of young plants; hyoscyamine being always the predominant component
Daucus carota	Anthocyanins	Increase of 63.41% in production of anthocyanins by addition of 1.0 nM Co^{2+}
Digitalis lanata	Digitoxin	Addition of Mn^{2+} (10 mM) at day zero of culture increased the digitoxin content
Dioscorea deltoidea	Diosgenin	Hypocotyl callus on RT+2,4-D (0.1)+ Cholesterol (10–100) +YE (0.5%) yielded higher diosgenin content
Ephedra andina	Alkaloids	Trace quantities of alkaloids were present in cultures.
E. distachya *E. equisitina* E. fragilis *E. gerardiana*	(1-ephedrine and d-pseudoephedrine)	The ability to produce alkaloids diminished to zero with successive subcultures

Plant	Active constituent	Culture conditions and yield of secon]dary metabolite
E. intermedia		
E. major		
E. minima	Lepidine	*E. saxatilis*
Lepidium sativum		Lepidine content was much higher in 8-month-old regenerants grown on ZnSO4 (900 μM) or CuSO4 (100 μM)
Papaver bracteatum	de-sanguinarine	Increase in concentration of Cu alone brought an increase in the content
Rauwolfia	Alkaloid	Increased alkaloid content in leaf callus *sellowii*
R. serpentina	Alkaloid	Total alkaloid content in the plantlets was higher as compared to field grown plants
		A group of new alkaloids, the raumaclines and some related alkaloids were isolated from cell suspensions fed with high level of ajmaline
Silybum marianum	Silybin	Higher silybin content in regenerants grown on $ZnSO_4$ (200 μM) or $CuSO_4$ (75 μM)
Solanum aviculare	Solasodine yield	Addition of cholesterol to the medium improved the
S. laciniatum	Solasodine	Decreasing the sucrose concentration increased the solasodine content significantly in shoot cultures
S. nigrum, and *S. nigrum* var. *judaicum*	Glycoalkaloids	Total glycoalkaloids were higher in plantlets
Stizolobium hassjoo	L-DOPA	Supplementation with 2.5 μM Co^{2+} stimulated 25 times the synthesis of L–DOPA
Withania somnifera	Withanolides	Maximum accumulation of withaferin A was noted in shoot tips proliferating on B5 medium; the withanolide D content was low. In MS medium withaferin A accumulation was low than in B5 medium, while withanolide D accumulation was higher Among the BA and Kn, BA favoured both shoot multiplication and withanolide synthesis. In the absence of any carbon source withanolide accumulation was very low in shoot tips (0.002%) Withaferin A accumulated maximum in the presence of 10% sucrose. The maximum accumulation of withanolide D was at 4% sucrose

tested for *supporting* growth include glucose, galactose and also complex carbohydrates such as milkwhey and molasses.

Increased sugar concentration favoured synthesis of shikonin in cell cultures of *Lithospermum erythrorhizon*, diosgenin production in *Dioscorea*, and anthraquinone in cell cultures of *Gallium mollugo*. On the contrary, lesser amounts of sucrose favoured the production of ubiquinone 10 in *Coleus blumei*.

Saccharose as sugar source has shown strongest effect for secondary metabolite content increase in cultures of *Catharanthus, Nicotiana, Chenopodium, Thalictrum, Dioscorea, and Rhamnus* in tandem with the concentration supplied, and with a parallel increase in dry weight. Higher concentrations of phosphate results in an increase in the production of indole alkaloids in *Catharanthus roseus*, whereas in callus cultures of *Peganum*, low phosphate levels stimulate the secondary metabolism.

Transfer of suspension cultures of *Thuja occidentalis* from MS to B5 medium induced the synthesis of terpenoids. Both, different NH_4^+ content and the stress due to transfer to specific media, seemed responsible for accelerated shikonin production in suspension cultures of *Lithospermum erythrorhizon*.

The type and amount of N source seems to affect the yield of secondary products. The ratio of nitrate and ammonia in the culture media also influences growth and secondary metabolite production. Fujita et al. report increase in the yield of shikonin with increase in the concentration of sole nitrogen source, nitrate till 6.7 mM, but the production decreased with above 10 mM nitrate level.

Decreased levels of N are reported to stimulate the production of secondary metabolites such as, certain polyphenols, anthocyanins, etc. Manipulation of concentrations of microelements in the nutrient media offers a strategy to increase the production of secondary metabolites in plant cell cultures.

Trace elements have indeed been considered as abiotic elictors or as inducing factors that trigger the biosynthesis of secondary metabolites. There are results showing the effect of divalent ions; Co^{2+} and Cu^{2+} seem to have received more attention because of their positive effects on the production of secondary metabolites.

Increase in Co^{2+} from 1 to 5 μM resulted in the enhanced production of betalains in *Beta vulgaris*. Enhanced shikonin production in the cultures of *Lithospermum erythrorhizon* have been attributed to the increased concentration of both copper and sulphate. Phytoxicity by heavy metals due to industrial pollution has caused degradation of cultivable land.

Plants allowed to grow on such soil receiving sludge high in heavy metals show reduction in the quality and productivity. Efforts thus are required to raise metal tolerant plants. Tissue culture *techniques* have helped not only in raising metal tolerant plants but have also demonstrated that subjecting the cultures of medicinal plants to abiotic stress can be crucial in increasing the yield of secondary metabolites.

Several investigations have indeed demonstrated the possibility to raise metal tolerant plants *in vitro*. Heavy metals have different role in metabolic functions. Some of them including Cu and Zn are required as micronutrients in biological systems to act as cofactor and/or as part of prosthetic groups of enzymes in a wide variety of developmental pathways, Cu a constituent of the medium is an essential microelement for plant growth.

It is required for several biochemical and *physiological* pathways. Cu at higher *concentrations* exhibits strong toxicity and hamper plant growth as do some other heavy metals, such as Cd, Pb or Hg which have no function in plant metabolism. Copper is released as particulates in stack effluents primarily from Cu smelters.

Greater concern of Cu comes from prolonged applications in fungicidal treatments. Addition of Cu in the medium is reported to promote somatic embryogenesis as well as its subsequent development in *Citrus*. Cu stimulated regeneration in wheat, *Nicotiana tabacum and Bacopa monniera*. This was also so at lower concentrations with *Dioscorea bulbifera*.

Cu has proved to be more effective than Zn in enhancing the yield of xanthotoxin in *Ammi majus* and lepidine in *in vitro* cultures of *Lepidium sativum*. Heavy metals and others have also induced a positive effect on alkaloid production in *Catharanthus roseus*. Fe^{2+} and Cu^{2+} induced positive effects on the synthesis of shikonin. Endress and Obrenovic have already demonstrated profitable role of Cu^{2+} on the accumulation of betacyanins in callus cultures of *Portulacca grandiflora and Amaranthus caudatus* seedlings.

Higher concentrations of Cu^{2+} in the media supported increased accumulation of sapogenin steroid in the *in vitro* cultures of *Agave amaniensis*. Plant growth regulators (auxins and cytokinins) are also effective triggers of secondary metabolites. An optimum concentration of 2,4-D (25 mgl^{-1}) favoured the production of L-Dopa in cell cultures of *Mucuna*. Low concentration of 2, 4-D (0.1 ppm) proved favourable for alkaloid production in cell cultures of *Cinchona ledgeriana*.

In addition to concentration, the type of auxin used also exerts a strong influence on secondary product formation. 2,4-D in general proved less suitable for protein synthesis than IAA. Zenk et al. have reported that in *Morinda citrifolia* presence of 2,4-D reduced the production of anthraquinones but NAA enhanced the accumulation of anthraquinones.

The alkaloid synthesis and biomass accumulation increased on nutrient media containing NAA as compared to 2,4-D in *Nothapodytes foetida*. Like auxins, cytokinins also influence secondary metabolite production. BAP enhanced shikonin production in *L. erythrorhizon* and kinetin promoted L-Dopa synthesis in callus cultures of *Stizolobium hassjoo*. Likewise, in the presence of BAP maximum accumulation of withanolide occurred.

There was a decline in withanolide in the cultures of *Withania somnifera* with an increase (2.0–5.0 mg l^{-1}) in the concentration of BAP. In experiments conducted by Decendit et al. Zt or BAP proved more effective than Kinetin in *Catharanthus* cell cultures. At 1 μM Zt or BAP production of alkaloids was doubled.

Higher concentrations resulted in the decrease of alkaloids. According to Bhatt et al. besides growth regulators, a combination of IAA and sucrose in the medium can also stimulate the production of solasodine in the tissue cultures of *Solanum nigrum*. Higher concentrations of NAA + Kn or IAA + Kn promoted the yield of diosgenin in *D. bulbifera*.

Among the two auxins tried, NAA + Kn induced much higher content (Narula, unpublished). Corroborative results were obtained in *D. deltoidea* tissue cultures grown in the presence of 2,4-D, IBA, BA and GA singly and in combinations. The medium with 2,4-D favoured diosgenin production most consistently. GA and high BAP concentrations proved toxic. GA or kinetin are otherwise reported to increase the steroid content in *Phaseolus aureus and Corylus avellana* and doubled production of diosgenin in *Solanum xanthocarpum* tissue cultures. Zhao et al. observed that an increase in jaceosidin production was accomplished by increased concentration of NAA.

This concurs with the results of Matsumoto et al. who used cell suspension cultures of *Populus.* Addition of precursors of desired compounds to the culture medium also enhances the yield of secondary products. Ajmalicine production in *Catharanthus roseus* could be stimulated to approximately 10-fold by supplying secologanin.

Quinine in *Cinchona* cultures, rosemarinic acid in *Coleus blumei* and capsaicin production by cell cultures of *Capsicum frutescens,* and addition of loganin (precursor of secologanin) into the medium for enhanced yield of secologanin are some examples where precursor addition caused an increase in the yield of related metabolites.

Addition of various precursors (L-ornithine, L-arginine, L-phenylalanine, DL-β-phenyllactic acid and tropinone) alone was ineffective in stimulating hyoscyamine production in *Datura innoxia.* But, a combination of these precursors alongwith DL-β-phenyllactic acid and Tween 20 increased the yield. The recognition that certain specific secondary metabolite products, such as phytoalexins are produced by plants which are active against microorganisms has led to the concept of using such stimulators for *in vitro* cultures also.

These compounds have been described as 'elicitors' by Keen et al.. Elicitors can be of biotic or abiotic origin. Biotic elicitors are prepared from fungal, yeast or bacterial cultures, fungal mycelial extracts, culture filtrates, and fractions or compounds obtained from microbial cell walls. Autoclaved fungal mycelia induced the accumulation of diosgenin in *Dioscorea deltoidea* cultures. The production of berberine and shikonin enhanced in the cultured cells treated with fungal extracts.

A beta-glucan elicitor prepared by ethanol precipitation of yeast, *Saccharomyces cerevisiae* elicited alkaloid production in cultured cells of *Eschscholtzia.* In *Tabernaemontana divaricata* cultures, reserpine accumulation increased by treating the cells with an elicitor prepared from *Candida albicans.*

Purified fractions from bacteria also elicited diosgenin and capsaicin production. Elicitation of capsaicin in *Capsicum frutescens* cultures could be achieved by supplementing the culture medium with chitosan, curdlan and xanthan. The abiotic elicitors include physical and chemical stresses such as UV radiation, exposure to heat or cold, ethylene, fungicides, antibiotics, salts of heavy metals, salinity, etc..

It has also been recorded that the synthesis of alkaloids can be similarly elicited with jasmonic acid and its esters playing a key role in regulating the response. In fact, it is reported that fungal cell wall elicitors and methyl jasmonate (MeJa) can activate inducible secondary metabolism in soybean cell cultures by different mechanisms.

Treatments with exogenous MeJa can elicit the accumulation of several classes of alkaloids in a wide range of plant species. Hairy root cultures of *Datura stramonium* showed maximum alkaloid in the presence of MeJa followed by fungal elicitors and oligogalacturonide. Jasmonate

Table 11.4: Examples of some cryopreserved medicinal plants.

Plant	Explant/Culture	Method used
Anisodus acutangulus	Cell suspensions	Liquid nitrogen (–196°C)
Atropa belladonna	Pollen embryos Protoplasts	Liquid nitrogen (–196°C)
Catharanthus roseus	Cell suspensions	Low temperature (0-30°C), –196°C
Datura innoxia	Protoplasts	Exposed to vapors, immersed in liquid nitrogen
Dioscorea alata	Shoot tips	Encapsulation Dehydration
D. balanica	Callus	Direct immersion in liquid nitrogen
D. bulbifera	Shoot tips	Encapsulation Dehydration
D. floribunda	Shoot tips	Encapsulation Dehydration
Eucalyptus sp.	Shoot tips	Encapsulation Dehydration
Ipomea batatas	Shoot tips	Vitrification
Medicago sativa	Somatic embryos	Encapsulation
Mentha sp.	Shoot tips	Encapsulation Vitrification
Nicotiana tabacum	Protoplasts	Liquid nitrogen (–196°C)
Panax ginseng	Cell suspensions	Hardening, –30, –70, then –196°C
Trifolium repens	Shoot tips	Vitrification

can elicit natural product formation not only in plants but also in cell cultures. Methyl jasmonate therefore could be an useful tool for the enhancement of lignan production in biotechnological processes. Feeding experiments with the precursor coniferyl alcohol resulted in fast increase in the pinoresinol content. Some of the examples where elicitors caused enhancement in the yield of medicinal compounds are cited in Table elsewhere in this chapter.

It is not only the chemical milieu but also the physical factors which play a significant role in secondary metabolite production. Light as physical source, for example, has an effect on growth and development of plants as well as in stimulation of secondary metabolite production.

In fact, quality, intensity and duration of light play a decisive role in the accumulation of secondary compounds. Production of diosgenin and related compounds seem to be controlled by different media ingredients as well as by light. In some cases, direct effect of hydrogen ion concentration on secondary compound production has been demonstrated.

For example, alkaloid synthesis in *Lupinus polyphyllus* cultures rose with a decrease in pH from 5.5 to more acidic, 3.5. Even physical conditions of the medium have proved crucial for the production of secondary metabolites in cultures.

Table 11.3. Some examples of *in vitro* production of medicinal compounds when elicitors were used in cell suspensions.

Plant	Elicitor Used	Active Principle
Catharanthus roseus	*Botrytis* species homogenate	Catharanthene
	Fungal homogenate	Terpenoid, indole alkaloid
Eschscholtzia californica	Yeast	Sanguinarine
Hyoscyamus albus	*Phytophthora cinnamomi*	Lubimin
Lithospermum erythrorhizon	Oligogalacturonides	Dihydroechinofurane
Morinda citrifolia	Polysaccharides	Anthraquinones
Papaver bracteatum	Fungal	Sanguinarine
Verticillum	Sanguinarine	
P. somniferum	Fungal homogenate	Sanguinarine
	Botrytis species homogenate, *Pythium aphanidermatum*	Sanguinarine
Sanguinaria canadensis	*Verticillum*	Sanguinarine
Thalictrum rugosum	Yeast carbohydrate	Berberine
Tripterygium wilfordii	*Botrytis* species	Oleanane triterpenes
	Trichoderma virideae	
	Rhodotorula rubra	
	Sclerotinia sclerotiorum	

Cell suspension cultures have been favourites for the production of valuable secondary metabolites in cultures. These cultures initiated by transfer of most friable sector of an established callus tissue into an agitated liquid medium received more homogenous stimuli.

A close correlation between the growth of cultures and yield of products has been envisaged. Since the product accumulates through the growth cycle, the product and biomass show a close correlation. The first commercial production of a natural plant product by cell suspension cultures was developed in Japan for the production of naphthoquinone, shikonin.

In suspension cultures of *Rauwolfia sellowii* alkaloid content was maximum at the end of the exponential growth phase.

It has been argued that for industrial scale production of plant secondary metabolites, the cells should be suspended in liquid so that the entire operation of harvesting, inoculation and other treatments could be accomplished by pumping the suspended cells.

Immobilized plant cells used in the same way as immobilized enzymes have also played an important role in the secondary product formation. Although the enzymatic activity of immobilized cells is about half that of suspending cells, these have the advantage of being reusable as a biocatalyst over a considerable period.

Table 11.5: Application of molecular markers in some medicinal plants.

Plant	Marker	Application
Achillea ospenifolia	Oligonucleotide finger printing, RAPD	Stability of micropropagated plants
Allium sativum	RAPD	Genetic diversity in plants regenerated by somatic embryogenesis from long-term-callus
Artemisia annua	OPGMA-RAPD	Artemisinin and chemotypic variants
Azadirachta indica	AFLP	Genetic diversity
A. indica	AFLP	Clonal fidelity in tissue culture raised plants
Cichorium sp. group	AFLP	Diagnostic marker for endive and chicory
Codonopsis pilosula	RAPD	Geographic variation
Datura sp.	AFLP	Genetic diversity
Digitalis obscura	RAPD	Genetic variation
Dioscorea bulbifera	RFLP	Linkage (physical) map
	RAPD	Genetic variability and relationship within the species
D. rotundata and	AFLP	Genetic diversity *D. cayenensis*
Duboisia	RFLP	Hybrid origin identification
Moringa oliefera	AFLP	Genetic variation
Panax ginseng	RAPD	Genetic stability in micropropagated plants
P. ginseng and	RFLP	Ginseng drug *P. quniquefolium*
Plantago major	RAPD	Identifying subspecies
Rehmannia sp.	RAPD	Homogenity
Tylophora indica	RAPD	Genetic variation

Synthetic Seed

The concept of 'synthetic seed' was first introduced by Toshio Murashige in 1977 and later the use of synthetic seeds or artificial seeds was realized by Redenbaugh and coworkers and others. Synthetic seeds help in reducing the cost of transport and in maintaining the uniformity.

Besides, of much importance is the ability to provide large-scale delivery of elite genotypes selected from hand pollinated hybrids or genetically engineered plants. The first successful examples of synthetic seed technology have been in alfalfa and celery.

Various vegetative propagules like axillary buds, shoot tips, bulbs, protocorms have been used. The production of 'Syn' seeds has been reported in several medicinal plants like, *Atropa belladonna, Hyoscyamus muticus, Menthaarvensis, Picrorhiza kurroa. Dioscorea alata, D. floribunda, Clitoria ternatea* and *Guazuma crinita.*

Cryopreservation

Cryopreservation offers long-term conservation of germplasms. In addition to germplasm

Table 11.6: Some examples of *Agrobacterium-mediated* transformation in medicinal plants.

Plant	Strain	Result
Ammi majus	*Agrobacterium rhizogenes* A4 (20233)	Hairy roots produced higher content of visnagin
Artemisia annua	*A. rhizogenes* LBA 9402	1-month-old transgenic produced more artemisnic acid and arteannuin B
A. annua	*A. tumefaciens* C58 , N2 73	Artemisinin content was slightly higher in shoots
Atropa belladonna	*A. rhizogenes*	Higher atropine levels A4 , TR 105
A . belladonna	*A. tumefaciens*	Higher scopolamine LBA 4404
A . belladonna	*A. rhizogenes*	Increased scopolamine content 15834
A . belladonna	*A. rhizogenes* 15834 and	Higher alkaloid *A. tumefaciens rol ABC* genes
Catharanthus roseus	*A. rhizogenes*	At reduced pH more alkaloid released
Cinchona ledgeriana	*A. tumefaciens* A6	Five times more alkaloids (cinchonine and cinchonidine)
C. ledgeriana	*A. rhizogenes* LBA 9402	Quinine, cinchonidine and quinidine reached a maxima after 45 days
Datura candida hybrid (*D.candida* ×	*A. rhizogenes*	Scopolamine and hyoscyamine showed increase *D.candida*)
D. innoxia *D. stramonium* *D. ferox*	*A. rhizogenes* LBA 9402	Maximum hyoscyamine content in *D. stramonium* and scopolamine in D. innoxia D. wrightii
D. innoxia	*A. rhizogenes* A4, 15834 and A4–24 A4 and 15834 strains more effective	Higher hyoscyamine content
D. innoxia	*A. rhizogenes* LBA9402, A41027, R1601 R1601 gave best response	Hyoscyamine and scopolamine content was higher and among the two alkaloids hyoscyamine content was much higher
D. innoxia	*A. rhizogenes*	Permeabilization with Tween 20 for 30 hr period increased the alkaloid concentration in the medium
D. stramonium	*A. rhizogenes* TR-105	Heat shock given to the cultures resulted in higher hyoscyamine release in the medium
D. stramonium	*A. rhizogenes* TR-105, ATCC 15834, A4, 1855, A41027, ATCC 13333	Hyoscyamine and scopolamine bioproductivity was higher in hairy root culture Among these strains TR-105

(Table Contd.)

		proved most effective
D. stramonium	*A. rhizogenes*	Release of alkaloids increased at low pH (3.5)
D. stramonium	*A. rhizogenes* LBA 9402	Live fungal pellets caused enhanced hyoscyamine production
D. stramonium	*A. rhizogenes A4 rol*	Higher hyoscyamine production *ABC* and *tms* gene
D. stramonium	*A. rhizogenes* TR-105	An inverse relation between alkaloid accumulat-ion and growth, hyoscyamine content showed an increase
D. stramonium	*A. rhizogenes* ATCC 15834	Highest hyoscyamine yield with culture medium in which $SO4^{2-}$ and K^{+} was dominant
D. stramonium	*A. rhizogenes A4*	Lower calcium concentrations reduced the hyoscyamine synthesis
D. quercifolia	*A. rhizogenes* LBA 9402	5% sucrose in Gamborg B5 medium proved best for growth and higher hyoscyamine accumulation
Hyoscyamus albus, H. desertorum, H. muticus	*A. rhizogenes* LBA 9402	Hyoscyamine and scopolamine content was highest in *H. albus*
H. albus	*A. rhizogenes* MAFF 03-	Higher yield of hyoscyamine 01724
H. muticus	*A. rhizogenes* LBA 9402, C58Cl, pRTGUS 104	High hyoscyamine content at 3% sucrose in two of the clones, high nitrogen content had negative effect on hyoscyamine production and growth. Copper (11 μM) stimulated hyoscyamine production
Hyoscyamus × gyorffyi (*H. niger × H. albus*)	*A. rhizogenes* LBA 9402, A41027, R 1601 Among these strains R 1601	In 14 clones of *H. gyorffyi* hyoscyamine percentage being much higher than scopolamine gave the best response
Panax ginseng	*A. rhizogenes*	Produced saponin, and ginsenosides more effectively
P. ginseng	*A. rhizogenes A4*, 15834 A4 proved more effective	Higher content of glycosides
P. ginseng	*A. rhizogenes A4*	Faster growth of callus and higher yield of ginsenosides
Pgq (*Panax hybrid*) (*PP ginseng × P. quinquefolium*)	*A. rhizogenes ATCC 15834*	Ginsenoside content was higher
Rauwolfia serpentina	*A. rhizogenes 15834*	Increased levels of ajmaline and serpentine
Solanum eleagnifolium	*A. tumefaciens T 37*	Transgenic shoots showed higher solasodine cont-ent
Scopolia lurida and	*A. rhizogenes* LBA *9402*	Produced little alkaloids *S. stramonifolia*
Withania somnifera	*A. rhizogenes* LBA *9402*	Productivity of withanolide D was higher

conservation, it also ensures genetic stability and retention of biosynthetic potential. Cryopreservation has been achieved by using various explants. The period over which the cultures retain viability vary widely with the species and a maximum of 3 years has been recorded in *Digitalis.* Meristems have been preferred over cell and callus cultures because they are genetically more stable.

Shoot tips of medicinal plants such as *Cichorium* sp., *Dioscorea deltoidea, D. floribunda, Holostemma annulare* and *Mentha* sp. have been cryopreserved successfully. Genetic erosion due to periodic subculture and storage can be overcome by freeze preservation of callus and cell suspensions in liquid nitrogen. Cell suspensions of medicinal plants, e.g., *Atropa belladonna, Datura innoxia, Nicotiana tabacum, Panax ginseng,* etc. retain their biosynthetic potential after freezing.

Cryopreservation of somatic embryos helps in storage at appropriate stage that can be used whenever required. The somatic embryos of carrot, orange and asparagus frozen in liguid nitrogen yielded high viability and regenerated complete plants.

The potential of zygotic embryos is manifold in plants with recalcitrant seed, in fruit and timber trees and plantation crops. In wide hybridization programs, especially dealing with intergeneric crosses which are incompatible due to degeneration of embryos, can be possibly dissected out at immature stages and cryopreserved. Zygotic embryos of rice, wheat, barley, mustard and coconut cryopreserved by quick freezing, followed by thawing at 35-40°C produced viable plants but viability varied considerably.

The storage of pollen has been of prime interest to plant breeders. Cryopreservation of pollen enables en masse production of haploid plants, maintenance of stability of haploids and conservation of genetic resources.

Segments of anthers and pollen embryos of *Atropa belladonna, Brassica campestris, Nicotiana tabacum and Primula obconica* have been successfully frozen and entire plants have been regenerated after one year of storage.

Freshly isolated protoplasts of *Atropa belladonna, and Nicotiana tabacum, and Datura innoxia, and Glycine max* subjected to freezing in liquid nitrogen for various time periods have survived and retained their morphogenetic potential.

Molecular Markers

As micropropagation developed from a laboratory curiosity to commercial industry, different considerations became important concerning the feasibility of approaches for long-term economic benefits. The foremost concern has been the maintenance of the genetic integrity of micropropagated plants with regard to the explant source so that the advantages (high yield, uniform quality, shorter rotation period, etc.) in the use of elite genotypes over natural seedlings is maintained.

Rani and Raina have emphasized that micropropagation cannot be rewarding unless complete genetic fidelity is maintained. Thus for obtaining true-to-type plants, axillary branching or somatic embryogenesis have mostly been adopted. These two methods have generally been considered to be immune to genetic changes that may arise during cell division or differentiation under *in vitro* conditions.

Rani and Raina showed that the field-transferred enhanced axillary branching derived plants of *Eucalyptus camaldulensis* were genetically stable in terms of genome size, RFLPs of nuclear and organellar genomes and RAPD and oligonucleotide fingerprinting patterns.

The concept of uniformity among micropropagated plants, however, received a jolt when somaclonal variations were reported. Somaclonal variations can pose a threat to the genomic integrity of regenerated plants. Several strategies were therefore adopted to detect variants based on morphological traits, cytogenetical analysis for the determination of numerical and structural variation in the chromosomes and isozymes.

But, these met with severe limitations. Molecular markers have thus been used to study genetic diversity, phylogeny and fingerprinting as well as to construct physical genetic maps in medicinal plants. The range of marker system includes RAPD, AFLP, microsatellites and RFLP. RFLP was introduced as hybridization based marker for single copy loci.

Since RFLP is capable of detecting multiple alleles, it reveals greater level of heterozygosity and has a higher information content. The major drawback of RFLP is that it screens very few loci per assay. It is expensive, labour intensive and technically complex as it involves the use of radioactive probes.

It also requires larger amounts of genomic DNA making its application impractical for efficiently cataloguing of genetic resources. RAPD technique is quite simple, inexpensive but less reliabile. AFLP has many advantages that make it applicable in assessment of genetic diversity, genetic mapping and tagging studies.

AFLP has now become a preferred technique as it combines RFLP and RAPD. AFLP markers offer best method for detecting mutations by randomly surveying the genome. This technique does not require prior sequence information. Besides, it has wide genome coverage as compared to other DNA-based markers which makes it an ideal tool for detecting genetic variation.

This technique has been used for analyzing genetic variation in somatic embryoids of pecan. Singh et al. reported application of AFLP markers for ascertaining clonal fidelity in tissue culture raised progenies of a medicinally important plant, *Azadirachta indica.* AFLP markers are now being routinely employed for assessment of genetic variation in economically important plant species including chichory, *Withania* sp., etc..

Genetic Engineering in Medicinal Plants Through *Agrobacterium*

The stable introduction of foreign genes into plants represents one of the most significant developments in plant biotechnology. Attempts have been made to manipulate pharmaceutically important medicinal plants for their secondary metabolic pathways by using transgenic technique.

Since secondary products are often biosynthesized in mulit-step enzymatic reactions in specifically differentiated cells, manipulations of such pathways to alter metabolic production is complex, complicated and unpredictable. Transformation has many advantages over conventional cell culture systems that may include fast growth and stable high level production of secondary metabolites making them favourable for biotechnological exploitation.

Agrobacterium tumefaciens and *A. rhizogenes* have proved efficient and have provided highly versatile vehicles for introduction of genes into the desired plant genome. As a consequence of transfer and integration of genes through plasmids into the plant DNA, the transformed tissues and hairy roots have provided encouraging results.

These transformed tissues have thus become potential sources for stable production of plant metabolites. Hairy root cultures of *Trigonella-foenum-graecum L.* produced twice the amounts of diosgenin than the non-transformed roots. Several studies have indicated *that Agrobacterium rhizogenes* affects the levels of polyamine in transformed plants that may influence growth and the production of secondary metabolites.

Atropa baetica hairy roots synthesized and accumulated a conspicuously high amount of tropane alkaloids. In *Hyoscyamus albus*, hyoscyamine content was more in the transformed roots followed by stem and leaves.

Doerk-Schmitz et al., however, reported low proportion of scopolamine in hairy roots of *Hyoscyamus albus* but there was high content of hyoscyamine even after several subcultures and the transgenic plants could be regenerated directly from such roots via organogenesis. Strains of *Agrobacterium* are reported to affect the growth behaviour and production of secondary metabolites.

Influence of *A. rhizogenes* strains on biomass and alkaloid prductivity in hairy root lines of *Hyoscyamus muticus and H. albus was* also studied by Zehra et al.. A4 induced hairy root lines of *H. albus and H. muticus* were faster growing than those induced by strain LBA 9402. The atropine yield of A4 induced lines of *H. albus was* significantly higher (3.5-fold) than the LBA 9402 induced lines. Cu^{2+} enhanced both, the growth and the alkaloid yield in *Hyoscyamus albus* hairy roots.

Similar results have been obtained in the production of shikonin derivative by cell suspension cultures of *Lithospermum erythrorhizon*. Copper concentration up to 11 μM stimulated hyoscyamine production but had no influence on growth of hairy root cultures of *Hyoscyamus*. Two-year-old transformed root cultures of *Catharanthus roseus* accumulated higher ajmalicine and catharanthine than the non-transformed cultures. Addition of MeJa increased the yield of both the alkaloids.

A positive correlation between STR activity and alkaloid accumulation has also been found in tissues of *Cinchona ledgeriana and C. roseus* seedlings. TDC (trytophane decarboxylase) activity in developing *Cinchona* seedlings increased after a large pool of tryptophan was formed. It fell to undetectable levels once the tryptophan was converted into tryptamine.

Serotonin content enhanced if the hairy root cultures of *Peganum harmala* were fed with tryptamine. But the alkaloid content was not affected. In *Panax ginseng* roots were transformed with *A. rhizogenes*. Inomata et al. found that periodic changes of medium maintained the high growth rate and the ginsenoside production varied during different stages of growth.

Mallol et al. also observed that the capacity to produce and accumulate ginsenoside is associated with biomass. The results concur with other investigations as well as our results with *Datura*. Transformation stimulated increased biomass and tropane alkaloid production in axenic root cultures of *Calystegia sepium and Atropa belladonna*.

Compared to transformed plants, non-transformed plants contained low amounts of tropane alkaloids, especially 6 β-hydroxy hyoscyamine and scopolamine in the roots. In transgenic lines of *Nicotiana tabacum* feeding of lysine to root cultures with low LDC (lysine decarboxylase) activity enhanced cadaverine and anabasine levels.

Several hairy root cultures of *N. tabacum* having lDC gene increased cadaverine levels and this was used for the formation of anabasine to obtain a 3-fold increase of this alkaloid. Transformation has indeed helped in the enhancement of secondary metabolites in a number of cases though not to commercial levels. In *Artemisia*, use of arnesyl diphosphate synthase gene promoted artemisinin 3-4 times higher in hairy roots.

In *Catharanthus roseus* where *str* (strictocidine synthase) is highly desirable for increased terpenoid indole alkaloid (TIA) production, high STR activity positively influenced the flow of metabolites through the indole pathway. Subroto and Pauline reported the production of steroidal alkaloids in *Solanum aviculare* that was growth associated.

It has been shown by Schaller et al. that the introduction of extra copies of a chimeric *hmgr* gene (obtained from *Hevea brasiliensis*) increased the accumulation of sterols by 6-fold in tobacco plants. HMGR β-hydroxy-3-methylglutaryl-coenzyme A reductase) plays a major role in the regulation of sterol biosynthesis in plants.

In *Solanum aviculare*, Cavalcante Argolo obtained transgenic hairy root clones that grew faster and accumulated up to 4.2 times more solasodine when grown under dark. Upregulation of the *hmgr* gene in tobacco has also been shown to give rise to highly significant increase in sterol accumulation.

odc and adc genes play important role in the biosynthetic pathway of alkaloids. A stable transformation system has been developed by us for *Datura innoxia* using androgenic callus that was transfected with *Agrobacterium tumefaciens* strain LBA4404 carrying *odc and adc* genes.

Transformed cultures showed higher amounts of hyoscyamine and early regeneration. Tiburcio and Galston reported that in *Nicotiana tabacum* ODC pathway is important for cell division and growth, the effects of inhibitors on alkaloid biosynthesis show that ADC is more important in synthesis of pyrrolidine alkaloids.

Imanishi et al. in tobacco and Robins et al. in *Datura stramonium* also found that arginine decarboxylase activity is more important for hyoscyamine formation. However, expression of yeast *odc* gene in *Nicotiana rustica* roots induced an increased accumulation of nicotine that shows that plant secondary products can be elevated by means of genetic manipulation.

EPILOGUE

Biotechnology of medicinal plants has not received the attention it deserves. While other group of plants have been the area of concern for yield improvement including disease and pest resistance, no organised technology has been adopted for improving the yield of medicinal plants. The methodology should include credible selection, micropropagation and studies on abiotic stress related yield as stress has been implicated in the biosynthesis of secondary metabolites. Recombinant DNA technology, molecular biology and metabolic engineering need to be integrated to make a combined concerted effort that will help in improving the productivity of drug components.

12

Chapter

IMPROVING THE SYNTHESIS OF PHYTOCHEMICALS

Higher plants are inexhaustible sources of a wide range of biochemicals such as flavors, fragrances, natural pigments, pesticides and pharmaceuticals. Currently many of these compounds are isolated by solvent extraction from the naturally grown whole plants. This continued *destruction* of plants has posed a major threat to the plant species getting extinct over the years.

Clearly, the development of *alternative* methods to whole plant extraction for the production of these compounds, especially of medicinal value, is an issue of *considerable* socio-economic importance. These factors have generated *considerable* interest in the use of plant cell culture technologies for the *production* of phytochemicals.

In plant cell culture, the isolated cells from the whole plant (or parts derived thereof) are cultivated under appropriate physiological conditions and the desired product is extracted from the cultured cells. The recent developments in plant tissue culture *techniques* and their *processing* have shown *promising* results to improve the productivity by many folds.

CELL SUSPENSION CULTURES

The first step in plant tissue culture is to develop a callus culture from the whole plant. A callus can be obtained from any portion of the whole plant containing dividing cells. To maximize the formation of a particular compound, it is desirable to initiate the callus from the plant part that is known to be a high producer.

However, from an engineering perspective, cell suspension cultures have more *immediate* potential for industrial application than plant tissue and organ cultures, due to extensive expertise which has been amassed for submerged microbial cultures. While tissue and root cultures offer genetic stability as well as, in some instances, superior metabolic *performances* over suspension cultures of the cell lines, the development of *appropriate bioreactors* and operating techniques for these systems involve high investment and laborious *experimentation*.

Accordingly, most of the research efforts have been directed towards *commercialization* of plant cell suspension cultures. A suspension culture is developed by transferring the relatively friable portion of a callus into liquid medium and is *maintained* under suitable conditions of aeration, agitation, light, *temperature* and other physical parameters.

However, various strategies may have to be adopted to obtain a fairly homogeneous suspension culture. Mitsui Petrochemical Industry, Japan was the first to produce shikonin (a dyestuff) on *commercial* scale.

While the large-scale cultivation of plant cell *suspension* cultures is desirable for industrial production of plant-derived biochemicals, the production technology comparable to that used for microbial systems needs to be further developed.

Although the basic equipment- and processrelated requirements for *suspension* cultures of plant cells are similar to those of submerged microbial cultures, some of the features used for microbial *cultures* are not suitable for plant cell cultures because of striking differences in the nature and growth pattern of the two types of cells.

The implications of these differences on culturing of the plant cells are *summarized* in Table elsewhere in this chapter. Certain *engineering* considerations are *normally* addressed before embarking on the mass scale *propagation* of plant cells.

ENGINEERING CONSIDERATIONS

Plant cell suspensions can now be *successfully* cultivated in bioreactors of various configurations. However, many of the unique properties of plant cells in culture such as sensitivity to shear, slow growth rates, and low oxygen *requirements* are manifested in complex ways at large scale cultivation.

As the scale of operation increases, mixing inside the bioreactor vessel becomes difficult, resulting in non-uniform concentration of the nutrients and limited oxygen transfer to respiring cells. Changes in the rheological nature of the fluid, wall growth, and clumping of cells resulting in *sedimentation*, lead to suboptimal *utilization* of the bioreactor.

These problems necessitate a more rigorous analysis of bioreactors to be used for the large scale cultivation of plant cells for metabolite production.

Aggregation

Plant cells are *significantly* larger and slower growing cells than most microbial organisms. Aggregation is common, largely due to failure of the cells to separate after division, although the secretion of *extracellular* polysaccharides, *particularly* in the later stages of growth, may contribute to increased adhesion.

This tendency of the plant cells to grow in clumps results in *sedimentation*, *insufficient* mixing

Table 12.1: Differences between the characteristic features of plant and microbial cells and their implications for bioreactor design

Characteristic features of a typical plant cell	*Implications for reactor design*
Lower respiration rate	Lower oxygen transfer rates required
More shear sensitive	May require operation under low-shear conditions by, for example, employing low-shear impellers and bubble-free aeration
Growth as aggregates	May have mass transfer limitations that limit the availability of nutrients to cells within the aggregates
Aggregation important for secondary metabolism	An optimal aggregate size may be required for product synthesis by manipulation of media constituents and environmental conditions
Volatile compounds (e.g. CO_2 or ethylene) may be important for cell metabolism	May need to sparge gas mixtures containing them
Product synthesis may be non-growth-associated	May require a two-step cultivation system for maximal product synthesis

and diffusion-limited biochemical reaction. This so-called cell-cell contact is desirable for the biosynthesis of many secondary metabolites by the plant cells. Hence controlled *aggregation* of plant cells is of interest from process *engineering* point of view.

Mixing

Mixing promotes better growth by enhancing the transfer of nutrients from liquid and gaseous phases to cells and the dispersion of air bubbles for effective *oxygenation*. Although plant cells have higher tensile strength in comparison to microbial cells, their shear sensitivity to *hydrodynamic* stresses restricts the use of high agitation for efficient mixing.

Plant cells are, therefore, often grown in stirred tank bioreactors at very low agitation speeds. Mixing of plant cells grown on a large scale is also hampered by the rheological characteristics of the culture broth. Plant cell suspensions are viscous at high *concentrations* and behave like non-Newtonian fluids.

NonNewtonian behaviour of the culture broth also restricts effective mass and heat transfer inside the bioreactor, leading to non-uniform nutrient *concentration* and *temperature*, and the development of dead zones inside the culture vessel. Excretion of polysaccharides at the later stages of cell growth, the extent and nature of which depend on the nature of the plant cells and the *carbohydrate* source used for growth, also results in a rapid increase in viscosity.

Inadequate mixing may lead to *clumping* of cells, thereby *complicating* the nature of the reacting system; also the inner cells of the clumps become nutrient deficient, which may have either an adverse or a positive effect on the cell growth and product formation.

Adequate mixing can be achieved by proper design of the impeller; *helical-ribbon* impeller has been reported to enhance mixing at the high density of plant cell suspension cultures.

Oxygen and Aeration Effects

Oxygen *requirements* of plant cells are comparatively lower than that of microbial cells due to their low growth rates. In some cases, high oxygen *concentration* is even toxic to the cells' metabolic activities and may strip nutrients such as carbon dioxide from the culture broth.

Hence, effective oxygen transfer in plant cell cultures must be carefully *analyzed* when a bioreactor system is being selected. The intensity of culture broth mixing, the degree of air bubble dispersion, the culture medium's capacity for oxygen, and the *hydrodynamic* stress inside the culture vessel affect proper aeration of the culture.

Effects of aeration on plant cell suspension cultures have focused largely on the influence of k_La, the mass transfer coefficient, in which the aeration and agitation are linked. The k_La value gives a direct measure of effective *oxygenation* of culture fluid and helps one choose a suitable *bioreactor* to cultivate plant cells.

Increased viscosity of the culture broth decreases k_La *and* signals the need for intensive agitation of the culture for better mixing and oxygen transfer. A balanced analysis of mixing and oxygen transfer as reflected in k_La value is, therefore, required to achieve reasonable cell yield and product formation. The effect of initial k_La on growth and alkaloid production by suspension cultures of *Catharanthus roseus* was studied in 12.5 liter stirred tank bioreactor using either a cross sparger or a sinter sparger, and a 6-bladed Rushton impellor for agitation.

It has been observed that, at higher k_La values, serpentine was produced when the cells were in the log phase, whereas production of serpentine and ajmalicine was maximum *at* k_La values of 16 h^{-1} and 4.5 h^{-1}, respectively. High aeration may lead to severe foaming, which has considerable influence on the cell growth and secondary metabolite production.

A number of antifoams such as polypropylene glycol 1025 and 2025, Pluronic PE 6100, and Antifoam-C have often been employed to control foaming; however, in some cases this resulted in reduction in cell growth and product formation.

Shear Sensitivity

The sensitivity of plant cells to *hydrodynamic* stress associated with aeration and agitation can be attributed to the physical characteristics of the suspended cells, viz. their size, the presence of thick cellulose based cell wall, and *existence* of large vacuoles.

Mechanically agitated vessels lead to damaging and breaking the cells through the hydrodynamic stress generated by aeration, agitation, and other operations. The air-lift bioreactor has also been used to achieve better *oxygen* transfer and good growth.

Bubble-free aeration of the culture fluid through a moving membrane provided another suitable alternative for transferring gas without inducing cell damage through shear stress. The immediate consequence of the shear effect on plant cells is cell damage, which has been *quantitatively*

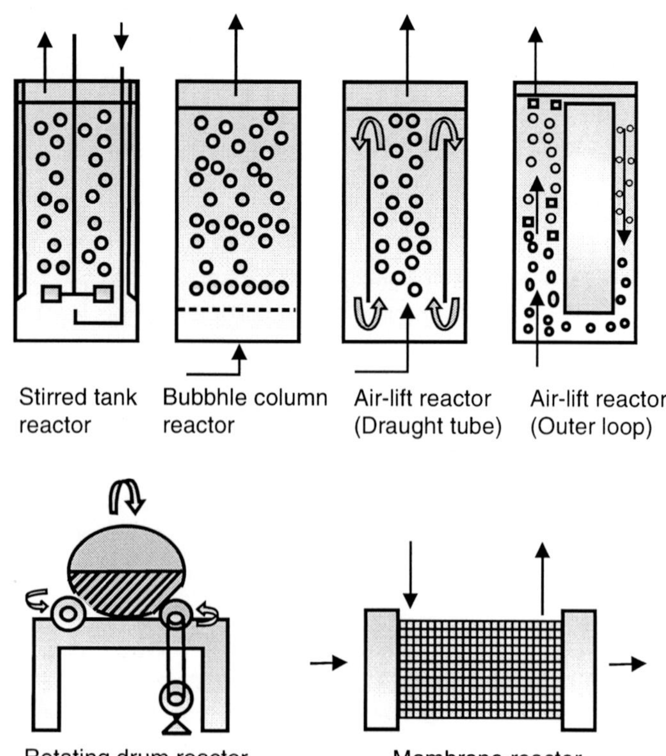

Figure 12.1: Configurations of different bioreactors used for plant cell cultivation.

measured by using a number of system responses such as reduction in cell viability, release of *intracellular* compounds, changes in morphology and/or aggregate patterns, and changes in metabolism.

The effects of *hydrodynamic* and interfacial stress on plant cell *suspension* cultures with various modes of *quantitative* analysis of system response at shake flask as well as bioreactor levels have recently been reviewed by Kieran and co-workers.

PLANT CELL BIOREACTORS

A suitable bioreactor can be designed for a specific plant cell system from the following considerations:

- optimum aeration-agitation with respect to capacity of oxygen supply and intensity of hydrodynamic stress effects on the plant cells.
- intensity of culture broth mixing and air-bubble dispersion.
- control of temperature, pH and nutrient concentration inside the bioreactor.
- control of aggregate size (which may be important to enhance secondary metabolite production).

- maintenance of aseptic conditions for relatively longer cultivation period.

A number of different types of bioreactors have been used for mass cultivation of plant cells taking the above *considerations* into account. Stirred tank *bioreactors* have been most extensively applied in order to achieve the optimum process parameters. In spite of the fact that stirred tank reactors exert more *hydrodynamic* stress on plant cells, they have great potential when used with low agitation speed and modified impeller.

The first commercial application of large scale *cultivation* of plant cells was carried out in stirred tank reactors of 200 and 750 liter capacities to produce shikonin by cell cultures of *Lithospermum erythrorhizon.* Cells of Catharanthus roseus, Digitalis lanata, Panax notoginseng, Taxus baccata and *Podophyllum hexandrum* have been cultured in stirred tank bioreactors with suitable modifications for production of phytochemicals.

Another type of reactor known as bubble column reactor has also been used for large scale cultivation of plant cells. The major advantages of this reactor are the absence of moving parts and ease of *maintaining* sterile *environment,* as no sealing parts are required. *Cudrania tricuspidata,* being highly shear sensitive, was cultivated in bubble column reactor.

A modification of bubble column reactor 'balloon type bubble bioreactor' has been recently adopted for the *production* of taxol by *Taxus cuspidata.* The major disadvantage of this reactor is *insufficient* mixing. A reactor having more uniform flow pattern with slight modification of stirred tank reactor (a draught tube is inserted instead of the impeller) is air-lift bioreactor.

The cells of *Catharanthus roseus, Digitalis lanata, Cudrania tricuspidata, Lithospermum erythrorhizon* and *Taxus chinensis* have been successfully cultivated in air-lift bioreactors for production of secondary metabolites.

The major disadvantages of this reactor are the development of dead zones inside the bioreactor, insufficient mixing at high cell densities and rupture of cells due to collision between air bubbles and the cells. Another type of reactor used in plant cell cultivation is rotating drum reactor, which has higher *oxygen* transfer ability and relatively lower *hydrodynamic* stress.

This consists of a horizontally rotating drum on rollers connected to a motor. Rotary drum reactor has been shown to be superior over other reactors for the cultivation of *Vinca rosea* and *Lithospermum erythrorhizon.* The performance of the different bioreactors has been summarized by Panda and co-workers.

PROCESS STRATEGIES

Selection of Cultivation Techniques

Various modes for *culturing* plant cells have been employed in suspension culture in order to *maximize* product formation. The fed-batch mode is used in cases where the addition of a high *concentration* of substrate affects the growth.

The technique of repeated batch cultivation (*semicontinuous* mode) provides an appropriate approach towards the continuous cultivation of plant cells when the rate of product synthesis (or *biotransformation* of added *precursors*) parallels the rate of growth. For non-growth-associated products, the use of a two-stage culture, where cells are propagated in a growth medium and

Table 12.2: Production of secondary metabolites by plant cell suspension cultures under different modes of cultivation

Plant cell	*Product*	*Bioreactor type, capacity and mode of cultivation*	*Product (mg/l)*
Anchusa officinalis	Rosmarinic acid	Stirred tank bioreactor, 2.5 liter, batch	3500
Aralia cordata	Anthocyanin	Jar culture vessel, 500 liter, continuous	1090
Catharanthus roseus	Ajmalicine	Air-lift bioreactor,	6.4
	Catharanthine	20 liter, batch	3
	Serpentine	1.6 Tryptamine	16.1
Coptis japoinca	Berberine	Stirred tank bioreactor, 2.5 liter	
		batch	800
		Fed-batch	2320
		Continuous	3500
Holarrhena antidysenterica	Conessine	Stirred tank bioreactor, 6 liter, batch	106
Lithospermum erythrorhizon	Shikonin	Stirred tank bioreactor, 200 and 750 liter, two-stage culture	4000
Nicotiana tabacum	*Cinnamoyl putrescines*	Stirred tank bioreactor	
		batch	160
		Fed-batch	400
Panax notoginseng	*Ginseng saponin*	Centrifugal impeller bioreactor, 2.5 liter, batch	800
		Turbine bioreactor, 2.5 liter, batch	490
		Air-lift bioreactor, 1 liter, batch	3120
		Erlenmeyer flask, 0.25 liter, batch	1570
Perilla frutescens	Anthocyanin	Erlenmeyer flask, 0.5 liter	5800
Podophyllum hexandrum	Podophyllotoxin	Stirred tank bioreactor, 3 liter	
		batch	13.8
		Fed-batch (intermittent feeding)	43.2
		Continuous with cell retention	48.8
Taxus chinensis	Taxane	Erlenmeyer flask, 0.25 liter	274.4
Taxus cuspidata	Taxol	Wilson type bioreactor	22

then transferred to a production medium, would be the ideal choice for maximizing product synthesis.

Obviously, it would be important to recognize the best *physiological* state of the cell for maximal product accumulation. Once the type of bioreactor is selected for a specific plant cell process, the mode of operation will depend on the dynamics of the specific culture. Batch cultivations are characterized by *constantly* changing *environmental* conditions, and are capable of *producing* metabolites associated with any kinetic pattern.

Therefore, a number of plant cell systems have been cultivated under batch mode to scale-up the process. Although batch cultivation strategy has been widely adopted for scale-up of plant cell bioprocesses, it has not always been *successful* in improving the production of desired metabolites; in many cases the production of *secondary* metabolites has been reported to be decreased in scale-up process.

A variety of plant cells cultivated under batch mode for production of secondary metabolites are *summarized* in Table elsewhere in this chapter. Stirred-tank *bioreactors* with modified impellers that impart improved mixing under low shear have been advocated for *cultivation* of fragile plant cells in large scale *suspension* cultures.

Panax ginseng has been successfully cultivated at a large scale in 2000 liter and 20000 liter stirred tank bioreactors to produce 500–700 mg/l of ginseng saponins. *Panax ginseng* cell lines have been cultivated in both stirred tank and air-lift bioreactors for the production of gingenoside. Different types of impellers (flat-blade, angled-blade disc turbine, anchor impeller) at various impeller speeds have been used for the cell growth of *Panax ginseng* and it has been observed that angle-blade disc impeller at 100–150 rpm resulted in highest cell growth, indicating the shear sensitivity of the cells.

Another cell line of *P. ginseng* cultivated in a 2 liter stirred tank bioreactor with a marine propeller grew fairly well up to an unusually high agitation speed of 1000 rpm, indicating shear-resistant nature of the cell line. The conditions derived from the batch cultivation can be used to design suitable fed-batch or continuous operation to overcome the inhibitions by controlled addition of a limiting nutrient.

Fed-batch cultivation has been able to improve the productivity of ginseng by *Panax ginseng,* and taxane by *Taxus chinensis*. Fed-batch cultivation of *Coptis japonica* had a significant effect on production of berberine at high cell density, as batch cultivation in stirred tank bioreactor damaged the cells due to high osmotic pressure of the culture medium.

Further, the biomass concentration was reduced due to accumulation of inhibitory products during cell growth. This problem was resolved by suitable fed-batch cultivation, which enhanced both cell growth and berberine production.

An increased production of cinnamoyl putrescines has also been observed by fed-batch cultivation of *Nicotiana tabacum* in stirred tank bioreactor. Production of podophyllotoxin has been enhanced to 43.2 mg/l by fed-batch cultivation of *Podophyllum hexandrum* in stirred tank bioreactor as compared to 13.8 mg/l in batch cultivation.

Steady state continuous flow or chemostat operation, with a constant withdrawal of culture medium and cells is commonly used for the production of growth-associated products, typically primary metabolites and biomass. It also provides a system to eliminate product inhibition, if any. The continuous culture technique has also been adopted for the cultivation of several plant cells such as, *Coptis japonica, Catharanthus roseus,* and *Nicotiana tabacum.* A high cell density of *Coptis japonica* produced 3500 mg/l berberine when cultivated in continuous mode in 2.5 l stirred tank bioreactor.

However, the cellular content of berberine in continuous culture decreased to less than 50% of that observed in batch *cultivation* because the production of berberine in *C. japonica was* a part of the non-growth-associated kinetics. Cell retention systems have been occasionally employed for the enhancement of growth and product yield in various microbial systems for their ability to achieve high cell density in *continuous* cultivation.

In situ cell retention systems have been particularly *successful* in improving the productivity of product *inhibited* cultivations, mainly because the bioreactor could be operated at high dilution rates to flush out inhibitory products and at the same time the cells could be retained by the filtration device.

Spin filter device has been applied for the somatic embryogenesis of plant cell suspension cultures and for industrial plant propagation. *Podophyllum hexandrum has* been cultivated in stirred tank bioreactor in continuous mode using cell retention device and this further enhanced the production of podophyllotoxin to 48.8 mg/l (authors' work).

Precursor Feeding

Precursors of biosynthetic pathways have been used in various plant cell suspension cultures to improve the production of secondary metabolites. Factors such as the concentration and the time of addition of the precursor are to be considered when applying the precursor to the cell culture medium.

The addition of loganin, tryptophan and tryptamine enhanced the production of secologanin, and indole alkaloids by *Catharanthus roseus* suspension cultures. Paclitaxel yields in the cell culture of *Taxus cuspidata* were improved up to six times by feeding phenylalanine and other potential paclitaxel side-chain precursors (e.g. benzoic acid, N-benzoylglycine and serine).

Cholesterol, a precursor of alkaloid biosynthesis, was found to have a strong effect on the production of conessine by *Holarrhena antidysenterica* cell suspension culture. The time of addition of cholesterol as well as its concentration had a significant effect on alkaloid synthesis.

A step feeding strategy, in which 50 mg/l cholesterol was added in 4 installments during different phases of growth, enhanced the production of the alkaloid from 63 mg/l to 106 mg/l in 6 liter stirred tank *bioreactor*; this study highlighted the *importance* of the *physiological* state of the culture for effective *transformation* of the precursor to alkaloid.

Permeabilization of Plant Cells

Plant secondary metabolites are normally produced *intracellularly* which adds up to the cost of downstream processing of a specific product. It is, therefore, desirable to extract the products into the culture medium. Removal of secondary metabolites from the vacuoles of the cells would also reduce the product inhibition and increase the productivity.

Many attempts have been made to permeabilize the plant cell membranes in a reversible manner with organic solvents. Dimethylsulfoxide (DMSO) has been used in many cases, because it is known to extract sterols from the membranes of the eukaryotic cells. Of various cells tested, only *Catharanthus roseus* survived the treatment of DMSO.

Taxol has recently been extracted by various organic solvents such as hexadecane, decanol and dibutylphthalate, in the range of 5–20% (v/v), in the culture medium of *Taxus chinensis*. Selection of a specific solvent system with due consideration to its effect on cell growth may lead to substantial release and increase in the production of secondary metabolites.

FUTURE PROSPECTS

Plant cell cultivation is a suitable alternative to whole plant cultivation for the production of desired compounds. However, due attention must be given to the relevant engineering parameters influencing cell growth and secondary metabolite production.

The inherent difficulties associated with *in vitro* plant cell cultivation, e.g., genetic variation of plant cell lines, sensitivity to shear stress, complex regulatory mechanism etc. are to be properly addressed for a specific cell line. Design of a suitable bioreactor with low-shear impeller, and selection of an appropriate mode of cultivation is required for increased metabolite production.

Selection of suitable metabolic precursors, extraction of intracellular metabolites by organic solvents can also lead to significant enhancement in productivity of secondary metabolites. The third author Prof. V.S. Bisaria along with Prof.

Saroj Mishra and Dr. A.K. Panda of National Institute of *Immunology*, New Delhi, initiated a collaborative project on production of alkaloids by cell cultures of *Holarrhena antidysenterica,* a plant growing in the lawns of Department of Botany, University of Delhi, Delhi, with the cooperation of Prof.

S.S. Bhojwani about 15 years ago. Since then the activity at IIT Delhi has *increased* many folds with substantial inputs of modeling and simulation expertise of the second author Dr. A.K. Srivastava, into the cultivation strategies of plant cells in bioreactors.

During the period of association, the authors were greatly benefited by the vast expertise of Prof. Bhojwani. The authors, therefore, feel honored to dedicate this article to Prof. Bhojwani at the time of his *superannuation* from a very fulfilling and *academically* rewarding experience.

13

Chapter

IMPROVING OIL SEED PLANTS

Production of crop varieties with increased sustainable production is the most challenging task facing the plant breeders in the current century. Considering the limited resources such as diminishing and deteriorating cultivable land, water supply, fertilizers etc., *improvement* in terms of yield and quality within a limited time frame, is the demand of the present and future *generations*.

Since the increased yield alone may not sustain the needs of *human* nutrition, *improvement* of *nutritional* quality and value addition for *diversified* uses are of prime importance. The oilseeds form the second largest agricultural *commodity* in India.

Among the nine annual oilseed crops grown in the country, oilseed brassica rank second in importance *contributing* about 30% to the total oilseed produced. It is one of the best edible oils available, having lowest amount of saturated fats as compared to other vegetable oils, provides both *essential* fatty acids and also the animal feed through oil free meal rich in protein having well balanced aminogram.

The oleiferous Brassicas being the provider of edible oil to a major proportion of our population are prime targets for quality *improvement*.

The presence of high amounts of two *nutritionally* undesired elements in Indian varieties (40–50% erucic acid in the seed oil and upto 300 µm/g glucosinolates in the deoiled meal) pose a huge challenge to plant breeders working on improving oil and deoiled meal quality in Brassicas.

The canola quality exotic rapeseed cultivars, commonly known as double low or 'oo', having less than 2% erucic acid in the seed oil and less than 30 µm glucosinolate/g oil free meal were not found suitable for cultivation under Indian agroclimatic conditions.

Since, among the oilseed Brassicas, B. juncea acquires the *maximum* share of cultivated area in our country, the improvement of *nutritional* quality in B. juncea is most desired to suit our needs. The brassica fatty acid profile is also amenable to alterations for developing designer crops for specific food or non-food industrial applications thus having prospects of diversified uses.

SEED OIL QUALITY

The nutritional quality of vegetable oils is considered significant in modern living. Oil quality is described in terms of saturated, *monounsaturated* and *polyunsaturated* fatty acids. Mustard oil contains the lowest amounts of saturated fatty acids as compared to other vegetable oils and also has a very good proportion of *n3* and *n6 polyunsaturated* fatty acids, thus *considered* beneficial for food consumption.

In most vegetable oils, the *unsaturated* fatty acids consists mainly of oleic and linoleic acid. However, mustard oil is an exception since in addition to oleic acid (8–15%), linoleic acid (13–20%) and linolenic acid (6–14%), it also contains erucic acid (41–50%), and palmitic and stearic acids in trace amounts. Erucic acid contributes *approximately* 50% of the total fatty acids in mustard oil. However, it is *nutritionally* undesirable and the high erucic acid *B. napus oil* is reported to be less *metabolisable*.

High erucic acid content is also known to cause impaired *myocardial* conductance, increased blood cholesterol and cardiac lipidosis with accumulation of erucic acid in *mammalian* system. High *concentration* of oleic acid is preferred for cooking *purposes* since it is thermostable. Both linoleic and linolenic acids are essential fatty acids that need to be supplied in diet from external sources.

However, high linolenic acid in the oil being prone to *peroxydation* causes flavor revision and oil *deterioration* and therefore 3 to 5% is preferred to meet the dietary *requirement.* Linoleic and linolenic acid are both produced by a common biosynthetic desaturation pathway. Therefore, selection for high linoleic acid has tended to increase the level of linolenic acid, while selection for low linolenic acid tends to decrease the level of linoleic acid also.

For this reason selection within the same *germplasm* may not be able to meet the breeding objectives. Therefore, the fatty acid scenario in mustard oil implies that efforts should be made towards development of cultivars having low levels of erucic and *linolenic* acids, high levels of oleic and moderate linoleic acids. The success of developing *B. juncea* with low erucic acid suitable for Indian agroclimatic condition has been limited due to search for appropriate gene pool.

Stefansson et al. and Downey identified genotypes with a genetic block in the biosynthesis of eicosenoic and erucic acid in summer rape *(B. napus)* and *summer* turnip rape *(B. campestris),* respectively. Studies for inheritance of erucic acid content have shown that it is controlled by multiple genes and the seed erucic acid level is controlled by the embryo genotype in *B. napus.*

Kirk and Hurlstone have reported two genes showing dominance and acting in an additive manner for erucic acid biosynthesis in *B. juncea.* Kirk and Oram *identified* zero erucic genotypes of *B. juncea* and following this low erucic acid genetic stock among Indian accessions of *B. juncea was* also identified. Recently the development of early maturing, low erucic acid strains of *B. juncea and B. napus, suitable* to grow under Indian agroclimatic conditions, have been reported and are under the advance stages of testing. In *B. juncea,* the *predominantly* grown oilseed brassica in India, the main emphasis has been on successful reduction of erucic acid and the work in the direction of developing cultivars with variable fatty acid profile for edible or industrial *purposes* is just beginning.

DEOILED MEAL QUALITY

The defatted Brassica meal contains about 40% protein with a well balanced aminogram and is used as animal feed. Brassica oil meal is particularly rich in lysine and methionine, which are essential amino acids not found in cereal grains.

For this reason, Brassica oil meal has been used for animal feed. However, the feeding value of rapeseed-mustard meal has been limited because of the presence of sulfur containing *compounds* called glucosinolates present in the vegetative tissues and seeds of cruciferous plants.

The various kinds of glucosinolates present in *B. juncea,* in decreasing order of their *abundance* are gluconapin, sinigrin, progoitrin, *napoleiferin* and *glucobrassicanapin.* At cellular level, glucosinolates are stored in the vacuole and myrosinase, a glycoprotein enzyme responsible for hydrolysis of glucosinolates is stored in a tonoplast-like membrane bound organelle called the idioblast.

On mechanical injury, myrosinase catalyzed hydrolysis of *glucosinolates* occur to form thiocyanates, isothiocyanates and nitriles. Although glucosinolates as such do not cause much harm, their breakdown products are undesirable in animal feeds. These compounds impart a characteristic flavor and odor to Brassica vegetables and condiments but may reduce palatability and adversely affect iodine uptake by the thyroid glands in *non-ruminant* animals such as swine and poultry.

Thus they reduce the feed efficiency in terms of development and weight gain. To avoid *glucosinolate* hydrolysis products to accumulate in Brassica oil meal, the myrosinase enzyme is heat inactivated as one of the first steps in oil extraction process.

However, this in turn also causes the breakdown of other proteins, which may adversely affect the nutritional value of the oil meal quality. In India heat treatment of seed before oil extraction is usually not done, therefore the extracted edible oil has relatively large proportion of *glucosinolates* breakdown products imparting the characteristic pungency in the oil.

In view of these facts, a prime breeding objective for *B. juncea* quality breeders is to develop low glucosinolate varieties. Work in the direction of *glucosinolate* inheritance in Brassicas was started in 1970's and was revolutionised by the discovery of a low glucosinolate *B. napus* cultivar 'Bronowski' from Poland. Since then, this genotype has provided the source of low *glucosinolate* gene for practically all cultivated Brassicas.

Kondra and Stefansson had proposed that in *B. napus* the maternal genotype rather than the embryo genotype controlled seed glucosinolates. They have proposed low glucosinolate level to be controlled by as many as 11 recessive alleles that do not show independent segregation. Rather than linkage to be operative, a *simultaneous* action of genes for a common biosynthetic pathway for synthesis of all glucosinolates has been suggested.

The formation of individual glucosinolates is thought to occur through a chain break at the end of the biosynthetic pathway. Further, Lein has also determined an additional influence of cytoplasm on glucosinolate synthesis. Till date no germplasm source for low *glucosinolate* genes has been reported in *B. juncea*. However, Love et al. developed the low *glucosinolate B. juncea* line BJ-1058 using interspecific *hybridization* between Indian mustard and a low glucosinolate strain of *B. campestris* having the Bronowski gene block.

Glucosinolates also show tissue level variation within the same plant and the leaf glucosinolate quantity and profile can be correlated to the seed *glucosinolate* level only in small seedlings suggesting that the *glucosinolate* content in the leaves and seeds may be under different genetic control.

The glucosinolate profile at the seedling level may serve as a tentative tool to predict glucosinolate profile of seeds, but its authenticity is doubtful since *differentiation* is not clearly understood and may produce *unpredictable* and drastic changes.

There have been some reports indicating that the genes for *glucosinolate* contents in vegetative tissue are pleiotropic or linked with the grain filling stage, and that glucosinolates may contribute towards resistance to insect pests and pathogens.

QUALITY STATUS IN B. JUNCEA

Most of the work related to quality improvement has been globally *concentrated* on *B. napus* and the work on genetic *enhancement* of *B. juncea* quality, the predominant species of Asian subcontinent, is somewhat limited. The facts discussed above suggest that an ideal genotype of mustard from the point of view of nutritional quality would be one having low erucic acid in the seed oil, low levels of glucosinolate in the seed or reproductive tissue and high glucosinolate content in the vegetative tissue.

This may seem to be a mammoth task but it has already been accomplished in *B. napus* and is being extensively researched on for *B. juncea.* Several double low strains/cultivars of *B. napus* are available globally, however, the progress of work to develop double low *B. juncea* has not been very successful as yet, primarily due to the lack of suitable donor germplasm.

Following the successful introgression of low glucosinolate genes, the double low *B. juncea* strains have been developed in Canada through cross breeding of BJ-1058 and LDZ (a zero erucic acid, high oil content *B. juncea* strain). The progeny of this cross was backcrossed to the *B. juncea* var. Cutlass, in order to incorporate white rust resistance genes. This material has shown promising results in field trials, and is being improved for its fatty acid profile.

In India also, attempts have been made to introgress the double low characteristics in various Indian mustard cultivars but the desired success is yet to be achieved and these low erucic/low glucosinolate/double low strains are being improved for agronomic *characteristics*.

CONVENTIONAL APPROACHES FOR DEVELOPMENT OF DOUBLE LOW CULTIVARS

The conventional breeding techniques for quality improvement vary greatly and have evolved from simple mass selection to hybrid cultivar development. The breeding strategies depend on the objective and practical scientific considerations such as inheritance pattern of genes responsible for a particular trait. The *backcrossing* approach has been *successfully* used to transfer simply inherited traits such as low erucic acid.

The erucic acid content of the seed is controlled by the genotype of the embryo, that is, the individual F_2 seeds borne on F1 plants have different erucic acid level. This fact led to the development of the half seed technique. This approach has been used by Kirk and Hurlstone to develop low erucic *B. juncea* lines.

The use of backcross technique for development of low *glucosinolate B. juncea* is limited due to the non-availability of any natural low glucosinolate source and polygenic inheritance, but it has been successfully used for development of low glucosinolate *B. napus*. Both *B. napus and B. juncea* are *predominantly* self-pollinated species and thus the commonly used breeding tool of pedigree selection can be employed for cultivar development.

A clearly defined breeding objective and identified suitable parent is a pre-requisite to start a pedigree selection program. Backcrossing in conjugation with pedigree selection has been used *successfully* for the development of early *maturing* canola quality *B. napus* cultivars in India. Further, modifications in the methods can be done as per available germplasm resources or breeding objectives.

However, due to the involvement of multiple recessive genes, development of double low *B. juncea* by conventional methods alone is proving to be a lengthy process, thus necessitating the need for incorporation of suitable *biotechnological* tools such as doubled haploids production, *mutagenesis* and molecular approaches to *facilitate* the quality *improvement* in a targeted manner.

QUALITY IMPROVEMENT USING DOUBLED HAPLOIDS

The efficient production of doubled haploid plants from anther or *microspore* cultures has become an important new tool for *Brassica* breeders. After initiation of work for this school of thought in late 1970's, efficient protocols to induce *embryogenesis* in isolated microspore cultures of *B. napus* have been reported by several workers.

A promising double low variety of *B. napus* (cyclone) developed through doubled haploid technique using isolated microspore culture, is being commercially cultivated in Canada. Doubled haploids provide several advantages over conventional breeding approaches.

The selection of desired genotypes at F1 haploid level followed by diploidization fixes the desired genes i.e., leads to the production of pure lines that do not segregate further. Hence homozygosity can be achieved in one step equivalent to repeated in-breeding for several generations (8–10 years). Doubled haploids being *homozygous*, also considerably reduce the time required for parental *identification* for *hybridization* programmes. This technique also offers the advantage of significantly smaller population size required to find the least likely recombinants particularly when several genes are involved.

Since both glucosinolates and erucic acid are multiple recessive gene governed traits, doubled haploids offer a powerful tool to reduce the perfect population size to *approximately* 70 to 80 fold than what would be needed to be handled via conventional methods. An integrated approach involving application of doubled haploid *technique* with early selection for high erucic acid in the cotyledons of microspore derived embryos obtained from the F_1 hybrids of winter oilseed rape established a positive correlation in the erucic acid content of embryos and the seeds derived from them, thus *elucidating* the efficiency of selection at microspore embryo stage.

In addition to the complicated inheritance of *glucosinolates*, additional effects of maternal inheritance and cytoplasmic influence on seed glucosinolates have been reported. Since glucosinolates in seed are governed by maternal genotype rather than the seed embryo's genotype, the F_1 seeds would show glucosinolate content as per maternal parent genotype.

This means that effective selection can only be done in F_3 seeds produced by the F_2 population and in order to follow this procedure under field conditions at least 3 years would be required to reach initial screening.

However, the pollen/microspore is not the target site for *glucosinolate* storage and has minimal cytoplasm, therefore seeds produced by the doubled haploids would reflect the genotype of the doubled haploid plant rather than the parent. Moreover, since haploids would express recessive genes, transgressive segregants for recessive traits can efficiently be recovered through *diploidization* of recessive haploids.

QUALITY IMPROVEMENT THROUGH MUTAGENESIS

Mutagens are also being effectively employed to generate considerable variability in fatty acid composition. Chemical *mutagenesis* has been used to produce *B. napus* lines with reduced linolenic and increased linoleic acid contents.

The low linolenic acid lines have been used as genetic base for the development of *B. napus* with less than 3% linolenic acid and more than 22% linoleic acid. Doubled haploid lines of *B. carinata* with modified erucic acid content have also been identified through chemical mutagenesis by EMS treatment of isolated microspores. Mutagens have not only been used to produce variable fatty acid composition but also to substantially increase the oil content.

Kumar et al. have reported an increase in oil content upto 4.55% using gamma irradiation in *B. juncea*. An increase in oleic acid content coupled with decrease in erucic acid was also observed in the treated varieties. Wong and Swanson and Auld et al. recovered high oleic acid producing doubled haploids through chemically induced *mutagenesis* in microspore cultures of *B. napus*. The use of induced mutations for altering fatty acid profile allows for the selection of variants with either complete or incomplete sets of functionally altered genes responsible for fatty acid synthesis.

However, a major limitation of *mutagenesis* is that apart from the genes controlling the target trait, it may cause several changes in the genetic *background* thus affecting the non-target traits. For example, mutants for the high oleic acid content have been shown to be associated with undesirable agronomic *characteristics*.

It is considered likely that several genes code for Δ12 desaturase enzymes (that are responsible for conversion of oleic to linoleic) in *B. napus* seed and that some of these genes also regulate production of Δ12 desaturase in the vegetative tissue. Mutation exposure would lead to non-tissue specific changes in both the seed and vegetative tissue Δ12 desaturase genes, which could have detrimental effects on the vegetative tissue where the correct fatty acid composition is required for normal membrane structure and function.

As discussed above, mutagenesis aims at altering the existing fatty acid profile and does not have the ability to add genes for new biosynthetic pathways for production of novel fatty acids. Although mutagenesis has been fairly successful for *producing genotypes* with altered fatty acid compositions, its non-tissue specific action restricts its use for cultivar development.

Nevertheless, the lines derived from mutation breeding programs serve as important donor material in *forthcoming* crop improvement *programmes*, and the abovementioned bottlenecks can be quite satisfactorily overcome by using the transgenic approach.

QUALITY IMPROVEMENT THROUGH GENETIC ENGINEERING

The potential use of genetic engineering to modify plant seed oil composition has been recognized for a number of years. The oilseed crops have the potential to produce high quality edible oils as well as speciality oils having commercial applications.

For instance jojoba is a rich source of wax esters, coconut is rich in capric, lauric and myristic fatty acid, palm has a high *proportion* of palmitic, oleic and stearic acid, whereas linseed is a rich source of linoleic acid. These fatty acids are used in a wide range of products ranging from the production of soaps, detergents, *cosmetics*, surfactants, lubricants, plastics, varnishes and *pharmaceuticals*.

Due to the nondomestication of most of the potential sources and their restricted availability, at present the fatty acids for industrial applications are mostly derived from petrochemicals. However, in the near future, with the biased use of global reserves of fossil derived hydrocarbons *alternative* sources of industrial fatty acids from the *environment* friendly oil crops are sought after.

This can be achieved either by altering the existing fatty acids profile or by adding new genes for synthesis of novel fatty acids. In most of the oil bearing crops, the biosynthetic pathway of fatty acid synthesis is similar and their differential accumulation in the seed is genetically controlled depending upon the species.

During the seed development process, photosynthetically fixed carbon is imported into the seed in the form of sucrose, and is converted into the storage products with the help of *enzymes* present in the seed. The seed contains all the enzymes that are required for the conversion of sucrose into any of the storage products.

However, it is the rate of sucrose uptake by the various *biosynthetic* pathways that lead to the differential accumulation of a particular storage product in the seed. Thus the genetic *manipulation* of any of the biosynthetic pathway can lead to a specific ratio of seed storage product, according to the end use of the seed.

This can be done either by modifying the length of the existing hydrocarbons in fatty acid chain (modifying the chain elongation enzymes) or by changing the position of double bonds (modifying desaturase enzymes). The seed specific or tissue specific genetic modifications may be used for creating changes in endogenous fatty acid *biosynthesis* pathway or addition of new biosynthetic pathways.

The use of seed specific antisense *technology* has allowed for the selective *modulation* of key enzyme activities in the developing seed, while keeping the rest of the genetic background of the plant absolutely constant. Co-suppression based on post-transcriptional gene silencing of endogenous desaturase gene has shown promising results in developing high oleic acid genotypes of *rapeseedmustard*.

The recently derived RNAi approach has also shown a great potential for endogenous desaturase silencing. Using this concept total silencing of the Δ12 desaturase gene in *B. napus* has been acheived, resulting in the production of genotypes *accumulating* 89% oleic acid in the seed oil. The rapeseed oil normally contains low levels of lauric acid (C12) and stearic acid (C18) at a *concentration* of 1-2% and 0.1-0.2%, respectively.

High lauric rapeseed can be used as a substitute in detergent markets, leading to displacement of conventional lauric oils derived from coconut or palm kernel, whereas high stearic rapeseed is a useful substitute in *margarine* markets and replaces *conventional* hydrogenated rapeseed oil.

The two most notable achievements in oil modification to-date are the 40% stearic and 40% lauric rapeseed varieties (laurical) first produced and entered in field trials by Calgene in 1993-94. Thus laurical was the first genetically *manipulated* rapeseed variety given permission for commercial cultivation in 1995 in US.

The Δ9 stearoyl ACP desaturase gene which normally converts stearic to oleic acid was partially inactivated in rapeseed using antisense technology, resulting in the *accumulation* of a seed oil containing up to 40% stearic acid. This high stearic variety contains an antisense copy of a *Brassica* stearate desaturase gene which inhibits the function of the normal rapeseed stearic desaturase gene, resulting in an *accumulation* of stearic acid, rather than their saturation to oleate.

The resulting high stearic oil has many advantages over the normal rapeseed oil for the production of certain solid fats, such as margarines. With the advent of transgenic technology, the genes coding for enzymes that *synthesize* industrially important fatty acids can be transferred from non-traditional crops into more important oil crops.

The canola oil having low erucic acid has food applications in margarine, salad and salad dressings while the high erucic rapeseed has industrial application. The canola quality rapeseed has also been *genetically* modified for containing high levels of β-carotene.

This high carotenoid canola oil may prove very beneficial to combat the vitamin A deficiency in developing world. Various species of Brassicaceae have been *transformed* with mutated Sn-2 acyltransferase gene from yeast and have been reported to show increase in seed oil content, seed weight and erucic acid content. Lauric oils are mainly used in soaps and detergents although their use in confectionary fats and milk formulas is also being investigated.

Lauric acid which is present at *insignificant* levels in rapeseed is found at high levels in the seed oil of the California Bay plant, *Umbelluria californica,* due to the presence in the latter species of a lauryo-ACP thioesterase. This gene has been cloned from the Bay plant and inserted into rapeseed causing premature chain-termination, resulting in a novel variety with a seed oil containing almost 25% lauric acid.

Following this an Sn-2 acyl transferase gene (LPAAT) from coconut has been introduced in lauric rapeseed to increase the accumulation of lauric acid in the seed triacyl glycerol molecules.

Similar to the development of lauric acid producing rapeseed, several novel genes coding for altered fatty acid synthesis have been used for altering seed fatty acid profile.

Some worthy examples are Caprilic and Capric acid (from *Cuphea* spp.), myristic acid (from *Myristica fragrans)*, Crepenylic acid (from *Crepis alpira)*, Richinolic acid (from Castor), Vernolic acid (from *Crepis palaestina)* and petroselenic acid (from *Coriandrum sativum)*. Thus, in future, plant derived oils may be an important source of industrial oil derived chemical or oleo chemicals.

CONCLUSION

Genetic *enhancement* for *improvement* in the quality of rapeseed-mustard is a prime breeding target for *Brassica* breeders all over the world. In addition to being the second most important edible oilseed crop in India, the rapeseed-mustard oil also finds its use in industrial applications.

The advent of biotechnology has provided the plant breeders with new and more accurate tools that have the ability to compress the time taken in directed evolution of crop species. Efforts towards developing improved quality rapeseed varieties have been consolidated and expedited at global level through the use of biotechnological techniques such as doubled haploid and mutagenesis in *conjugation* with the *conventional* methods.

The advances in molecular approaches, the genetic engineering and *transformation*, has made it possible to develop many designer rapeseed varieties with specific fatty acids profile for edible and industrial purposes.

The work is in progress towards such quality *improvement* in Indian mustard, *B. juncea* also. Such targeted value addition in the quality of oilseed Brassicas will not only provide for an improved source of human nutrition but also for non-food, fuel/non-fuel industrial products that could reduce the load on ever depleting natural oil and gas resources.

Chapter 14

IMPROVING WHITE RUST RESISTANCE

Oleiferous Brassicas are the important cash crops of India and stands second only to groundnut among the nine annual oilseeds being cultivated. It contributes 27 and 25.3% to the total oilseed *production* and *hectarage, respectively,* and is cultivated in about 6.81 million ha with 6.96 m tons production of oilseed.

The productivity level of 1022 kg ha^{-1} is far below that of the developed countries (2500–3000 kg/ha) and the world average of 1500 kg/ha (*Economic* Survey, 2000–2001, GOI). This is mainly due to certain abiotic and biotic factors that adversely influence the average yield of cultivated varieities. Amongst the abiotic factors, drought, frost and salinity are a major cause of concern since they may cause yield losses to the magnitude of 20–70%.

The important biotic factors are weeds and insects-pests causing 17–41% and upto 60% loss, respectively, whereas fungal diseases alone can cause major damage to the crop contributing to a yield loss of upto 70% under favourable conditions for the disease infestation. The fungal diseases that attack Brassica species in India throughout the cultivated areas include *Alternaria* blight caused by *Alternaria brassicae and Alternaria brassicicola,* white rust caused by *Albugo candida* and Downy mildew caused by *Peronospora parasitica.*

The other diseases that attack Brassicas, but are distributed more commonly in the temperate regions include sclerotinia stem rot caused by *Sclerotinia sclerotiorum,* blackleg by *Leptosphaeria maculans,* club root by *Plasmodiophora brassicae* and powdery mildew caused by *Erysiphe cruciferarum.* Among the abovementioned fungal diseases white rust has emerged as a major limiting factor in production of Brassicas causing a loss of 17–34% which may reach upto 60% depending upon the severity of infection and environmental conditions. In addition, Downy mildew that alone does not cause much of damage, when combined with white rust causes synergistic damage resulting upto 35% yield loss. *B. juncea,* the most predominantly grown Brassica species in India, is highly susceptible to white rust disease.

Although *B. nigra, B. oleracea, B. napus, B. carinata and* some species of *B. campestris* have been reported to be comparatively tolerant to this disease, adequate amount of resistance is not available in cultivated Brassica species.

This article discusses the white rust disease in terms of its symptoms, effect on plant system, its *physiology*, inheritance, available sources of resistance along with the biotechniques utilized to achieve the adequate amount of resistance in Brassicas.

WHITE RUST

Symptoms

White rust caused by fungal pathogen *Albugo candida* (Pers.) Kunzee belonging to family Albuginacae appears in almost all rapeseed mustard growing states of India. *A. candida can* infect all above ground parts of the plant, *producing* characteristic white blisters known as sori.

The fungal pathogen attacks the plant at both vegetative and reproductive phase. In the vegetative phase the fungal pathogen infects leaves and cotyledons causing local infection resulting in the appearance of white to creamy yellow pustules on the abaxial (lower) surface corresponding to tan yellow pustules on the adaxial (upper) surface of the leaves such that disease can be easily *recognized* from the upper surface of the affected leaves.

The pustules rupture after maturity and release white coloured dust of spores known as sporangia. With the increase in duration of disease, tissues around the pustules become necrotic and lead to senescence of leaves. At the flowering stage the fungus causes systemic infection, leading to *extensive* distortion, hypertrophy, *hyperplasia* and sterility resulting in severe inflorescence malformation known as staghead.

This leads to early foliar infection and *abnormalities* in *reproductive* organs leading to complete sterility. This systemic staghead infection of the inflorescence is often in association with *Peronospora parasitica.* However in a recent report it has been *elucidated* that the inflorescence *malformation* in *B. juncea* is due to *A. candida* and not because of *P. parasitica.*

Effect on Plant

White rust has a significant impact on the yield and quality of seeds. It also has a profound effect on important end *products* such as total oil content, fatty acid *composition* and seed protein content. The fungal infection tends to decrease dry matter, and increase erucic acid.

High proportion of erucic acid is reported to cause impaired myocardial conductance and increased blood cholesterol and is thus *nutritionally* undesirable. A positive correlation exists between the amount of chlorophyll, sugars, flavonoids, waxy deposition on leaves, total phenols and the extent of infection by *Albugo candida.*

The moderately resistant cultivars contain higher amount of the abovementioned biochemicals

Table 1. Various pathotypes of white rust and their specific host species

White Rust Pathotypes	*Host Species*
Race 1	*Raphanus sativus*
Race 2	*Brassica juncea*
Race 3	*Armoracia rusticana*
Race 4	*Capsella bursa pastoris*
Race 5	*Sisymbium off cinale*
Race 6	*Rorrippa islandica*
Race 7	*Brassica campestris*
Race 8	*Brassica nigra*
Race 9	*Brassica oleracea*
Race 10	*Sinapis alba*
Race 11	*Brassica carinata*
Race 12	*Brassica juncea* (Indian isolates)
Race 13	*Brassica campestris var. toria*

than the susceptible cultivars at all stages of growth. Phenols, in particular, have been reported to impart resistance whereas more proteins led to higher disease severity. Thus, white rust *infection* not only damages the plant *morphology* but also disrupts its physiological metabolism.

Biology of the Fungus

The biggest challenge in breeding white rust resistant brassicas is in the fact that as many as 13 pathotypes of *Albugo* parasitize different *cruciferous* plant species. Besides infecting cruciferous plant species, *Albugo* also finds its host in several wild species of different families such *as Portulacaceae, Chenopodiaceae, Amaranthaceae, Convolvulaceae, Boraginaceae* to name a few.

The white rust races are classified based upon their ability to infest different host species. The different races that infect Brassica species are given in Table elsewhere in this chapter. However, these races at times, may not retain their species specificity and can also attack the related species, i.e. host specificity in *Albugo candida* is not an absolute adaptation to a particular species especially when the races are from hosts sharing a common genome.

Inheritance of Resistance

The information on the genetics of host parasite interaction for white rust has centered on the level of specificity between the races of pathogen and genotypes of related host species. Genetic analysis of available white rust resistance through biometrical techniques has elucidated a digenic mode of inheritance with duplicate gene action in *B. napus* and monogenic dominant resistance in *B. juncea*. Cheung et al and Prabhu et al. have confirmed this through gene mapping.

The white rust resistance in the three Brassica species, *B. campestris, B. nigra and B. carinata,* is reported to be under the control of a single dominant gene. It is suggested that a few major genes in *Brassica* are responsible to initiate the disease resistance whereas other minor genes may be involved in the control of the intensity of sporulation of the fungus in the plant.

However, additive genetic variations were also found to be predominant for the intensity of white rust resistance and thus differential expressions have been obtained.

Sources of Resistance

The traits for resistance to white rust are found to be present in some species of Brassica as well as in related weedy and wild speices. Among the various *Brassica* species grown in India, *B. napus* and most cultivars of *B. oleracea*, some species of *B. campestris and B. carinata* have been reported to exhibit moderate resistance and thus utilized as a source of resistance to white rust.

Recently moderate resistance has also been found in *B. tournefortii* and in certain species of related genus *Diplotaxis and Sinapis alba. Eruca sativa has* been identified as a potential source of white rust resistance and all the accessions of this genera are reported to be resistant to race 2 that attacks *B. juncea.*

DISEASE CONTROL STRATEGIES

The different strategies adopted to control plant diseases include non-chemical and chemical control. The non-chemical control includes hot water treatment and biological control. The chemical control, though found to be effective, results in *development* of resistance in the pathogens and residual *toxicity*, thus having detrimental effect on non-target species. Besides this, the fungicide sprays affect crop *physiology* independent of disease occurrence.

These may decrease the triacylglycerol fraction of the oil and increase the *diacylglycerol* fraction, thus affecting the oil quality. Owing to the *abovementioned* problems associated with chemical control, focus has been to develop new biotechnological techniques for crop *protection* and production.

An upcoming alternative approach to crop *protection* is the use of externally applied biotic and abiotic stress inducers that activate plant's natural defence mechanism.

They create a *hypersensitive* response in the plant thus leading to systemic acquired resistance. For instance, actigard, an isonicotinic acid derivative identified by Syngenta has been recently *commercially* utilized to prevent downy mildew on spinach.

Under such biological stresses, plant synthesize a variety of compounds that include phytoalexins and *pathogenesis-related proteins.*

However, work in this direction is still in infancy and commercial products are yet to be realized on a large scale. Among the biological approaches, *exploitation* of genetic resistance, present in the existing plant species for its incorporation in the cultivated varieties, is seen as the *eco-friendly* and environmentally safe approach.

This includes sexual hybridization, wide *hybridization*, somatic *hybridization*, somaclonal variations and genetic engineering. The possibility of using these biotechniques to enhance the scope and efficiency of transfer of desired traits with special emphasis on white rust for improvement of crop Brassicas are briefly discussed.

Selection and Hybridization

Several germplasm lines and popular cultivars have been screened for white rust resistance and varying degree of response to *A. candida has* been reported in *B. juncea*. However, it was found that the selected lines are not stable for the trait, and breakdown of resistance occurs in successive years.

The breakdown of resistance may be due to mutations in the existing pathotypes leading to new pathotypes. This indicates that there is a continuous need to expand the genetic base for white rust resistance. Intervarietal transfer of disease *resistance* has been attempted and resistant F_2 generation plants have been selected by Chauhan et al..

However, response of the plants to pathogen is yet to be studied under field conditions. *B. juncea* cultivars have also been *hybridized* with other species of *Brassica* such as *B. napus* and advanced progenies of the cross were identified to possess similar degree of response to white rust as the resistant donor.

B. carinata has also been utilized for transfer of disease resistance in *B. juncea* and moderate disease tolerance was observed in the hybrids. However, *Ba juncea* accessions having *resistance* to white rust are under *different* stages of development.

Wide Hybridization

Genes conferring resistance to biotic and abiotic stress are frequently scattered in weedy and widely related species that can be used for the incorporation of resistance in cultivated varieties. However, majority of these belong to *secondary* and tertiary gene pools.

Their exploitation is problematic because of the difficulties in obtaining hybrids and subsequent gene transfer in desirable genetic *background* due to pre- and post-fertilization barriers.

Pre-fertilization considerations include spatial separation, asynchrony of flowering, pollination system, floral characteristics and competitiveness of pollen whereas post-fertilization considerations include genetic/sexual *compatibility*, hybrid viability, fertility of progeny and successful introgression.

For successful gene introgression all pre- and post-fertilization requirements must be met, failure of any one requirement will lead to non-introgression of the gene, and thus would not produce the desirable results.

A large number of interspecific and intergeneric sexual hybrids have been produced using *in vitro* techniques to study the *compatability* barriers that exists between the species.

These techniques have been scantily utilized in Brassicas for transfer of disease resistance traits, however, there are a few reports for transfer of *Alternaria* blight resistance.

Chevre et al generated hybrids between *B. napus* and *S. alba* through ovary culture to transfer resistant traits for *Alternaria* blight. Similar study was made utilizing *B. campestris and B. spinenscens* through sequential embryo rescue technique by Agnihotri et al..

However, *Alternaria blight resistant* genotypes are yet to be realized and only a preliminary report by Gupta and Agnihotri is available for transfer of resistance to white rust in *Brassica* species utilizing this technique.

Somatic Hybridization

Somatic hybridization involves enzymatic removal of the cell wall and the resulting spherical protoplasts are fused together. Fusion of *protoplasts* at the level of plasma membrane is *nonspecific*, and there is no barrier to interspecific, intergeneric or even intertribal fusion of cells.

The resulting hybrid cells are cultured and subsequently regenerated to give rise to somatic hybrids. The use of this technique can bypass both pre- and post-fertilization barriers. Among the cultivated *Brassica* species, the main focus so far has been on *B. napus and B. oleracea* and this technique has not been utilized effectively in other *Brassica* species.

Attempts have been made to transfer resistance traits to some fungal diseases in Brassicas through somatic hybridization such *as Leptosphaeria maculans* (Black leg) in *B. napus and B. olearacea; Plasmodiophora brassicae* in *B. napus and B. oleracea; Alternaria* blight in *B. napus and B. oleracea*. Therefore, as apparent several studies have been undertaken to transfer black leg, downy mildew *and Alternaria* blight disease resistance, mainly in *B. napus and B. oleracea*, and only a few reports are available for transfer of white rust resistance in *B. oleracea and B. juncea*.

However, in both the cases the somatic hybrids obtained were sterile and could not be utilized further. Hence, production of hybrids that are either sterile or do not survive, mainly due to meiotic irregularities, is the major drawback of this technique.

Somaclonal Variation

Somaclonal variation, regarded as the spontaneous epigenetic variations that occur *in vitro*, have been a source of genetic variation suitable for crop improvement. Somaclonal variations have been utilized for many abiotic stress resistance traits, however, it has been scantily used for disease resistance.

Somaclones have been selected for salt tolerance, high yield and for transfer of *Alternaria* blight disease resistance in *B. juncea*. So far only one study has been published for resistance to white rust in *B. juncea* through *generation* of somaclones, reporting a stable and heritable resistance till R_2 generation in the field.

Molecular Techniques

Recent developments in DNA marker technology has led to a better understanding of the complex genome of various crop plants. Molecular markers that are tightly linked to the trait of interest, besides helping in identifying the desired species at any growth stage of the plant, also helps to select for the trait under strict quarantine laws.

However, even then the crop plants have to be tested for virulence against the pathogen to confirm the effectiveness of the marker *associated* with the resistant gene. Marker assisted selection, or MAS as it is *commonly* known, has been successfully utilized in identifying oil quality in *B. napus and B. campestris*, seed coat colour in *B. napus* and *B. juncea*, and for fungal disease *Leptosphaeria maculans* in *B. napus*. Work is in progress to identify the genes *responsible* for resistance to white rust for use in molecular assisted selection.

In *B. juncea*, resistance to white rust race 2 was observed to be controlled by a single dominant allele. With the help of restriction fragment length *polymorphism* (RFLP) a locus Acr and Ac21 have been *identified* in *B. juncea*. Recently, flanking markers have been identified for a white rust resistant locus, AcAl in *B. napus* and in *B. campestris,* and Ac2t in a Polish *Ba juncea* accession.

Similarly, 3 genes namely Ac71, Ac72 and Ac73 have been identified for resistance to white rust race 7 in *B. campestris.* However, the use of these markers in molecular assisted selection has not been successful as yet mainly because of their specificity to their respective host species. Work has been undertaken to identify the molecular markers that could be used in precise and efficient screening.

Two markers, WR2 and WR3 and OPNO11000 and OPBO61000 linked to white rust resistance have been identified which flank the resistant locus. Prabhu et al. have reported that although these markers were effective in *identifying* the presence or absence of the resistance gene in the population of the cultivars, these are specific to the Russian source of white rust resistance.

Work is in progress to study the *mechanism* of resistance response and mapping of the loci responsible for resistance to white rust. Although, a few *markers* linked to white rust resistance locus have been identified in some species of Brassica, work has to be *consolidated* to employ these markers in routine marker-assisted selection for efficient utilization.

Furthermore, the focus has now been shifted from identifying trait linked markers to the mapping of the genes to utilize them more efficiently in developing new cultivars. During the past decade, different strategies have been used to produce *transgenic* plants that are less susceptible to disease caused by *phytopathogenic* fungi and bacteria.

For achieving transgene derived resistance, genes from organisms other than plants and endogenous plant genes have been utilized. The basic concept of utilizing these genes revolves around induction of *systematically* acquired resistance *utilizing* transgene mediated production of *pathogenesis* related (PR) proteins.

Almost 14 distinct PR-protein groups have been identified from different plants and have been utilized for transgene mediated production of PRproteins. This technique has been successfully utilized in cereals. However, transgene mediated resistance for white rust has not been exploited in crop Brassicas because of poor understanding of pathogenesis related proteins and their role in trigerring systematically acquired resistance towards *Albugo candida.*

CONCLUSION

Oilseed Brassicas contribute to about 30% of the edible oilseeds being produced in India. However, in spite of the horizontal increase in the area and production, vertical increase in productivity per unit area has remained far below the yield potential of presently cultivated varieties.

This is mainly due to various abiotic and biotic stresses, fungal diseases being one of them. The major fungal diseases affecting oilseed Brassicas are *Alternaria* blight, white rust and downy mildew, which together cause severe yield losses under environmental conditions favouring disease infestation.

White rust caused by *Albugo candida* is reported to be under the control of digenic inheritance with duplicate gene action in *B. napus* and monogenic dominant resistance in *B. juncea.* Upto 13 races of *Albugo candida* affecting different *Brassica* species have been reported that are host specific.

Strategies for controlling white rust have mainly focussed on development of disease resistant cultivars, exploiting the resistance available within crop species and also utilizing the modern biotechnological tools to tap resistance from secondary or tertiary gene pool.

Utilization of resistance genes from wide species has been a promising proposition since some of the widely related species of crop Brassicas such *as Eruca sativa,* species of *Diplotaxis and B. tournefortii* have been reported to have resistance/tolerance to white rust.

These sources of resistance have been utilized by various scientists for introgression of resistance genes in the cultivated varieties. Some work has also been undertaken to identify and clone the resistance genes and develop molecular markers for precise selection. Systematic *characterization* of the Indian gene pool of Brassicas and its related species for identification of white rust resistant genes is important and work in this direction is being pursued at *various* national and *international* institutions.

Utilization of these genes through the use of *biotechnological* tools will help in *expediting* the development of varieties having resistance to white rust.

IMPROVING TROPICAL FRUIT TREES

Commercial cultivation of fruits is still in infancy and even at present the yield of fruits in most cases remains low and are not within the means of working classes of the developing world. Many tropical fruits remain under utilized due to the complex *circumstances* that *encompass* their production and marketing.

Moreover, the green revolution could make a relatively little impact on fruit cultivar development. Increase in fruit production can be achieved by advances in *horticultural* practices, post harvest *handling* and disease and pest control. Conventional *propagation* methods, i.e. grafting, air layering and removal of suckers, for improving the tropical fruit crop trees already exist for many important tropical fruits but the long juvenile period has made these *techniques* time *consuming* and cumbersome.

Clonal propagation and selection of fruit crops using tissue and organ culture *techniques* have considerable potential for the improvement of *economically* important fruit trees that have been under *cultivation* for many generations. Improvement of plant quality and yield by cell *manipulation* through the sophisticated methods of genetic engineering has to rely on tissue culture for the final product.

Generation of new variability through somaclonal variant selection, production of *androgenic* and gynogenic haploids to achieve *homozygosity*, rapid fixation of specific traits in hybrids, freeing plants from disease causing organisms by shoot tip culture and production of industrial compounds by cell culture are some well-known applications of plant tissue culture.

Tissue culture technique and other biotechnological intervention have proved fairly successful and could be commercialised for some temperate fruit crops. However, due to difficulty in controlling normal somatic embryo development and achieving high rates of their germination the progress in the application of tissue culture for clonal *multiplication* of tropical fruit trees and *biotechnological* tools has been rather slow.

The purpose of this review is to present the current status of *in vitro* regeneration and improvement of tropical fruit trees.

IN VITRO REGENERATION OF TROPICAL FRUIT TREES

One of the earliest attempts to regenerate tropical fruit trees through *in vitro* culture technique was made by Maheshwari and Rangaswamy. Subsequently, several species of tropical fruits have been regenerated through the process of organogenesis as well as somatic embryogenesis.

Organogenesis involves adventitious and axillary shoot production. The adventitious shoot production comprises *de novo* shoot meristem formation from callus tissue or directly from organized tissues such as epidermal or subepidermal cells. The axillary shoot production involves shoot formation from axillary buds, shoot tips and meristems.

The regenerated shoots are excised and used to produce additional shoots. The axillary shoot production is a direct method involving multiplication of preformed buds, usually without any callus formation and produces in general, genetically stable cultures.

It produces the smallest number of plants, since the number of shoots produced is limited by the number of axillary buds placed in culture. Although the initial multiplication rate is low, it increases during the first few *subcultures* and eventually reaches a steady state, which may be maintained through numerous subcultures. Somatic embryogenesis is the process in which structures are formed containing a shoot and root *connected* by a closed vascular system (directly analogous to zygotic embryos).

REGENERATION VIA ORGANOGENESIS

The main factors that influence the mode and rate of *in vitro* regeneration are the nature of explant, composition of the medium and the physical conditions in which the cultures grow. Organogenesis has been induced *in vitro* both from seedlings and mature tree explants.

Adventitious shoots have arisen directly from internode segments without a callus phase in *Citrus*. Direct shoot organogenesis and plant *regeneration* have also been reported from seedling leaf explants of *Annona squamosa and Garcinia mangostana* and from hypocotyl and seedling petioles of *A. cherimola.*

Adventitious shoots have differentiated following callus initiation and proliferation in *Citrus.* New vegetative growth that occurs from the base of the main stem during the period of vigorous vegetative growth in guava serves as a reliable source of shoot tip and nodal explants.

Papayas have been decapitated in order to stimulate lateral *branching* and to increase the number of explants from stock plants. Shoot tip culture is the basic technique for *Musa* propagation. It has been successfully applied to the rapid propagation of AA and AAA bananas, cooking ABB

Table 15.1: In vitro regeneration of tropical fruit trees: Organogenesis

Species	*Explant*	*Mature/ Juvenile*	*Medium*	*Growth Regulator*
Annona cherimola	H, P	J	MS	NAA, BA
Annona squamosa	L	J	MS	BA
Annona squamosa	H	J	WPM	BA, NAA, IBA
Artocarpus heterophyllus	ST	M	MS	BA, KIN, NAA
Carica papaya	S	J	MS	KIN, IAA
Carica papaya	C	J	MS	BA, NAA
Carica papaya	N	J	MS	BA, KIN, IBA, NAA
Carica papaya	L, P, S, R	M	MS	BA, IBA
Citrus acida	Ep	J	MS	BA, NAA, IAA, 2, 4–D, GA_3
Citrus aurantifolia	S, R	J	MS	BA
C. aurantium	S	J, M	MS	NAA, KIN
C. grandis	S, L	J	MS	NAA, BA
C. grandis	S, T	J	MS	BA, TDZ, NAA, GA_3
C. halimii	H	J	MS	BA, NAA
C. jambhiri	S, R	J	MS	BA, KIN, NAA
C. limetoides	S	J	MS	NAA, KIN
Citrus limon	S	J, M	MS	NAA, BA
Citrus limon	S, R	J	MS	BA, KIN, NAA,
C. madurensis	S	—	MS	BA, NAA
C. paradisi	S, L	MS	MS	BA, NAA
C. reticulata	S	J,M	MS	NAA, KIN
C. reticulata	ST	M	MS	BA, KIN NAA, IBA
C. sinensis	S, L	M	MS	BA, NAA
C. sinensis	S	J, M	MS	BA, IBA
Citrus sinensis × Poncirus trifoliata	S	J, M	MS	BA
C. sinensis × P. trifoliata	R	J, M	MS	BA, 2, 4-D
Garcinia mangostana	L, C	J, M	MS	BA
Garcinia mangostana	L	M	WPM	BA, IBA
Garcinia mangostana	L	J, M	*	BA, auxin
Garcinia mangostana	Seed	—	MS	BA, NAA
Garcinia mangostana	L	J	MS,	WPM BA, TDZ, NAA

(Table Contd.)

Species	Explant	Mature/ Juvenile	Medium	Growth Regulator
Litchi chinensis	Seed C	J	MS	BA, IBA
Mangifera indica	L	M	MS	KIN, IAA, IBA
Poncirus trifoliata	ST	M	MS	BA, IBA
Psidium guajava	ST	M	MS	BA, NAA, IBA
Psidium guajava	N	M	MS	BA, NAA, IBA
Psidium guajava	N	M	MS	BA, NAA, IBA
Psidium guajava	N	J	MS	BA
Psidium guajava	ST	J	MS	BA, NAA, IBA
Psidium guajava	Seedling	J	MS	
Psidium guajava	S	M	MS	BA, NAA, IBA
Musa	ST	—	MS, Knop's	BA, NA
Syzygium cumini	ST, N	J	MS	BA, BAA, IBA

bananas and to a limited extent to AAB plantains and 'Silk' and 'Pome' AAB dessert bananas. Organogenesis of tropical fruit species have generally been based on MS medium.

In a few cases (mangosteen, *Musa)* other media have been used for optimum morphogenesis. In most studies callus initiation and shoot induction have been reported on the same medium which contains cytokinin, BA or a cytokinin together with an auxin.

A high cytokinin to auxin ratio favours caulogenesis. Occasionally, shoot formation can occur following subculture of callus initiated on a medium with either a high auxin to cytokinin ratio, or high cytokinin to auxin ratio, or with cytokinin alone. Usually, the auxin, NAA has been preferred for its synergistic effect on shoot induction. Some tropical fruit trees which have been regenerated via organogenesis have been listed in Table elsewhere in this chapter.

Regeneration via Somatic Embryogenesis

Somatic embryogenesis has several distinct advantages over organogenesis. In woody species somatic embryogenesis is achieved less frequently than other methods of regeneration.

However, most of the tropical fruit trees have been regenerated via somatic embryogenesis. Among the tropical fruit trees *in vitro* somatic embryogenesis was first reported in *Citrus*. The initial attempt on induction of somatic *embryogenesis* in *Citrus was* made by Stevenson.

Later on, Maheshwari and Rangaswamy reported the induction of somatic embryogenesis in *Citrus* by showing the formation of *subcuticular* globular proembryos from nucellus explants. Since then, the list of species has been extended and numerous *publications* have appeared on the initiation of somatic embryogenesis (both direct and indirect) using diverse explants. Among the different explants used to induce somatic *embryogenesis* in tropical fruit trees, nucellus has been the most appropriate.

Somatic *embryogenesis* has been induced directly in cultured nucelli of *Citrus* and indirectly in mango and papaya. Immature *zygotic* embryo has also proved to be regenerable tissue for

Table 12.2: In vitro regeneration of tropical fruit trees: Somatic embryogenesis

Species	Explant	Mature/ Juvenile	Medium	Growth Regulator
Carica papaya	S	J	MS	KIN, IAA
Carica papaya	ZE	J	MS	2, 4–D, KIN
Carica papaya	Protoplasts isolated somatic embryos	J		
Carica papaya	P	J	MS	2, 4-D, BA
Carica papaya	H	J	MS	2, 4-D, IBA
Carica papaya	H	J	MS	2, 4-D, ABA
C. papaya × C. cauliflora	ZE	J	MS	BA, ABA
Citrus aurantifolia	Nu	M	MS	IAA, KIN, GA_3
Citrus aurantium	Nu	M	MT	
Citrus clementina	Nu	M	MS	
Citrus grandis	Nu	M	MS	
Citrus jambhiri	Nu	M	MT	
Citrus limon	Nu	M	MS	
Citrus limon	In (style)	M	MS	BA, NAA
Citrus limon	ST	M	MS	BA, KIN, NAA, IBA
Citrus limon	Nu	M	MS	–
Citrus microcarpa	Nu	M	W	–
Citrus nobilis	Nu	M	MT	–
Citrus paradisi	Nu	M	MT	–
Citrus reticulata	Nu	M	W	–
Citrus reticulata	ST	M	MS	BA, KIN, NAA, IBA
Citrus reticulata	L, E, C, R	M	MS	KIN, NAA
Citrus sinensis	Nu	M	MS	–
Citrus sinensis	Nu	M	MS	–
C. unshiu	Juice vesicle	M	MS	KIN, GA, NAA
Cocos nucifera	Inf	M	MS	2, 4-D, BA, zip
Cocos nucifera	Inf	M		
Eugenia spp.	ZE	M	MS	2,4-D
Euphoria longan	L	M	B5	2, 4-D, KIN
Eriobotrya japonica	Nu	M	MS	2, 4-D, BA

(Table Contd.)

Species	Explant	Mature/ Juvenile	Medium	Growth Regulator
Feijoa sellowiana	ZE	J	MS	2, 4-D, KIN
Mangifera indica	Nu, ZE	M, J	MS	2, 4-D
Mangifera indica	Nu	M	MS, B5	2,4-D, KIN
Mangifera indica	Nu	M	MS, B5	BAP, 2, 4–D GA_3
Mangifera indica	Nu, ZE	M, J	MS, B5	2, 4-D, GA_3
Mangifera indica	Nu	M	MS, B5	2, 4-D, GA_3
Mangifera indica	Protoplasts isolated from pro embryo-genic masses	J	MS, B5	2, 4-D, NAA, KIN GA3
Musa (AAA, ABB)	Rh, Basal Sheath	M	SH, MS	Dicamba, Zea
Myrciaria cauliflora	Nu	M	MS	2,4-D

many species. The culture of zygotic embryo is a relatively easy *in vitro* procedure. Embryo culture has been used to multiply *Litchi* which is one of the most recalcitrant tropical fruit species. Somatic embryogenesis is reported to follow two different patterns. In the first, embryogenesis proceeds from the cells that are embryogenic in origin and in the second, embryogenesis is induced in highly *differentiated* tissues such as leaf, stem, nucellus and inflorescence. Embryogenesis from *proembryogenic* determined cells (PEDC) requires only *an in vitro* environment to follow the requisite pattern of cell division.

Since mature tissues are highly *differentiated* than those of proembryos, embryogenesis from the former tissues proceeds via the other route described by Sharp et al., i.e. through induced embryogenic determined cells (IEDC). These highly *differentiated* tissues must undergo major epigenetic changes to initiate somatic embryogenesis. Therefore, IEDC requires *an in vitro environment* initially to dedifferentiate and then to *redifferentiate* quiescent cells to an *embryogenic* state.

Direct and indirect embryogenesis, are two additional terms used to describe PEDC and IEDC embryogenesis respectively. A number of media have been used for the induction of embryogenic cultures. However, most of the *successful* reports are based on Murashige and Skoog's (MS) medium.

The effect of medium composition and strength on induction of somatic *embryogenesis* has been demonstrated in some species, e.g. *Citrus,* papaya and mango. Generally, embryogenic callus has been obtained following explanting onto the medium containing 2,4-D or other synthetic auxins, like dicamba, NAA, etc..

The requirement of exogenous auxin for the induction of somatic embryogenesis depends on the nature of the explant used. Although cytokinins have sometimes been incorporated into the induction medium, they are probably not critical for induction. But, in a few cases, e.g. in longan, induction of embryogenic callus has been shown to be cytokinin-dependent. Nitrogen in the form of glutamine has been shown to be essential for somatic embryogenesis in mango. Addition of *polyamines* to the culture media promoted somatic *embryogenesis* in coconut and papaya.

The complex organic nutrients such as coconut water, casein hydrolysate, malt extract, etc., have also been used in the induction medium for some species. Sucrose is the commonly used carbon source and a relatively high concentration of sucrose (5–6%) is optimum for somatic *embryogenesis* in guava, *Citrus,* mango and longan. In addition to culture medium and explants, different genotypes of a species influence the ability of somatic *embryogenesis*.

Among the tropical fruit trees, regeneration of viable plantlets from somatic embryos is a more frequently encountered problem than the production of somatic embryos from somatic *embryogenesis*. The problem may occur at any stage of *development* like maturation, *germination*, shoot apex elongation or *acclimatization*.

Although somatic embryogenesis has been reported for several tropical fruit tree species, the quality of somatic embryos with regard to their *germinability* or *conversion* into plants has been very poor This is because the apparently normal looking somatic embryos are actually incomplete in their development.

Unlike seed embryos, the somatic embryos normally do not go through the final phase of *embryogenesis* called 'embryo maturation' which is *characterised* by the accumulation of embryo specific reserve food materials and proteins which impart desiccation *tolerance* to the embryos.

Abscisic acid (ABA) which prevents precocious germination and promotes normal development of embryos by suppression of secondary embryogenesis and *pluricotyledonary* is reported to promote embryo *maturation* in several species.

A number of other factors such as temperature shock, osmotic stress, nutrient *deprivation* and high density *inoculation* can substitute for ABA, presumably by inducing the embryos to synthesize the hormone.

ABA is known to trigger the *expression* which is normally expressed during down phase of seeds. Cytokinin can be *important* for somatic embryo *maturation* and has been *demonstrated* to influence development of *cotyledon* and shoot apex.

Anther Culture

In vitro androgenesis has been described as a process of deviation of *development* from normal *gametophytic* to a sporophytic pathway. This deviation *generally* leads to callus production or embryo formation. The plants can *subsequently* be obtained either via *organogenesis* or *embryogenesis* from the androgenic callus or via direct *germination* of androgenic embryos.

In the tropical fruit trees androgenesis and plantlet *regeneration* have been reported in *Citrus,* sugar apple, papaya, longan and *Litchi.* The androgenic callus formation from *in vitro* culture of anthers has been reported in guava and *Feijoa.*

This meagre progress with anther culture *particularly* in woody tropical fruit species that are difficult to culture suggests that the technique could be a reproducible method in *regeneration* of tropical fruit trees, but an extensive research in this area is still needed.

Anther culture following pollen storage has potential for conservation. Cryogenic storage of pollen would be space efficient and economical.

Table 12.3: Tropical fruit trees in which stable transformed plants have been obtained

Species	*Explant*	*Transformation method*	*Foreign gene*	*Result*
Citrus reticulata CVS 'Onta' (Ponkan) 'Kara' (mandarin)	Electroporation Embryogenic callus sub-cultured in liquid medium	Direct DNA transfer by Electroporation	gus	Reduced colony formation
Citrus jambhiri (rough lemon)	Protoplast of nucellar callus	Direct DNA transfer with 20% PEG6000	cat and npt II	Selection of micro colonies with paramo mycin (20-40 tg/ml). Transgenic plants
Citrus sinensis CVS 'Trovita' 'Washington navel'	Cell suspension culture derived from embryo callus	*Agrobacterium*	npt II and hpt	Transgenic plants, embryoids resisting Kan
Citrus sinensis CV 'Pineapple'	Internodal stem segments of seedlings	*Agrobacterium*	gus with intron and npt II	Transformed shoots grafted *in vitro* onto seedling rootstocks
Citrus sinensis × *Poncirus tritbliata* (root stock)	Internodal stem segments of 5 week old seedlings	*Agrobacterium*	gus with intron and npt II	Transformed shoots grafted *in vitro* onto seedling rootstocks
Poncirus tritbliata (root stock)	Epicotyl segment	*Agrobacterium* gus,	npt II	Transformed plants (Resistance to Kan)
Carica papaya	Zygotic and somatic embryos and hypocotyl	Microprojectile bombardment	gus, npt II and the coat protein of papaya ring spot virus	Transformed somatic embryos and leafy shoots.Resistance to Kan

(Table Contd.)

Species	***Explant***	***Transformation method***	***Foreign gene***	***Result***
Carica papaya	Immature zygotic embryos	Particle bombardment	coat protein of papaya ring spot virus gus, npt II	Transgenic papaya plants having increased resistance to PRV
Mangifera indica	Somatic proembryos	*Agrobacterium*	gus, npt II	Proembryos resistant to Kanamycin
Musa (AAA group)	Embryogenic cell suspension immature male flower	Microprojectile bombardment	npt II, Vid *A* or BBTV	Resistance to Kanamycin initiated using

SOMACLONAL VARIATION

The term 'somaclonal variation' refers to the phenotypic and genotypic variation observed in plants *regenerated* from any form of cell culture. The degree of variation has been shown to depend on tissue being cultured and also on the length of time that the cells or tissues have been *maintained in vitro*. Somaclonal variation may be a viable approach for *obtaining horticulturally* useful traits in tropical fruit trees.

In addition, a long generation time for most fruit species like, *seedlessness* in *Musa,* etc. make this approach even more appealing for many species. Progress has been made with a few fruit species to use this *technique* to obtain disease resistance, salt tolerance, thornlessness and toxin resistance. Additional research still needs to be *conducted* to assess the *phenotypic* and genotypic stability of these traits.

SYNTHETIC SEED

The 'synthetic' or 'artificial' seed technology is an exciting and rapidly growing area of research in plant cell and tissue culture. Production of artificial seeds has unravelled new vistas in plant *propagation*. It is an excellent technique for *propagation* of rare hybrids, elite *germplasm* and genetically engineered plants. Germplasm can be stored *effectively* in the form of *synthetic* seeds.

They serve as the most efficient delivery system. Synthetic seeds have been produced using either of the two methods: a hydrated system or a desiccated one. In the tropical fruit trees, the artificial seed technology is progressing well. Encapsulation of somatic embryos and plantlet regeneration have been reported in guava, mango and papaya. Plants were also regenerated from encapsulated shoot tips of banana.

TRANSGENIC PLANTS: ACHIEVEMENTS IN TROPICAL FRUIT TREES

The development of recombinant DNA technology and efficient systems of controlling *morphogenesis* from the culture of cells and tissue have opened the *opportunity* for genetic *manipulation* of plants at the cellular level.

The goal of gene transfer *techniques* is to produce improved varieties through the incorporation of horticulturally important genes (such as pest and disease resistance, drought and cold tolerance, herbicide resistance, improved fruit quality, reduced juvenility, dwarfism, etc.) into existing cultivars.

Methods available for plant *transformation* are arranged in three main groups: (i) those using biological vectors (virus- or *Agrobacterium*mediated transformation), (ii) direct DNA transfer techniques (chemical-, electrical-, or microlaserinduced permeability of protoplasts or cells), and (iii) non-biological vector system (microprojectiles, microinjection or liposome fusion).

A comprehensive review on *transformation* methods has been compiled by Potrykus. *Agrobacterium* based *transformation* shows an advantage over other methods since it targets transgenes to the nucleus and integrates them into the host DNA. Several trasformations have been reported based on *Agrobacterium-mediated* transformation of cells or explants, e.g. in *Citrus,* papaya and mango. The recovery of transgenic plant is mainly dependent on the frequency of gene introduction and the ability of the *transformed* cells to differentiate into plants, i.e. an efficient *in vitro* regeneration protocol is a pre-requisite. Pang and Sanford were the first to demonstrate *transformation* of papaya by co-cultivating leaf discs, stems and petioles with *A. tumefaciens.*

Although transformation was confirmed by nopaline assays, they were not able to regenerate the callus into plant. Fitch et al. first demonstrated papaya with the neomycin phosphotransferase II (NPTII) and (3glucuronidase (GUS) genes using *immature* embryo explants via *microprojectile bombardment.* Fitch et al. regenerated papaya plants resistant to papaya ring spot virus by incorporating PRV cp gene. The frequency of transformation in both cases was very low.

In *Citrus,* successful *transformation* is reported using different methods, but transformation frequencies were much lower. Transformation has been reported in a few tropical fruit trees, some of which are listed in Table elsewhere in this chapter. Although elegant protocols have been worked out using the biological vector *Agrobacterium tumefaciens* as well as direct gene transfer in basic and applied science, there are still many problems which have to be solved in terms of a reproducible method, but these problems are more related to the *biological* or genetical phenomena than to the delivery of DNA into plant cells. The different methods could deliver DNA into the cells, but the events in the cell and the genetic *compartments,* organelles and nucleus are not controlled and the genetic integration of foreign DNA is random. Targeted transformation is still at its infancy.

Gene silencing and interactions between different transgenes result in unexpected expression patterns of foreign genes. Several independent transformants with a specific gene construct are still necessary to find one transgenic plant with the proposed expression pattern.

Transgene-mediated *suppression* of a gene by antisense constructs can be achieved. Up to now, plant biotechnology has mainly focused on a single gene strategy. It is still cumbersome to change *physiological* traits which are *determined* by multiple genes and/or *quantitatively* inherited.

CONCLUSIONS

Considerable progress has been made in the recent past on *in vitro* plant *regeneration* via *organogenesis* and somatic *embryogenesis* in tropical fruit trees by *manipulation* of growth media and culture conditions as well as testing a variety of explant sources.

To improve the propagation system and to overcome the main bottlenecks, in particular, maturation and low *germination* frequency, the knowledge of developmental *physiology* need to be enhanced. Refinements in protocols are also necessary to get good quality embryos to facilitate storage, *germination* and encapsulation of these embryos.

Numerous characteristics in tropical fruit trees which cannot be improved by *conventional* breeding need *biotechnological* intervention. Besides the fundamental aspects, a wide array of practical problems need to be solved such as mechanical handling and automated planting. In addition, it would be necessary to reduce the *production* cost for commercial application.

16

Chapter

BIOPOLYMER PRODUCTION IN PLANTS

It is nowadays almost taken for granted that plastics are made from mineral oil. However, this has not always been the case, as one of the first plastics, called collodion, was made from cotton cellulose in the *mid-nineteenth* century. The body of a 1941 Ford *demonstration* vehicle consisted of plant fibers, soy protein polymers, and rubber tires made from the plant Goldenrod.

The low cost and reliable supply of fossil fuels put an end to that. In less than 20 years, petroleum-derived plastics almost completely replaced plant-based materials. Now, the pendulum appears to be swinging back.

Three factors are of importance in the resurgence of the use *biopolymers* with plastic or elastomeric properties (*referred* to as *bioplastics*) in industrial and consumer products: economics, public acceptance, and regulation.

Price and properties already allow some bioplastics to successfully compete with *petrochemical* plastics, due in part to a strong increase in oil price.

For most bioplastics, however, significant efforts on the raw materials side and on *processing technology* are still required to make them competitive. Public acceptance of non-food applications of agricultural products is not a big issue.

However, public acceptance of the use of transgenic plants for non-food purposes is not assured, especially in the European Union.

Life cycle *assessments* and a mounting concern over climate change due to greenhouse gas production may exert increasing regulatory pressure to shift from *petrochemicals* to renewable materials (e.g., by CO_2 taxation). In general, production of plastics from plant *biopolymers*

promises to offer the potential of reliable (domestic) supplies, jobs in rural communities, sustainable production, lower *greenhouse* gas production, and competitive prices.

ROUTES TO BIOPOLYMERS: WHITE VS. GREEN BIOTECHNOLOGY

Biopolymers from Bacterial Fermentation

White or industrial biotechnology also provides routes for obtaining biopolymers. Plant biomass can be converted to glucose, fatty acids, or other small molecules, either as the main product or as a waste stream from other *production* processes.

These small compounds may then be converted to bioplastics via microbial *fermentation* or chemical *polymerization*. For example, poly-b-hydroxyalkanoates (PHA), biocellulose, xanthan, silk, and polythioesters, can be produced by recombinant or wild-type *microorganisms* in fermentation processes, while polylactic acid, *polycaprolactone*, and other (partially renewable) polyesters, such as polytrimethylene terephtalate (e.g., Sorona by Dupont) and polybutylene succinate (e.g., Bionolle by Showa), are produced using chemical *polymerization* of substrates that are, at least in part, renewable and generated by fermentation.

It is likely that the production processes of bioplastics will be part of future biorefineries, which are now in an early stage of development (with the exception of starch and paper mills). This early stage implies that in *biorefineries* the processing costs still determine the economic viability of bioproducts, and a great potential for *streamlining* and improved process integration exists.

As biorefineries mature, the focus will shift away from processing to the raw materials, as has happened in the *petrochemical* industry.

Why Biopolymer Production in Plants?

Prices of raw materials for the production of bioplastics using white *biotechnology* are already on the rise. For example, sugar prices have become very volatile due to the strong demand. In the USA alone, $50{\times}10^6$ t of corn will be used in 2006 to produce ethanol fuel.

At the same time, world production of grains in 2006 is expected to fall short of consumption by 60×10^6 t on a total of approximately $2{\times}10^9$ t, leading to upward price pressure. Similarly, increasing amounts of vegetable oils are being converted to biodiesel. Again, the current world production of vegetable oils is barely higher than the demand for food applications.

In other words, it is likely that the price of sugars and vegetable oils (and energy-rich waste streams) will become tightly linked to the price of oil. Direct production of polymers in plants may circumvent this price issue to some extent. Another factor to consider is the life cycle assessment: does the production of bioplastics really consume less raw material and energy, and produce less CO_2, than the production of petroleum-based plastics?

Some analyses have shown that if the amount of polymer in plant material is high enough and the remaining biomass is used to generate energy for polymer processing, the life cycle *assessments* favour plant biopolymers over *petrochemical* plastics. Life cycle assessments also favour the production of biobased polymers over biofuels if land-use is also included in the analysis.

However, new methods could also provide highly efficient chemical routes to polymers, such as for poly-β-hydroxybutyrate (PHB).

The Role of Transgenic Plants in the Production of Biopolymers

What is the potential role of transgenic plants in the production of novel or improved *biopolymers* from crops? Simple targets are increased amounts of the desired *biopolymer* relative to other plant components (e.g., starch content), or decreased amounts of other *compounds* in the plant that interfere with *processing* (e.g., lignin, proteins, pectin, hemicellulose).

More complicated research targets can be considered as well. Genes may be altered or *introduced* to change the substrate range or processivity of polymerases, the structure and amount of precursors available for *polymerization* may be adjusted, new genes maybe introduced in plants to obtain polymers with different properties (e.g., by changing the ionic *charge, composition, chemical reactivity, stability, solubility, melting* and other *thermoplastic properties*), and gene regulation may be altered.

Potentially, much can be accomplished. However, do these changes improve the *economics* of *biopolymer* production in crop plants? Any polymer *modification* could lead to adverse effects, such as lowered *concentrations* of the polymer, increased difficulty in processing, reduced plant growth and seed *germination*, or other undesired effects.

Other aspects of the application of plant biotechnology for biopolymer production must also be taken into account, such as crop identity preservation, gene transfer to other noncrop plants, limited flexibility of production in plants versus bacteria, length of time to market for transgenic plants, transgene methods versus fast-track breeding and tilling, the use of non-food plants to avoid controversy or litigation, the cost and time frame of registering and patenting transgenic crops, low marginal costs for established technologies, and the role of the technology development time gap.

In other words, demonstrating the technical feasibility of producing a modified polymer is probably the easiest step, but bringing the transgenic plant to market entails many difficult and expensive steps. Important key questions that should be *addressed* at an early stage in the *development* of crop-based bioplastics are:

1. Is it possible to gain sufficient control over the properties of biopolymers in planta compared to the relative ease of control over *composition* and properties in chemical *polymerization* and in fermentation?
2. Is the significant *investment* of creating transgenic plants or plant breeding for bioplastic production justified by the economic value of the product, in view of the current main use of *bioplastics* in low-cost applications?

PLANT BIOPOLYMERS

In this chapter, we have singled out four specific (classes of) *biopolymers* for special attention: starch, natural rubber, protein-based polymers, and PHA. Starch, natural rubber, and proteins such as zein, gluten, and soy-protein, are naturally *synthesized* by plants.

For these products, polymer productivity and quality may be optimized by plant breeding, targeted genetic changes, and improved processing technology. In contrast, PHA, fibrous proteins such as silk and elastin, and non-ribosomally synthesized proteins are not naturally *synthesized* in plants but may be produced in transgenic plants. Cellulose, *hemicellulose*, and lignin are other major plant biopolymers, which will not be considered here.

Only cellulose has important *applications* in its unmodified (e.g., cotton, fibers, and wood), and modified (e.g., cellulose acetate, which is produced at about 750000 t/year) forms. Plants produce many other biopolymers that presently have relatively few *applications* in the non-food sector.

This could change if larger amounts of the materials become available, for example as co-products of biofuel *production*. Other biopolymers that are now isolated from fungi or bacteria could also be produced in plants.

Starch

Starch is the second major *agricultural* commodity after cellulose, is the least expensive food commodity, and has numerous industrial applications. It is the cheapest and easiest to handle biopolymer. Due to its *abundance* and low price (world production is 57 × 10^6 t/year, at around 0.30 •/kg depending on the source of the starch), it has found numerous applications in the nonfood sector.

To give a size *perspective*, non-food uses of starch in EU15 (the 15 member states of the EU before May 2004) amounted to 3.6 × 10^6 t/year, or about 13% of the total starch market in these countries. Currently, only about 40000 t/year are converted to plastic materials by a range of small and large companies worldwide.

Most of this bioplastic is marketed as *biodegradable*, and is used for packaging films and foams, and for disposables (e.g., cups and plates, plant pots, and bags). The growth potential of this market is high, with many studies referring to future market sizes in the range of 1 × 10^6 t/year. Due to the importance of starch, its *biosynthesis* and ways to modify its properties have been studied in depth.

A great effort has gone into genetic *modifications* affecting starch biosynthesis in plants. The so-called starch-enhancement *technology* has increased the amount of starch relative to the other components in potato, yielding more starch per hectare and lower *processing* costs. Efforts to change the properties of starch in planta have focused on the ratio between amylose and amylopectin, the *branching* pattern of *amylopectin*, synthesis of phosphate-substituted starches, and the production of starches from new crops.

Until now, only the high-amylose and amylose-free starches have been *commercialized*. A major conclusion of research in this field is that the effects of a single ge-netic lesion on starch biosynthesis are much more complex than expected.

In addition, the structures of starch and starch granules are still not completely understood. Most of the research on the in planta modification of starch was carried out with food applications in mind, but could aid the production of thermoplastic starch (TPS). For example, high-amylose TPS was reported to have better properties than "standard" TPS: films were less sensitive to water, and less subject to cracking and shrinking. One of the main barriers to applications of TPS is its high moisture sensitivity and difficult processing.

Table 16.1: Selection of plant biopolymers and their applications.

	Chemical structure and source	*Applications as material*
Cellulose	Polysaccharide: 1,4-linked ,6-D-glucose, most abundant component of terrestrial biomass. Can be derivatized to ethers and esters (with acetate, propionate, butyrate, etc.)	Nitrocellulose, cellophane,carboxy methylcellulose, Tencel fiber, cellulose acetate
Hemicellulose	Polysaccharides: xylan, glucuronoxylan, arabinoxylan, glucomannan, and xyloglucan, present in almost all cell walls along with cellulose	Limited use as source of chemicals
Lignin	Complex (irregular) polyphenolic macro-molecule making up a quarter to a third of the dry mass of wood	Limited use as polymer and source of chemicals
Pectin	Various polysaccharides containing 1,4-linked α-D-galacturonic acid units, and L-rhamnopyranose units, linear and branched molecules.	Edible films
Inulin	Polysaccharide: linear β (2→1)-linked fructose chains attached to a sucrose molecule. Belongs to fructan-group: alternative storage carbohydrate in the vacuole of ~ 15% of flowering plant species.	Mainly used to produce inulin syrup. Carboxy methyl inulin is used as antiscalant.
Cutin	Polyester found on the surface of plants	None
Suberin	Complex (irregular) biopolymer consisting of ω-hydroxyalkanoates, di-carboxylic acids and aromatic compounds. It is a waste product available in large amounts (80000 t/year from cork production alone)	None
Pullulan	α (1→4)-linked glucose trimer, linked by α-(1→6) bonds, fungal polymer that could be produced in plants	Edible films, fibers
Hyaluronic acid	Repeating disaccharide unit consisting of an N-acetyl-hexosamine and a hexose or hexuronic acid, either or both of which may be sulfated	Surgery

Such problems can be remedied by chemical derivatization, e.g., by *introducing* ester and ether-groups. Blending TPS with polycaprolactone or other biodegradable hydrophobic polymers, or by coating TPS films with a waterbarrier is also extensively used. Both types of research have been carried out for many decades and are covered by *numerous* patents.

Is it possible and worthwhile to aim for chemical *derivatization* or blending in planta? Theoretically, a linear starch chain can be decorated with side-groups using enzymes that are co-

Table 16.2: Thermoplastic starch.

Chemical composition	Amylose: linear α-(1,4)-linked D-glucose polymer, molecular weight 10^5 10^6 Amylopectin: α-(1,4)-linked D-glucose polymer, u-branches, molecular weight 10^7-10^9
Annual production	40000 t/year
Price	0.20-0.50 •/kg, depending on source
Main sources	Maize, potato, wheat, cassava, rice, pea, waxy and amylo maize, etc.
Main industrial uses	Diapers, cardboard, paper, fabrics, plastics, plaster, water treatment, detergent, oil drilling, filler for tires
Main producers of TPS or starch foam	Novamont, BIOP, Biotec, Rodenburg Biopolymers, Green Light Products, National Starch and Chem., Earthshell
Main use as bioplastic	Foams (for the loose fill foam market), mulch films, shopping bags, moldable products (pots, cutlery, fast food packaging)
Advantages	Cheap, widely available, many variant starches, many functional groups for derivatization, grafting, and interaction with plasticizers
Disadvantages	Mechanically weak, brittle, moisture sensitive, complex heterogeneous multiphase materials, sensitive to retrogradation, poor interaction with plasticizers and hydrophobic polymers, suitable only for short life applications (20% of the market), slow production rates in plastic film equipment
Important issues	1. The potential for starch bioplastics is several million t/year 2. Starch is a complex material (granule structure, amylose vs. amylopectin, crystallinity, chain-length) that is still not fully understood 3. Almost everything has been tried to improve properties 4. In planta modification of starch involves transgenic food plants 5. Starch yield should not be affected by modifications

expressed with the starch *synthesizing* enzymes. For example, enzymes could be used that O-acetylate cell wall polysaccharides.

It must be noted that such modifications would have to take place before the polysaccharide becomes part of the starch granule, because after granule formation, the amylose and amylopectin chains are probably not accessible for modification.

Other factors to keep in mind are the potential deleterious *consequences* of starch modifications. Starch granule structure is likely to be affected by the *modifications*, which in turn will affect the amount of the starch produced by the plant. Seed *germination* might be affected, as one of the

Table 16.3: Natural rubber.

Chemical composition	Major component: cis-1,4-polyisoprene, Minor components: proteins, polysaccharides, minerals
Annual production	9×10^6 t/year
Price	Up to 1.8 E/kg, depending on grade
Main source	*H. brasiliensis* (rubber tree)
Producing countries	Main: Indonesia, Malaysia, Thailand Minor: Sri Lanka, India, China, Ethiopia, Nigeria, Brazil
Main uses	Tires, gloves, thread, condoms
Advantages	High resilience, long fatigue life, very good tensile and tear properties, good creep and stress relaxation resistance, efficient heat dispersion, low-temperature flexibility, good balance of properties for demanding mechanical applications
Disadvantages	Compared to some expensive synthetic rubbers: doesn't age well, inferior resistance to sunlight, oxygen, ozone, solvents and oils, variable quality due to local production, re-use is difficult
Alternative plant sources	Guayule (10000 t/year in 1910, efforts during WWII and oil-crisis), Russian dandelion (WWII efforts), Goldenrod (R&D in 1930s)
Related	Gutta percha and Balata (poly-trans-isoprene) natural materials Chicle (mixture of *cis* and *trans)*
Synthetic alternatives	Synthetic rubber (total 10.4×10^6 t/year): styrene–butadiene copolymers (2.4×10^6 t/year), acrylonitrile-butadiene copolymers, and others

Important issues

1. *H. brasiliensis* is a genetically extremely narrow crop: SALB could destroy rubber production in South-East Asia
2. Rubber price strongly increases, a 25% shortfall in production is expected in 15 years
3. Increased competition for land-use by palm-oil plantations (for biodiesel and food applications)
4. Rubber production from *H. brasiliensis* cannot be mechanized, and work-force is getting more expensive
5. Synthetic rubber alternatives are non-renewable
6. Allergenic hypersensitivity to *H. brasiliensis* rubber is increasing

biological reasons given for O-acetylation is inhibition of cell wall degradation. In addition, the *processing* steps required to isolate the material could become less efficient. Here, it is useful to consider the effects of the currently available in planta *modifications*. For example, reducing the number of branching points in amylopectin resulted in potato plants producing smaller but more numerous tubers.

On the other hand, waxy and high-amylose maize variants are *commercially* grown. In considering modified-starch production, it should be noted that all starch plants are food plants, and that many of the *modifications* discussed entail the use of *transgenic* plants, which may not be well accepted by the public when crops that could enter the food chain are used.

Rubber

Rubber from Hevea brasiliensis

Natural rubber (hereafter simply referred to as rubber in contrast to synthetic rubber) consists mainly of cis-polyisoprene, with many minor additional *components* that are the key to the superior properties of this material compared to all synthetic rubbers.

Nearly 80% of all rubber is produced by only three countries (*Malaysia*, *Indonesia*, and *Thailand*), and from one biological source: the Brazilian rubber tree *(Hevea brasiliensis)*. The yield per hectare varies from 500 kg/year in *smallholder* plots to more than 1500 kg/year in large plantations. Rubber is a highly valuable biomaterial: in contrast to the other *biopolymers* discussed, it is essential for many industrial *applications*, and cannot be replaced by synthetic materials.

For example, heavy-duty tires for trucks, buses, and airplanes, as well as latex products for the medical profession, cannot be made with synthetic rubber. The rapid economic development in Asia, especially in China (the world's largest rubber consumer imported 1.5×10^6 t in 2005) and India, is *resulting* in strongly rising prices.

According to the International Rubber Study Group, the production deficit for 2006 is estimated to be 250000 t. Because rubber is essential and one region *dominates production*, rubber is *considered* a strategic commodity.

In 1934, South American leaf blight (SALB) wiped out the production of rubber in Brazil, and it has not been possible to restart large-scale production due to the endemic leaf blight pathogen *Microcyclus ulei* (the present production on marginal lands in Brazil, where SALB is less of a problem, is only 96000 t/year). SALB could cause a disaster in Asia, as *H. brasiliensis is* genetically very homogeneous: the millions of hectares of rubber *plantations* are all derived from a small sample of seeds collected in Brazil by Dr. Henry Wickham in 1876. Production in Africa is quite limited, although climate and soils would permit large-scale production.

Attempts in the 1980s and 1990s in Brazil to develop SALB-resistant *Hevea* clones did not meet with success. Although some progress has been made, all *promising* lines finally succumbed to the fungus in the field. Apart from efforts in Asia on common plant diseases, yield, and agronomics, *H. brasiliensis* is studied in France and Brazil to generate leaf-blight *resistant* varieties, increased yield, and altered properties.

Recently, efficient transformation of calli and regeneration of plants was shown to be possible. However, the narrow genetic base, prolonged breeding cycles and *juvenile* period, and highly

Table 16.5: Protein co-products potentially available for the production of bioplastics or biopolymers.

Protein	Total crop harvest	Protein content	Uses of protein as material (t/year)	Price and volume
Zein (maize)	692×10^6	4	Films, bioplastic, fibers	10-20 •/kg, < 1000 t/year
Soy protein (soybean)	209.5×10^6	38-45	Films, extruded foams, injection molded products	Price is slightly higher than con ventional plastics
Gluten	626×10^6	9-15	Films, coatings, (wheat)	Not available bioplastics, resins
Switchgrass leaf	Not protein available	10	Not available	Not available

heterozygous nature of *H. brasiliensis* make breeding complex, time-consuming and labor-intensive. In view of the critical importance of rubber, these efforts appear extremely limited: it makes sense to investigate alternative *production* methods.

Guayule as an Alternative Source of Rubber

Only one other plant has been used in large-scale commercial production of rubber. In 1910, 10000t/year of rubber was produced from natural stands of the guayule shrub *(Parthenium argentatum)*. As production from *H. brasiliensis* became more efficient, and natural stands of guayule were exhausted, this production strategy was gradually abandoned.

Guayule was studied *intermittently* for strategic reasons during WWII and the oil-crisis, and more recently also because many consumers are allergic to *H. brasiliensis* rubber, but not to guayule rubber. Over the years, guayule breeding efforts have improved rubber yield to 1000 kg/ha/year (compared to 1500 kg/ha/year for *H. brasiliensis)*.

In Europe, guayule has not attracted much attention, except for limited *cultivation* studies in Spain and Greece. As the plant is quite vulnerable to cold winters, the initial priorities might include the development of more hardy strains that can be grown in Southern Europe, or the *identification* of more suitable regions for growing this crop (e.g., North Africa). General research areas requiring attention are breeding for higher yield, harvesting methods, processing, and co-product utilization.

Natural Rubber from Plants Growing in Temperate Climates

The last major research activity of Thomas Edison was the development of natural rubber production from Goldenrod *(Solidago virgaurea minuta)*. Extensive research proved that Goldenrod, a common weed growing to an average height of 1 m, produced 5% yield of latex.

Through *hybridization*, Edison produced Goldenrod in excess of 3 m, yielding 12% latex. However, Goldenrod rubber never went beyond the *experimental* stage, mainly because the rubber was of low quality. Another potential source of rubber is the Russian dandelion *(Taraxacum kok-saghyz)*.

Table 16.4: Alternative sources of poly-cis-isoprenes.

Source	*Production in t/year (year)*	*Price $/kg*	*Current R&D related to rubber*
Rubber tree *H. brasiliensis*	9×10^6 (2005)	1.80	Resistance to SALB, rubber polymerase
Guayule shrub *P. argentatum* Gray	10000 (1910)	n.a.	Processing technology, rubber polymerase
Goldenrod *S. virgaurea minuta*	Demonstration project (1931)	n.a.	None
Russian dandelion *T. kok-saghyz*	WWII emergency projects USSR/USA, 3000 (1943)	n.a.	Domestication

The root is a source of high quality latex (used for making rubber during WWII) with yields of between 150 and 500 kg/ha, and 45 kg of rubber per ton of roots. Unlike guayule latex, dandelion latex is probably less suitable for medical applications as it contains many proteins that are *apparently* related to *H. brasiliensis* latex proteins.

However, it has a shorter life-cycle than guayule, over 50 000 EST-sequences are available, and it has a relatively small genome. Research carried out in the 1930s and 1940s indicate that although high quality rubber could be produced, the agronomics are not favourable.

Production of rubber in *transgenic* sunflower, lettuce, or chicory has been considered. However, the use of a transgenic food-crop for the production of rubber may not be acceptable in the EU.

PROTEIN-BASED BIOPLASTICS OR BIOPOLYMERS

Three groups of protein-based plastics and biomaterials can be distinguished: (1) derivates of natural plant proteins obtained as co-products of starch, vegetable oil, or biofuel production; (2) fibrous proteins with potential uses in *engineering* (e.g., spider silk, mussel adhesive protein, collagen, elastin); and (3) non-ribosomally produced *polypeptides* (e.g., *cyanophycin* and polylysine).

Protein Co-products

Examples of materials that can be derived from natural plant proteins are plastics and resins based on zein (corn protein), *soy* protein, and gluten from wheat. These materials are typically produced by *crosslinking* proteins with *glutaraldehyde*, formaldehyde, or other chemicals, in *combination* with starch, polyphosphate, or other fillers.

Zein is the major protein in corn. In 1950, about 2700 t/year of zein plastics (glossy, scuffproof, grease-proof coatings) and 2200 t/year of Vicara fiber were produced. If produced on the same scale as in the 1950s, and as a by-product from ethanol production, zein would cost about 2.5•/

Table 16.6: Poly-β-hydroxyalkanoates.

Chemical	Linear polyesters of 3-hydroxyalkanoates and related hydroxy acids composition 1. Poly-β-hydroxybutyrate (PHB), high crystallinity 2. PHB-co-valerate (PHBV), high crystallinity 3. PHB-co-hexanoate (PHBH or Nodax), moderate crystallinity 4. Medium-chain PHA (mclPHA), C6-C16 monomers, elastomers, low crystallinity
Annual production	< 1000 t/year (Metabolix, Biomer, Biomatera, Kaneka) Monsanto stopped production of PHBV in 1998 ADM & Metabolix announced construction of a 50000 t/year plant in 2006
Price	1.5 $/kg (expected), currently 10-20 $/kg
Main source	Bacterial fermentation using sugars and oils as starting material
Main produ-	USA, Brazil, Germany, Japan, China, Thailand, presently all at a very cing countries small scale
Main (industrial) uses	1. Thermoplasts for bottles, packaging material, cutlery, cups, bags, mulching films 2. Latex for coatings and films 3. Blending with other biodegradable polymers 4. For mclPHAs: source of monomers, paints, pressure-sensitive adhesives, biodegradable cheese coatings, and biodegradable rubbers
Advantages	1. Hydrophobic and moisture-resistant compared to other biopolymers 2. Choice of feed strategy and host organism allows many different monomer compositions, resulting in a wide range of properties: for example, PHBH (Nodax) is easier to process than PHBV due to lower melting temperature and lower crystallinity, and has greater toughness and ductility 3. High oxygen impermeability 4. Processing on conventional equipment for polyolefins possible
Disadvantages	General: high production costs, hydrophobicity makes blending with cheap hydrophilic polymers such as starch and proteins difficult PHB: brittle, stiff, decomposes just above melting temperature, unfavourable aging PHBV: slightly lower melting temperature than PHB, long processing times mclPHA: weak, sticky, rubbery
Related materials	Polylactate (PLA), polycaprolactone (PCL), other polyesters produced by condensation of diacids and diols, or hydroxy acids
Important issues for production of PHAs	1. Transgenic food plants will not be accepted in the EU 2. LCA and land-use favour plant GMO over bacterial fermentation 3. Deleterious effects on plant growth at high PHA levels 4. Lack of control over monomer composition in plants 5. Processing 6. Stability in harvested material

kg, the actual cost now being ten times higher. Henry T. Ford used soy protein as a source of bioplastics to construct car parts. However, after a brief bloom in the 1930s and 1940s, petroleum-based plastics replaced protein-based plastics, in part because of microbial degradation and water *permeability* issues.

Glutenbased bioplastics suffer from the same general problems and are also currently too expensive for large-scale use. The amount of protein co-products from future large-scale biofuel production (potentially millions of tons of protein per year from Switchgrass or *Miscanthus)* can be expected to greatly exceed the amount that can be absorbed by the food and feed markets, enabling the development of a protein-based bioplastics industry.

The role for genetic *engineering* specifically to improve bioplastics derived from these proteins appears quite limited, *especially* if the primary goal is biomass production.

Fibrous Proteins

The second group of protein biopolymers consists of fibrous proteins that are typically composed of short blocks of repeated amino acids. Silk, elastin, adhesin, and numerous other fibrous proteins show great promise in that these materials have unique strength-to-weight, elastic, or adhesive properties.

These are potentially very attractive *materials*, but expensive and labor-intensive to produce from their natural sources. Therefore, quite some effort has gone into the heterologous production of these proteins. In most cases, *microorganisms* (but also cell cultures, animals, and plants) were tested as host.

Problems such as clone *instability* because of repetitive sequences, inclusion bodies, and difficult processing have thus far prevented breakthroughs. It has proven difficult to obtain materials (*fibers, glues, elastic tissue*) from *recombinant* material with the same quality as the original material except on a small scale.

It must be kept in mind that the properties of fibers such as silk depend in large part on how different types of proteins are assembled and spun together. Thus, beyond the production of the individual protein *components*, advances in *microspinning technologies* are essential.

At present, production of fibrous proteins in plants suffers from the same problems, i.e., low yield and difficult processing (e.g., spinning of heterologously produced silk). Concerning yield, approaches such as seed-specific expression and the use of ER-targeting sequences may provide valuable solutions.

Genetic engineering can also be used to produce completely new materials such as block-copolymers, *combinations* of different proteins like silk and elastin, completely synthetic sequences with even better properties, and thus perhaps also sequences optimized for production in specific organisms, including plants.

Heterologous *expression* in plants would enable *production* on a much larger scale and open up new markets. However, the question should be asked if any of the fibrous proteins has a (potential) market size that would justify the development of a transgenic germplasm. Moreover, it should be noted that one of the most interesting aspects of the fibrous proteins is the ability to specify properties through the DNA template.

This allows tailoring to specific applications and processing, but at the same time clearly favours production in more flexible organisms, such as bacteria or yeast. In addition, much higher product concentrations can be attained in these organisms without compromising growth, the downstream processing is likely to be easier, as is the genetic engineering (especially in view of the multitude of different proteins in this class).

In addition, if these proteins are to be used as highend engineering materials, and thus needed on a relatively small scale, the fermentation costs are less relevant than the material properties. Thus, production in plants should be envisaged only if the fibrous protein is to be used on a commodity-scale.

Non-ribosomal Polypeptides

The third group of protein *biopolymers* consists of non-ribosomally produced *polypeptides* such as cyanophycin, a protein-like copolymer composed of a polyaspartate backbone and arginine side-groups produced by cyanobacteria and a few *non-photosynthetic* bacteria, as well as polylysine and polyglutamate.

The latter are now used in food but have many potential *applications* ranging from hydrogels, biochip coatings, drug carriers, *cryoprotectant*, etc.. Polyaspartate derived from *cyanophycin* can be used as superadsorbant or antiscalant. Recombinant *E. coli* can produce *cyanophycin* up to 29% of the cell dry weight on protamylasse, a waste product of starch production from potato.

Transgenic plants have been created that contain up to 1.1% cyanophycin dry weight. Due to the low-price applications of these compounds, the critical question is whether production levels in plants can be high enough for cheap production. Again, production in crop plants versus bacteria makes sense only if the *polypeptides* or their derivatives are used as commodities.

POLY-F-HYDROXYALKANOATES

Poly- β-hydroxyalkanoates (PHA) are polyesters naturally produced by *microorganisms*, primarily as carbon and energy storage material. The polymer properties depend strongly on the nature of the monomer, which can range from linear C4-C16 β-hydroxy fatty acids, to β-hydroxy acids substituted with aromatic rings, other *functional-groups*, or containing double-bonds.

The simplest PHA, poly-β-hydroxybutyrate (PHB), is a relatively hard and brittle material with a melting point slightly below the thermal decomposition temperature. Inclusion of C_5-monomers gives slightly better properties. Adding small amounts of longer *monomers* (C_6 and longer) has resulted in materials with further *improved* processing and material properties.

PHA consisting of higher molecular weight monomers (C_6-C_{16}, referred to as medium-chain PHA or mc1PHA) typically are rubber-like materials with an amorphous soft-sticky *consistency*. PHAs are very attractive *polymers* for consumer products such as bottles, films, and fibers, due to their water and air impermeability, as a source of chiral monomers, and as components of paints.

If it is possible to produce PHAs at a cost of 1-2C/kg, many of these potential *applications* become *commercially* viable. Presently, PHAs produced by *microbial* fermentation are clearly too expensive, estimated at 10 $/kg. However, *according* to some industry specialists, the lower price range is feasible with current, large-scale and fully *integrated bioreactors,* and downstream processing *technology.*

Present efforts to develop cellulosic ethanol, and the rapid development of biogas *technology* to convert waste biomass into heat and electricity, should make PHA *fermentation* technology much more energy and CO_2 efficient.

As a potential large-scale commodity, it is logical to consider production of PHA in plants. The critical question to ask is: can PHA *production* in plants compete with *established* and future *fermentation* methods? If the answer is positive, many technical hurdles need to be addressed.

These issues are generally related to production levels in plant tissue, control over monomer *composition,* deleterious effects of PHA production on plant growth, and processing *technology.* In *A. thaliana* PHB levels of 40% based on dry weight of leaves were obtained, but plant growth was severely affected. It is *conceivable* that better control over targeting (in the cell organelle or plant part where the PHA is produced) will solve this problem.

PHB up to 8% in seeds of rape has been reported without deleterious effects on seed germination or viability. Production of PHA containing several types of monomers (from C4 to C16) has been reported for a variety of plants. Polyesters with different monomer compositions are easily obtained by using different bacterial hosts, feeding regimes, and co-feeding specific monomers.

The breadth and precision in monomer composition that can be attained by bacterial fermentation appears to be hard to replicate in plants, because in some cases at least two independent metabolic pathways supplying the intermediates would have to be quantitatively controlled during production of the polymer if it is to contain two or more monomers in defined ratios.

This requires a much better *understanding* of and control over metabolic *pathways* and fluxes in plants than is presently available. Isolation of PHA from plant tissues is bound to be more complicated than isolation from bacteria where there is no need to break up tissue. Further, much higher *concentrations* can be reached in bacteria without affecting the viability of the host organisms (up to *85%* for PHB).

The timing of *production* in a *bioreactor* is also much easier as the typical *substrates* for bacterial growth (sugars and *oil-containing* wastes, or purified *compounds*) can be stored, and production can take place *throughout* the year.

A related issue is whether the PHA is stable in plant material after harvesting: if not, the plants must be processed immediately after harvest (this is also an issue for rubber and heterologously produced proteins). Taking into account the cost to create a *transgenic* plant and the time required to generate a *commercial* germplasm, it seems advisable to concentrate on the production of only one or two standard PHA polymers in plants (PHB and perhaps mc1PHA), leaving *production* of the wide range of other PHA polymers to *fermentation* schemes.

Which plants are most suitable for PHA production? Since production of PHAs in plants by definition involves the use of *transgenic* plants, from the EU perspective it is best to focus on a non-food crop, such as Switchgrass chosen by Metabolix, energy-crops such as *Miscanthus,* or a non-food oil crop such as *Crambe.*

CONCLUSIONS

Bioplastics and materials derived from biopolymers typically have low value *applications*, but potentially large markets (the exceptions are fibrous proteins, which are more valuable but have smaller markets). In most cases, the bioplastics have to compete with petrochemical plastics on price and properties. The role for transgenic plants differs strongly depending on the *biopolymer*. Starch has rather unfavourable *properties* for use as a *thermoplastic* except for its low price.

It is difficult to envisage in planta modifications that will drastically improve the material properties of starch. In the case of natural rubber, the first priority appears to be the *development* of alternative crops such as guayule or Russian dandelion. Genetic *engineering* may help the *development* of improved germplasm.

The only polypeptide where transgenic plants appear useful are the non-ribosomal protein cyanophycin; it seems unlikely that protein co-products of biofuels or food production can be modified to improve their *usefulness* as a bioplastic (although other *applications* can be *considered*).

For fibrous proteins, it makes more sense to concentrate on production in *microorganisms*, because markets are small and many different proteins (and derived sequences) must be considered. Finally, for PHA it makes sense to *concentrate* on one or two specific PHAs, for example PHB and mclPHA.

17

Chapter

GENETICALLY MODIFIED CROPS

The worldwide *commercial* cultivation of genetically modified (GM) crops has raised concerns about potential adverse effects on the environment from the use of these crops. Consequently, the risks of GM crops for the environment, and especially for *biodiversity*, have been extensively assessed before and during their *commercial* cultivation.

Substantial scientific data on environmental effects of the currently commercialized GM crops are available. Independent from the use of GM crops, modern *agricultural* systems have considerable negative impacts on global biodiversity. On a global scale, the most direct negative impact is due to the considerable loss of natural habitats, which is caused by the conversion of natural *ecosystems* into *agricultural* land.

The negative impact of modern agricultural systems in Europe cannot be ascribed to only one factor, but is caused by the interaction of a multitude of factors.

Several changes in the *management* of *agricultural* land over the last century have resulted in a decline in the diversity of plant, invertebrate, and bird species within agro-ecosystems.

The significant decline in floral diversity of grasslands and arable field margins, for example, was mainly caused by the adoption of high-yielding forage crop varieties, increased fertilizer inputs, frequent applications of herbicides, and the increased purity of crop seed.

Modern agricultural systems have produced a landscape in which many fields have very few weeds and very few invertebrates providing little food for birds. The shift in the type and density of weeds in the fields, as well as the disappearance of important habitats such as large stretches of hedgerows, was mainly responsible for the dramatic decline in bird populations.

Potential impacts of GM crops should thus be put in relation to the *environmental* impacts of modern agricultural practices that took place over the last decades.

Regulation of GM Crops

Generally, the approval of genetically modified crop varieties is more rigorously regulated than that of *conventionally* bred crops. Several reasons have lead to this regulation. The protection of human health and the *environment* is the primary reason for *government* oversight and regulation.

There are other factors besides the safety aspect that have supported government decisions to regulate GM crops. Among others, there is the novelty of *transgenic* crops, the uncertainty *accompanying* the *transformation* process, and public concerns about the safety of transgenic crops.

A thorough pre-market risk assessment of potentially unwanted effects of the GM crop on the environment is thus a prerequisite in obtaining permission to market any GM crop variety. GM crop growing countries generally follow the concepts of *familiarity* and of *substantial* equivalence, which state that a GM crop should be compared with its *traditional* counterpart that has an established history of safe use.

GM crop varieties that received regulatory approval are *considered* to present no more risks than comparable conventional varieties with a history of safe use.

Potential Environmental Effects of GM Crops

Potential environmental effects of the currently *commercialized* GM crops can roughly be subdivided into direct and indirect effects. Direct effects could result from the particular nature of the genetic change, i.e., from the resulting genotype and *phenotype* of the crop modified.

GM crops could be able to hybridize with sexually compatible wild relatives and these could subsequently suffer an increased risk of extinction. Introduced genetically modified traits could make a crop more likely to be more *persistent* (weedy) in *agricultural* habitats or more invasive in natural habitats.

Transgenic products, *especially* toxins produced to be active against certain pests, could be harmful to organisms that are not intended to be harmed. Target pests could develop resistances against the insecticidal proteins produced in GM crops resulting in a loss of *effectiveness* of the *transgenic* product.

Changes in the agricultural practice due to the adoption of GM crops (e.g., soil tillage, cropping intervals, or cultivation area) could result in a number of indirect effects. In the present review, the scientific knowledge of the environmental impact of GM crops deriving from 10 years of worldwide *experimental* field research and *commercial cultivation* is reviewed.

The sources of *information* included *peer-reviewed* scientific journals, scientific books, reports from regions with extensive GM crop cultivation, as well as reports from *international governmental organizations*.

The review is focussing on the currently commercially available GM crops that could be relevant for agriculture in Western and Central Europe (i.e., maize, oilseed rape, and soybean), and on the two main GM traits that are currently *commercialized*, herbicide tolerance (HT) and insect resistance (IR).

Where helpful, experiences gained with other crops such as Bt-cotton are considered. GM crops with minor worldwide acreage (e.g., virus-resistant papaya and squash) are not *considered.* Potential effects of GM crops are limited to the *environment* and to the following main topics: effects of GM crops on non-target organisms, effects of GM crops on soil ecosystems, gene flow from GM crops to wild relatives, invasiveness of GM crops into natural habitats, and impacts of GM crops on pest and weed *management.* In addition, this review identifies the possible ecological benefits that could be derived from the cultivation of GM crops.

EFFECTS OF BT-CROPS ON NON-TARGET ORGANISMS

Cry-proteins from *Bacillus thuringiensis (Bt)* are by far the most common *insecticidal* proteins that have been engineered into plants. They represent (up till now) the only insecticidal proteins that are commercially used in GM crops. *Bt cry* genes have been *engineered* into a large number of plant species such as maize, cotton, potato, tomato, rice, eggplant, and oilseed rape.

However, at *present, genetically* modified Bt-maize and Bt-cotton are the only crops that are commercially cultivated. Transgenic Bt-potato plants expressing Cry3Aa to control the Colorado potato beetle *(Leptinotarsa decemlineata)* were *commercialized* from 1996 to 2001, but were *withdrawn* from the market due to lack of consumer *acceptance* and the introduction of a novel insecticide able to control both the Colorado potato beetle and aphids.

Bt-maize *expressing* Cry1Ab was initially *developed* to control a *lepidopteran* pest, the European Corn Borer *(Ostrinia nubilalis),* but has also shown to be effective against various other *lepidopteran* pests such as *Sesamia nonagrioides, Spodoptera littoralis* and *Helicoverpa zea.*

Bt-maize expressing the beetle-specific Cry3Bb toxin to control corn rootworms *(Diabrotica* spp.) has received commercial approval in 2003 in the United States and in Canada. However, due to its recent approval, no *experience* from commercial *cultivation* is yet available. There are concerns that insect-resistant GM crops expressing Cry-proteins from *B. thuringiensis* could harm organisms other than the pest(s) targeted by the toxin.

The long-term and wide-scale use of Bt-crops over the past 10 years has been *accompanied* by extensive studies testing *potential* adverse effects of these crops. One factor of particular interest in this respect is the potential effect of Bt-transgenic crops on non-target organisms that provide important *ecological* and economic services within agricultural systems. This includes parasitoids and predators that are of *importance* for natural pest *regulation, pollinators,* and butterflies.

Effects of Bt-crops on Beneficial insects (Predators and Parasitoids)

Lower-Tier Studies in the Laboratory and Greenhouse

The effects of Bt-crops on predators have been assessed in a number of studies, most of them using a tritrophic system including a plant, a herbivore and a natural enemy, i.e., predator or parasitoid. Adverse effects on mortality, longevity or *development* of predators were only reported in studies using Bt-susceptible lepidopteran larvae as prey that had *ingested* the Bt-toxin.

In particular, the green lacewing *(Chrysoperla carnea),* an *important* predator in many maize growing areas, has thoroughly been studied since studies suggested that this *predator* was *negatively* affected by Cry1Ab. Results of subsequent studies using several different prey species reared on Cry1Ab-maize, however, showed that the *insecticidal* protein itself does not directly affect this predator, but that the green lacewing may be affected when feeding on prey species that are *susceptible* to *Bt*toxin.

The negative effect observed was thus entirely prey-quality mediated, i.e., caused by the suboptimal food quality of the lepidopteran larvae used in the *experiments*. Because *lepidopteran* larvae are not *considered* an important prey for *C. carnea* in the field, it is *unlikely* that Bt-maize poses a risk for this predator.

Similarly, effects of Bt-crops on mortality, development, weight or *longevity* of hymenopteran parasitoids developing in herbivores reared on transgenic plants were only observed in cases where *Bt*susceptible herbivores were used as hosts. This is not *surprising* given that host–parasitoid *relationships* are usually tight and parasitoids are very sensitive to changes in host quality.

The results of the performed lower-tier studies provide evidence that except for the lepidopteran species the toxin is intended for, Cry1Ab does not cause direct toxic effects on any of the *arthropod* groups examined.

Higher-Tier Studies in the Field

More than 50 field experiments, varying greatly in size, duration, and *sampling* efforts, have been conducted to determine the effects of Bt-crops on natural enemies. Most studies assessed the *abundance* of natural enemies using *different* methods, while only a few studies compared biological control functions of natural enemies in both *Bt-* and *conventional* crops.

These *experimental* field studies have only revealed minor, *transient* or *inconsistent* effects of Bt-crops when compared to a non-Bt control. Indirect effects were observed with *specialist* natural enemies which were virtually absent in Bt-fields due to the lack of target pests as prey or hosts.

Three studies in Bt-crops revealed consistent reductions in the abundance of different generalist predators that were also associated with the reduced availability of *lepidopteran* prey. A 6-year field study in Bt-cotton on the *abundance* of 22 arthropod natural enemy taxa indicated that an average decrease of about 20% in some predatory species did not appear to be *ecologically* relevant for the biological control function of the natural enemy *community*.

In general, many *natural* enemies are *polyphagous*, meaning they are able to switch to other preys in the field when one particular food source is scarce. The occurrence of indirect effects that are caused by changes in the availability and/or the quality of target *herbivores* is not restricted to GM *technology*.

Any pest-control measure will cause a reduction in the number of prey and host items, which could *consequently* affect population densities of natural enemies. Such indirect effects are thus generally not considered to comprise a *particular* risk of insecticidal GM crops. A number of *experimental* field studies have included *conventional* insecticides as a treatment.

Since Bt-crops are intended to replace or reduce applications of conventional insecticides commonly used in agriculture, insecticide treatments should be considered as one *reasonable* baseline for a comparative risk *assessment*.

Experiments that included broad spectrum insecticides, such as pyrethroids and organophosphates, have shown consistently reduced abundances of *different* groups of predators and hymenopteran parasitoids (Bt-maize; Bt-cotton). Side effects of more selective *insecticides* such as indoxacarb (*anoxadiazine*) or spinosad (*amacrolide*) largely depended on the spray frequency whereas systemic insecticides (such as *imidacloprid*, a *neonicotinoid*) were found to have no or little effect on natural enemies.

Although some of the field studies were limited in their spatial scale, and lack *statistical* power due to limited replication and high variability in the data, they clearly indicated that non-target effects of Bt-crops were *substantially* lower than those of broad spectrum insecticides.

This has been *confirmed* by recent large-scale studies conducted in commercially managed *Bt*- and non-Bt-cotton fields in the United States. The results of the various studies performed over the last years provide evidence that Bt-maize and Bt-cotton *expressing* insecticidal Cry1-proteins are more specific and have fewer side effects on non-target *arthropods* than most insecticides currently used.

Effects of Bt-crops on Pollinators

Many insect species are known to act as pollinators of various crops and wild plants. They are therefore of great ecological and economic importance. Among the various insect pollinators, honey bees are the best known, but it is now *recognized* that other species like bumble bees and solitary bees are also *important* in ensuring pollination of many plant species.

Due to their ecological and economic importance, honey bees are often used as test species in pre-market risk-assessment studies to assess direct toxicity of *insecticidal* proteins on non-target organisms. Such studies have been conducted for each Bt-crop prior to its *registration* in the United States.

Feeding tests with Cry1Ab proteins were conducted on both honey bee larvae and adults and in each case no effects were observed. Further studies with bees fed with purified Bt-proteins and with pollen from Bt-crops, as well as when bees were allowed to forage on Bt-crops in the field have confirmed the lack of effects.

Effects of Bt-crops on Butterflies

Butterflies are considered as a species group with a high aesthetic value serving as symbols for conservation awareness. Since Cry1Ab is selectively toxic to Lepidoptera (moths and butterflies), off-site pollen flow from Bt-maize fields might *potentially* have adverse effects on Lepidopteran species, if their larvae feed on host plants dusted with Bt-pollen.

The case of Bt-maize pollen and the monarch butterfly *(Danaus plexippus)* caused much public interest and led to a debate over the potential risks and the environmental impact of Bt-maize. Losey et al. found that when pollen from a *commercial* variety of Bt-maize (event *Bt* 11) was spread on milkweed leaves in the laboratory and fed to monarch butterfly larvae, the larvae consumed significantly less from these leaves compared with leaves dusted with non-transgenic pollen. In addition, after *4* days, almost half of the tested larvae died, which was *significantly* more than on the leaves with non-transgenic pollen where none of the tested larvae died.

The results of the study drew much attention to (potential) effects of Bt-crops on butterflies since the monarch is considered a conservation flagship species in the United States. However, the study also received much criticism and scientists questioned the validity of risk conclusions based on the data obtained in laboratory studies.

Later laboratory bioassays showed that the only transgenic Bt-maize pollen that consistently affected monarch larvae was pollen from Event *176,* an event that has meanwhile been withdrawn from the market. The results suggested that pollen from the most widely planted Bt-maize events *(MON810* and *Bt* 11) will have no acute effects on larvae in field settings since their pollen expresses 80 times less toxin than Event 176.

The results also suggested that pollen densities used by Losey et al. were in excess compared to pollen densities *present* in maize fields or that the pollen of event *Bt* 11 used may have been *contaminated* with non-pollen tissues. Excessive pollen densities of the currently commercialized events *(Bt* 11 and *MON810)* would be required to obtain relevant adverse effects on larval *developments*. The critics also felt that in addition to the mere toxicity (hazard), an ecological risk *assessment* has to consider exposure, i.e., whether the monarch larvae will encounter the Bt-toxin and at what level.

They also felt that the studies most likely did not address questions like the spatial and temporal overlap of monarch larvae and Bt-pollen. Extensive follow-up studies thus determined where the *monarchs* occur during their breeding season, and what *percentage* of the *population* of monarchs is possibly affected be the *Bt*toxin in areas where Bt-maize is presently grown.

The results showed that larval exposure to pollen on a population-wide basis is low, given the proportion of larvae in maize fields during pollen shed, the proportion of Bt-maize fields, and the levels of pollen within and around maize fields. The proportion of monarch *butterfly* population exposed to Bt-pollen was estimated to be less than 0.8%.

Field studies showed that continuous exposure of monarch butterfly larvae to natural deposits of Bt-pollen on milkweed plants within maize fields can affect individual larvae, but long-term exposure of larvae to Bt-maize pollen throughout their development is detrimental to only a fraction of the breeding population. It was concluded that the risk of exposure is low and that it is unlikely that Bt-maize will affect the *sustainability* of monarch butterfly *populations* in North America.

Furthermore, several authors claimed that effects of Bt-maize should be compared to mortality caused by other factors, which is very high in natural monarch butterfly populations, and averages around 80% over the entire larval development period. More important factors that may influence monarch butterfly survival include loss of over-wintering habitats in Mexico, use of *insecticides* to control *lepidopteran* pests and accidents such as collision with automobiles.

EFFECTS OF BT-CROPS ON SOIL ECOSYSTEMS

Similar to non-target effects above ground, concerns were raised that Bt-crops could have effects on soil organisms and soil functions. The following section discusses the concern that non-target soil organisms and processes could be affected by the *accumulation* of Bt-toxins in soils through the cultivation of the currently commercialized Bt-crops.

Release, Persistence, and Biological Activity of Bt-toxins in Soil

Bt-toxins expressed in Bt-crops can enter the soil system either via root exudates, via senescent

Table 17.1: Summary of results from studies assessing persistence, degradation, and inactivation of Bt-toxins in soil

Bt-crop/ Bt-toxin	*Study conditions*	*Toxin incorporation into soil*	*Bt-toxin detection*	*Persistence (days)*
Cotton tissue/ CrylAb and CrylAc	Laboratory	Experiments were carried out with field grown cotton tissue/soil/purified toxins in microcosms	Detectable residues (ELISA)	Detection of toxin and insecticidal insecticidal activity at termination of test - 28 d (CrylAb) and 56 d (CrylAc)
Microbial toxin and cotton tissue/CrylAb and CrylAc	Laboratory	Purified toxin and transgenic leaves added to soil in microcosms. Toxins extracted and measured for 140 days	Detectable residues (ELISA)	Initial rapid degradation, low percentage may persist for weeks/ months. Half lives at 22/40 d, depending on clay/organic content of soil
Maize tissue/ CrylAb 24-27°C	Laboratory/ Greenhouse	GM plants grown in greenhouse, harvest 2 weeks after pollen shed. Maize tissue was incubated with and without soil and mixed into artificial insect diet. Dose-weight response determined bioactivity. Soil: high *clay* content (25%)	Bioactivity test[b]	1.6 d (in soil) DT50 15.0 d (in soil) DT90 25.6 d (no soil) DT50 40.7 d (no soil) DT90
Cotton tissue/ Cry2A	Laboratory/ Field; Autumn/ winter	Protein incubation in soil for 120 d. Bioassay based on growth inhibition to determine DT50	Bioactivity test	15.5 d (lab) DT50 31.7 d (field) DT50 120 d: down to < 25% (field&Laboratory) MO, USA
Maize tissue/ CrylAb	Laboratory and field. Includes period of frost	Rhizosphere soil sampled from Bt-maize in a plant growth room and in the field	Western blot Bioactivity test	180 d: Bt-toxin detectable in rhizosphere soil samples from field (after first frost) around plants that had been dead for several months
Microbial toxin/CrylF	Laboratory 25°C	Mixture of CrylF pipetted onto soil samples representative of cotton fields	Bioactivity test	< 1 d DT50
Bt-cotton cultivation/ CrylAc	Field 16°C	Soil samples were collected 3 months after post harvest tillage for 3-6 consecutive years	ELISA Bioactivity test	Not detectable Bt-toxins in any of the samples
Maize tissue/ CrylAb	Litter bags in field (CH)	Leaves (growth chamber) sampled before/after pollen shed, cut&dried and placed in litter bags	ELISA Bioactivity test	45 d DT50 145 d DT90

(Table Contd.)

Bt-crop/ Bt-toxin	*Study conditions*	*Toxin incorporation into soil*	*Bt-toxin detection*	*Persistence (days)*
	~9°C	(5 mm mesh) and buried in soil in mid-October. Monthly analysis.		240 d : < 1.5% No degradation in winter (< 5 °C)
Maize tissue/ CrylAb	Soil cages in field (CH) ~9°C	Leaves sampled 3 weeks after pollen shed, cut&dried and added to surface of soil cages (1 mm mesh) with earthworm, tied up in field for 200 d, starting December	ELISA Bioactivity test	35 d DT50 105 d DT90 200 d: 0.3% Degradation continued in winter
Maize tissue/ CrylAb	Laboratory and field. No temperature indication	Laboratory: Bt-maize residues added to soil and incubated for 43 days. Field: soil samples from experimental fields after 4 years cultivation of Bt-maize	ELISA	Laboratory: 14 d: CrylAb not detectable Field: most Bt-toxin in subsurface soil at 0-15 cm depth. Not clear if Bt-toxin from previous year
Maize tissue/ CrylAb	Field. No temperature indication MO, USA	After ≥ 3 years commercial cultivation of Bt-maize, soil samples were collected during growth period and 6 weeks after harvest. Growth inhibition determined presence of toxin	Bioactivity test	No evidence of persistence or accumulation
Maize tissue/ CrylAb	Field. No temperature indication Germany	Samples were taken during a 3-year monoculture study with MON810 from bulk and rhizosphere soil at a) 9 leaves per plant, b) stem elongation phase, c) flowering/anthesis, d) ripening	ELISA	No accumulation during growing season despite potential binding to soil particles. Proportion of toxin persisted through winter but no indication of accumulation, toxin in rhizosphere remained consistently higher than in bulk soil

plant material, as well as via damaged and cast-off dead root cells. The supply of Bt-toxins by *senescent* plant material mainly occurs via decaying biomass remaining on or in the ground after harvest.

The toxin input from senescent plant tissue varies, depending on initial expression levels of the transgenic protein in different plant tissues, the *progression* of decay of the plant cells and the biomass *remaining* in the field.

Expression levels in the Bt-maize variety MON810 are estimated to be around 4–7 times higher in leaves than in roots. Persistence of Bt-toxins in soil is primarily depending on the protein quantity added and on the rate of *inactivation* and *degradation* by biotic and abiotic factors.

Degradation rates of Bt-toxins are known to be influenced by environmental conditions, soil type, the protein source (purified versus plant-produced) as well as by the particular Cry-protein chosen. Persistence in the environment can be *expressed* in different ways, which affects *comparison* between studies.

Terms such as dissipation time to 50% (DT50) or half-life are used to describe the time until 50% of the original amount of a substance is degraded. Persistence can also be described in terms of detectable residues.

While, for example, a DT50 of 1–2 days is an indicator for a rapid rate of dissipation, detectable residues after 2–6 months indicate that some small amounts of the protein last in a biologically active form (if detected by a bioassay) or in an *immunologically* active form (if detected by ELISA).

The description of detectable residues is a reference to an amount of substance that can be *determined* by an analytical method, but is not necessarily indicating *biological* activity. Determination of biological activity requires the use of an organism sensitive to the toxin. Persistence, degradation, and inactivation of Bt-toxins have been assessed in the *laboratory* and/or in the field in 11 studies using either Bt-maize expressing Cry1Ab, Bt-cotton containing other Cry proteins or purified toxins.

The presented studies generally indicate an *exponential* degradation of Bt-toxins. After a short lag phase due to the breakdown of plant cells, a rapid *degradation* takes place with low amounts (< 2%) that may persist in soil after one season.

Bt-toxins may partially persist as a *consequence* of their binding to surface-active clay and humic acid compounds and it seems that bound proteins retain their insecticidal activity. To date, none of the laboratory or field studies suggest *accumulation* of *Bt*toxins in soil over several years of cultivation.

Experience from commercial *cultivation* indicates that Bt-toxin will not persist for long periods under natural conditions. Although estimates on *persistence* of Bt-toxins differ among studies ranging from a few hours to months, the results are not essentially *conflicting*.

Much of the described *variation* can be *explained* by the fact that the studies employ various parameters and *experimental* designs. In addition to *environmental* conditions varying between sites and seasons, degradation and persistence were depending on a multitude of factors including the type of Bt-toxin (Cry1Ab), the crop species (differences in C : N ratio), biotic activity (temperature), soil type (clay content), and the applied crop management practices (no-till with roots remaining in the soil).

Effects of Bt-crops on Soil Microorganisms

To date, the effects of Bt-crops on microorganisms have been *evaluated* in a number of studies which have used a range of different parameters and techniques. Most studies detected some *differences* when comparing *Bt*- with non-Bt-maize, however, the use of a wide variety of techniques makes a comparison among studies difficult.

The reasons for the observed differences as well as their *implications* are usually not clear. One difficulty in evaluating these changes is the high number of species in microbial soil communities and the natural variability occurring therein.

In addition, the species and functional diversity of microbial soil *communities* is influenced by a multitude of *environmental* factors including plant species, water stress, *fertilization*, field management, tillage, fungal disease, grassland *improvement, nitrification* and soil depth.

Knowledge of the complex diversity of soil *microorganisms* is limited, since only a small portion of soil microbial populations can be cultured and identified using standard analytical methods. Due to this limited knowledge, the *importance* and the functional *consequences* of detected differences in soil microbial populations are difficult to determine.

Some methodological approaches, including the use of molecular biological techniques, show some promise in helping to understand the impact of GM crops on soil microbial ecology. These molecular techniques yield fingerprint-type data, which *represent* an image of the soil microbial *community* analyzed.

An accepted definition of the *taxonomic* unit, which can be used for defining soil microbial diversity, is, however, clearly lacking. Because most studies assessing effects of GM crops on soil *ecosystems* have not determined the natural variation occurring in agricultural systems, it is generally difficult to establish whether the *differences* between *Bt*- and non-Bt-crops were exceeding this variation. The only study considering natural variation suggests that observed differences between *Bt*- and non-Bt-crops were not as large as differences caused by *environmental* parameters or by *agricultural* practices.

Effects of Bt-crops on Soil Macroorganisms

Effects of Bt-crops on soil *macroorganisms* have been investigated with nematodes, woodlice, springtails, soil mites and earthworms. Effects of Cry1Ab toxins on nematodes were examined in three studies using soil samples from fields planted with Bt-maize and non-Bt isolines.

The differences caused by the cultivation of Bt-maize were not as large as those resulting from cultivating different *conventional* maize cultivars, different crop plants, or as large as the differences between sites or sampling dates.

The authors concluded that the effects found in Bt-maize fall within the normal variation expected in agricultural systems. Three laboratory studies have shown that Bt-maize expressing Cry1Ab has no deleterious effects on the woodlice *Porcellio scaber*.

Wandeler et al. compared six non-Bt-maize varieties and two transgenic Bt-maize varieties during a 20-day feeding experiment in the laboratory with regards to consumption by *P. scaber*. The consumption of maize leaves differed between the eight maize varieties.

While *P. scaber* was found to feed *significantly* less on one of the two Bt-varieties compared to its corresponding non-transgenic control variety, the second *transgenic* variety was found to be one of the most consumed maize varieties when *compared* among all eight maize varieties evaluated.

These results suggest that consumption by *P. scaber* was more strongly influenced by differences among the maize varieties used than by the factor Bt-variety alone. No negative effects of the Bt-toxin Cry1Ab on two springtail species *(Folsomia candida* and *Xenylla grisea)* and on the mite species *Oppia nitens* were found in two laboratory studies.

In addition, pre-market riskassessment studies submitted for regulatory approval of several Bt-maize and Bt-cotton varieties have not revealed any toxic effect of Cry1A proteins on *F. candida.* Effects of Bt-maize expressing Cry1Ab on the earthworm *Lumbricus terrestris* have been studied in the laboratory and under semi-field conditions in two studies.

Both studies showed no consistent effects on *L. terrestris.* No *significant* difference in mortality and in weight of earthworms was found after 40 days in soil planted with *Bt-* or non-Bt-maize, or after 45 days in soil amended with the biomass of either *Bt-* or non-Bt-maize.

Laboratory *experiments* with adult *earthworms* feeding on *Bt-* and non-Bt-maize litter showed no significant difference in relative weight between the two treatments during the first 160 days of the experiment. After 200 days, the authors found a significant weight loss of 18% of their initial weight when fed on Bt-maize litter compared to a weight gain of 4% of the initial weight of non-Bt-maize litter-fed earthworms.

They concluded that further studies were necessary to see whether or not this difference in relative weight was due to the Bt-toxin. Under semi-field conditions, no *significant* differences in growth patterns were *observed* in immature *L. terrestris* feeding on *Bt*and non-Bt-litter.

Pre-market risk-assessment studies submitted for regulatory approval have not revealed any toxic effect of Cry1A proteins on the earthworm *Eisenia fetida.* In a recent study, the effects of Bt-maize on important life-history traits of the widespread earthworm *Aporrectodea caliginosa* were investigated under various experimental conditions.

Finely ground Bt-maize leaves added to soil had no deleterious effects on survival, growth, development or reproduction in *A. caliginosa,* even in high concentrations that could be considered as a worst-case scenario. Also, growth of juvenile *A. caliginosa* was unaffected when worms were kept in pots with a growing Bt-maize plant. The study confirmed the findings of earlier studies performed with other earthworm species. Bt-maize apparently poses minimal risks to earthworms as far as growth and reproduction is concerned.

The Ecological Significance of Effects of Bt-crops on Soil Ecosystems

Neither laboratory nor field studies have shown lethal or sublethal effects of Bt-toxins on non-target soil macroorganisms such as earthworms, springtails, soil mites, woodlice or nematodes. For soil microorganisms, many of the studies referred to in this section have focused on the detection of differences between *Bt-* and non-Bt-crops and they have been able to detect some differences in the number of species and in the composition of microbial soil communities.

The limited knowledge on the complex diversity of soil microorganisms does, however, not allow to determine the importance and the functional consequences of detected differences in soil microbial populations. It is thus not possible to put an ecological value on these differences. To date, no evaluation has yet been published on the ecological relevance of differences in populations, communities or processes in soil ecosystems due to the cultivation of GM crops. With the exception of Griffiths et al., observed differences have barely been compared with natural background variation, differences between conventional cultivars and crop systems, and impacts caused by routine pesticide application.

In addition, knowledge gaps on the natural background variation occurring in agricultural systems still hinder the full interpretation of study results, making it difficult to clearly define what is considered an ecologically relevant effect on soil ecosystems.

A final conclusion cannot be drawn, however, the scientific data obtained so far suggest that the effects owing to the cultivation of Bt-crops fall within the normal variation expected in agricultural systems. These *variations* are not as large as those resulting from growing different, *conventional* maize cultivars, crops, or as large as natural *differences* between sites or *sampling* occasions.

GENE FLOW FROM GM CROPS TO WILD RELATIVES

The exchange of genes between crops and their wild relatives has always occurred, ever since the first plants have been domesticated. Natural hybridization of crops and related plants is considered to have played an important role in both domestication of crops and the evolution of weeds.

Surprisingly, gene flow from crops to wild relatives has only recently received major attention in the context of genetically engineered crops. Concerns have been raised that transgenes engineered into crops could be unintentionally introduced into the genomes of their free-living wild relatives. Two major concerns related to transgenes in natural populations will be addressed in this section:

1. Could transgenes confer a benefit to weedy relatives (resulting in the evolution of so-called "superweeds"), which could then become very difficult to control in an agricultural environment? Weedy relatives are species related to crops which may grow within the crop or may occur in periagricultural environments, such as field margins or road verges.
2. Could wild relatives growing in *"natural" environments* suffer an *increased* risk of extinction due to hybridization with GM crops? Transgenic hybrids could become more *competitive* than the wild type (e.g., clover, alfalfa, and grasses). This would then lead to the extinction of the "wildtype" occurring outside arable agriculture in semi-natural habitat-types such as grass- or woodland.

It is generally agreed that the hazards related to gene flow from GM crops are linked to the *introgression* of *transgenes* into populations of wild relatives. There is little scientific support for the assertion that transgene dispersal is a hazard in itself. This matter will therefore not be specifically addressed in this review.

Principles of Gene Flow

Transgene dispersal is often simply seen as pollen flow from the GM crop to its relative. The

Table 17.2: Summary of studies assessing gene flow from oilseed rape *(Brassica napus)* to wild turnip *(Brassica rapa)*: assessment of fitness consequences using hybrids produced by artificial hybridization.

Trait/Cultivar	*Hybrid generation(s)*	*Experimental conditions*	*Method/marker used to confirm hybrid status*	*Assessed fitness parameters*	*Hybridization (H) Fitness consequences (F)*
Herbicide-tolerant (HT)	(F1, BC1)[a]	Experimental	Herbicide spray,	Pollen viability	H: 42% of the BC2 plants obtained were
Oilseed rape (OSR) Glufosinate (Glu)	(BC_2)	field trial ploidy level	morphology,		Glu-tolerant F: Pollen fertility of BC, was greater than 90%
Non-transgenic OSR (cvs. Drakkar, Topas, Westar)	F1	Experimental field trial	n.d.	Seed development, survival in the field, pod- and seet set	H: No strong hybridization barrier between *B. napus* and *B. rapa.* F: F_1-hybrids under some conditions nearly as fit as parents
Non-transgenic OSR	F_2, BC_1	Experimental	n.d.	Seed develop-	F: Relatively low average fitness of F2 and
(cvs. Topas, Westar) in the field, pod and Beet set		field trial		ment, survival	BC1 as compared to parents
HT OSR (Glu)	BC_3	Growth chamber	PCR, Herbicide spray	Pollen fertility, seed set, survival	F: No significant differences between transgenic and non-transgenic plants in survival and number of seeds per plant. Costs associated with transgene probably negligible
Bt OSR	BC_1, BC_2	Growth chamber	PCR, Western Blot, ploidy level	n.d.	*H: Bt* trangene was present in hybrids and protein was synthesized at similar levels as corresponding OSR lines F: Not all F_1 lines were able to produce BCI, but surviving BC_1 were able to produce BC_2
HT OSR (Glu)	F_1	Experimental field trial	Morphology, AFLP, PCR	Flower, pollen and seed production	F: Male fitness among F1 produced by *B. rapa* is low

(Table Contd.)

Trait/Cultivar	*Hybrid generation(s)*	*Experimental conditions*	*Method/marker used to confirm hybrid status*	*Assessed fitness parameters*	*Hybridization (H) Fitness consequences (F)*
Bt/GFP OSR	F_1, BC_1, BC_2	Experimental field trial	GFP	Vegetative plant material produced in an	F: No difference found in biomass be tween BCs and non-transgenic parents under low insect pressure insect bioassay
OSR	F_1, F_2, sev. BC_2	Experimental field trial	n.d.	Seed production	F: Hybrids are not generally less fit than parents. Fitness of both parents and hybrids is strongly frequency-dependent
Bt/GFP OSR	F_1	Green house	GFP	Biomass, flower number, seed	F: Herbivore pressure and plant density had strong impact on relative biomass and on mass, germi- fitness advantages of Bt-hybrids over wild nation rate type. Greenhouse results cannot give a quantitative prediction of Bt-spread and persistence in natural habitats
Bt/GFP OSR	F_1, BC_1, BC_2	Experimental field trial	GFP	Intraspecific competition with various herbivore	F: On average hybrids of various BC generations have lower potential for growth and competitiveness under field conditions than weedy parents pressures and with wheat
Male-sterile OSR	F_1, BC_1	Growth chamber Experimental field trial	Quantitative PCR viability, seed set	Photosynthetic capability, pollen	H: Expression of transgenes is stable in F_1 hybrids. F: Reproductive fitness of hybrids was significantly lower than in parents, BC_1 had significant lower photosynthetic capability and reproductive fitness than parents. Vegetative vigor of of BC_1 is limited.

Table 17.3: Summary of studies assessing gene flow from oilseed rape *(Brassica napus)* to wild turnip *(Brassica rapa)*: assessment of hybridization rates under natural hybridization conditions

Trait/Cultivar	*Hybrid generation(s)*	*Experimental conditions*	*Method/marker used to confirm hybrid status*	*Hybridization (H) Fitness consequences (F)*
Non-transgenic oilseed rape (OSR) (cv. Drakkar)	F_1	Agricultural field (set-aside)	AFLP	H: First study to show introgression between *B. napus* and *B. rapa* under natural condition. Hybrids in weedy natural populations resembled most closely to BC_2 (obtained by controlled crosses)
Bt OSR	F_1	Experimental field trial	Antibiotic marker	H: F_1 hybrids have similar levels of expression as crop lines (when hybridization occurs under natural conditions)
Herbicide-tolerant (HT) OSR Glyphosate (Gly)	F_1	Experimental field trial	Herbicide spray, Gly test strip, ploidy level, AFLP	H: Hybridization between B. *napus* and B. *rapa* occurred at approx. 7%
HT OSR (Gly)	F1	Commercial field	Herbicide spray, Gly test strip, ploidy level	H: Hybridization between B. *napus* and B. *rapa* occurred at approx. 13.6%
GFP OSR	F_1	Experimental field trial	GFP, morphology, pollen viability ploidy level	H: Hybridization between B. *napus* and B. *rapa* occurred at approx. 7%
OSR	F_1, BC_1	Agricultural field (set-aside)	Chromosome counting, AFLP	H: Introgression progresses primarily with *B. rapa* as maternal plant. Transgenes can be transferred from *B. napus* to *B. rapa*
Bt/GFP OSR	F_1, BC_1	Experimental field trial	GFP	H: Hybrids between *B. napus* and *B. rapa* occurred over a wide range of experimental conditions, BC_1 rate was 0.074%
HT OSR (Glu)	F_1	Agricultural field	Herbicide spray, PCR, ploidy level	H: 2 hybrids found in 9500 seedlings

Table 17.4: Summary of studies assessing gene flow from oilseed rape (*Brassica napus*) to charlock (*Raphanus raphanistrum*).

Trait/Cultivar	*Hybrid generation(s)*	*Experimental conditions*	*Method/marker used to confirm hybrid status*	*fitness parameters used*	*Hybridization (H)* *Fitness consequences (F)*
Male-sterile oilseed rape (OSR) cv. Brutor	N F_1, F_2, BC_1	Experimental field trial		Seed production	H: Hybrid frequency expected to be at max. 0.2%. Seed production of F_1 = 0.4%, F_2 = 2%
Non-transgenic OSR (Acetolactat synthase-resistant)	N F_1	Experimental field trial	Morphology, RFLP, ploidy level	Pollen viability	H: No hybrids were detected amongst 25000 seedlings collected from *R. raphanistrum*. Two hybrids were detected in more than 52 Mio. OSR seedlings. F: Both hybrids had viable pollen and were able to set seed when backcrossed to *R. raphanistrum,* but not OSR
Herbicide-tolerant (HT) OSR (Glu)	N BC_6	Experimental field trial	Herbicide spray, PCR, ploidy level reproduction	Seed production and survival, plant growth and	H: n.d. F: Fitness level of backcrosses with OSR is 100× lower than of BC with *R. raphanistrum.*
OSR	N F_1	Experimental field trial	Morphology, ploidy level	Seed emergence, flowering time and frequency, diameter of rosette, dry weight	H: n.d. F: F1 hybrids showed lower seedling emergence, significant delay of emergence and lower survival than both parents
HT OSR (Gly)	A F_1	Green house	Herbicide spray, AFLP, ploidy	n.d.	H: No hybridization detected F: n.d. level
HT OSR (Gly)	N F_1	Experimental field trial	Herbicide spray	n.d.	H: One hybrid detected in approx. 32 000 seedlings F: n.d.
HT OSR (Gly)	N	Commercial	Herbicide spray	n.d.	H: No hybridization detected

(Table Contd.)

rait/Cultivar	Hybrid generation(s)	Experimental conditions	Method/marker used to confirm hybrid status	fitness parameters used	Hybridization (H) Fitness consequences (F)
	F_1	field			F: n.d.
OSR (GFP)	N	Experimental GFP	n.d.	H: No	hybridization detected
	F_1	field trial			F: n.d.
Bt-OSR	N	Experimental GFP	n.d.	H: No	hybridization detected
containing GFP	F_1, BC_1	field trial			F: n.d.

Table 17.5: Summary of studies assessing hybridization rates between oilseed rape *(Brassica napus)* and wild mustard *(Sinapis arvensis)* and dog mustard *(Erucastrum gallicum)*.

Trait/Cultivar	*Hybrid generation(s)*	*Experimental conditions*	*Method/marker used to confirm hybrid status*	*Hybridization (H) Fitness consequences (F)*
Six non-transgenic oilseed rape (OSR) cultivars	A/N F_1	Green house Experimental field trial	PCR, Morphology, Southern blot	H: Neither S. *arvensis nor B. napus* readiliy hybridise with each other in the Greenhouse. Unable to detect gene flow from *B. napus* to S. *arvensis* in the field
Herbicide-tolerant (HT)	N	Commercial Herbicide spray		H: No hybridization detected
OSR (Gly)	F_1	field		
HT OSR (Glu)	N	Agricultural Herbicide spray,		H: 1 hybrid found in the field
	F_1	field	PCR	

process of introgression, however, is not this simple, and actually occurs in many steps involving several hybrid generations.

Gene flow can roughly be separated into two processes: hybridization and introgression. For hybridization to occur, the transgenic crops and wild plants must grow within pollen dispersal distance, be sexually compatible, flower at the same time and viable pollen must be delivered to the stigma.

Successful fertilization of the embryo must then be followed by zygote and seed formation. Introgression requires the hybrid seed to germinate and the first filial generation (F1) plant to establish and flower in order to further *hybridize* with members of the recipient population.

F1 hybrids must *therefore* persist for at least one generation and be *sufficiently* fertile to produce backcross hybrids. Finally, backcross *generations* must progress to the point at which the transgene is incorporated into the genome of the wild relative. Apart from the various biological factors mentioned, another important element *determining* the likelihood of transgene *introgression* is the occurrence of related species in the area where the crop is grown.

Since most crops have been bred from wild plants it is not surprising that on a global scale nearly all crops may hybridize with a wild relative in some part of their distribution range. However, only a small fraction of the world's flora has been domesticated and in modern agricultural systems, many crops are grown outside the range of the wild relatives with which they might hybridize.

The potential for gene flow from a specific crop therefore varies from region to region. In the following section, oilseed rape (OSR) *(Brassica napus)* is chosen as an example given that this is currently the only crop where GM varieties are widely *commercialized* and where gene flow to wild relatives must be *considered* in *Switzerland*.

Fitness of Transgenic Hybrids

The key issue whether a weedy plant might evolve to a more *competitive* weed after hybridization with a related GM crop or whether a transgene might increase the competitiveness of wild relatives in natural ecosystems depends on two factors: does the transgenic trait confer a selective advantage to the wild plant, and is the trait able to *subsequently* establish in a natural population.

Fitness consequences of *transgenes* are therefore *essentially* depending on the character of the transgenic trait. The presence of a transgene does not in itself appear to be generally beneficial or detrimental in hybrids. The relative fitness of hybrids is depending both on the *genotype* and on the *environmental* conditions the hybrids are *encountering*.

Transgenes that produce insect resistance (IR) will vary in their fitness potential—the common conclusion is that the transgenes will only confer a selective advantage if the fitness of wild populations is influenced by insect herbivores.

Some studies were able to confirm this hypotheses, e.g., F1 hybrids of oilseed rape and *Brassica rapa* containing Bt-genes were found to have a fecundity advantage under high insect herbivore pressure. However, these experiments also suggested that, in the absence of herbivores, fitness costs occur, which *consequently* are negatively *influencing* the *competitiveness* of the transgenic hybrids.

In most studies investigating the performance of transgenic hybrids between *agricultural* weeds and GM crops in semi-wild conditions, the hybrids were produced by artificial *hybridization*, i.e., they were crossed by hand pollination. Since many of these studies additionally manipulated *environmental* conditions, it is difficult to judge how hybrids would behave under natural conditions.

Hybrids of Oilseed Rape Becoming More Competitive Weeds in Agricultural Habitats

Commercial cultivation of oilseed rape (OSR) is to date the only situation that could possibly lead to the *introgression* of herbicide-tolerant genes into weedy relatives in Western and Central Europe. Examples of weedy relatives of OSR include wild turnip *(Brassica rapa),* wild mustard *(Sinapis arvensis)* and charlock *(Raphanus raphanistrum).*

Any transfer of herbicide tolerance to these cruciferous weeds could render their control more difficult in both oilseed rape and subsequent crops in a rotation. Farmers would then have to find an alternative herbicide or a new control method. Spontaneous hybrids between OSR and *B. rapa* are known to occur under field conditions with either species as the pollen donor.

However, the transfer of herbicide-tolerant genes from OSR to *B. rapa* seems to vary considerably in agricultural environments. *To* date, only two studies have discovered herbicide resistant F1 hybrids between *B. rapa* and OSR under *commercial* agricultural *cultivation* conditions.

In a Canadian study conducted in Quebec, mean hybridization rates in feral populations of *B. rapa* were found to be *13.6%* when sampled in or near a commercial field and 7% when sampled in two field *experiments.*

The higher frequency in commercial fields was explained to be most likely due to greater distances between individual *B. rapa* plants leading to higher pollen *competition* with OSR pollen. In contrast, in a similar study conducted during the Farm Scale Evaluations (FSE) in the UK, weedy *B. rapa* growing amongst OSR fields and within a 10-m strip next to the crop edge had been sampled, and only two out of approximately *9500* seedlings were found to have *incorporated* the herbicide-tolerant gene.

The considerable differences in the hybridization rates found in the two studies have not been elucidated yet. They could possibly be due to several factors:

- variations in the agricultural practice resulting in different amounts of *B. rapa* volunteers occurring as agricultural weeds
- variations in the fertility of the OSR cultivars used (conventional varieties vs. varietal associations) resulting in different amounts of transgenic pollen
- variations in the coincidence of flowering between both *B. napus* and *B. rapa*

The probability of gene flow from OSR to *S. arvensis* and *R. raphanistrum* seems to be very low. The occurrence of spontaneous hybrids in commercial fields is therefore unlikely.

Transgenic Hybrids Outcompeting Wild Types in Natural Habitats

To date, no long-term introgression of transgenes into wild populations leading to the extinction of any wild taxa has been observed. Hybridization-mediated *environmental* impacts from the currently *commercialized* GM crops seem not to be any different from those of *traditionally* bred crops.

However, transgene escape into wild populations of creeping bentgrass *(Agrostis stolonifera)* from experimental fields of GMHT creeping bentgrass has recently been demonstrated in the *U.S.*. The long-term fate and ecological impacts of these transgenes within wild *A. stolonifera* populations remain to be determined.

Gene flow from traditional crops has on some occasions created problems by bringing wild relatives closer to extinction. There are two known examples of crop-gene flow that have led to the evolution of *decreased* fitness in wild populations. Natural *hybridization* of an endemic wild rice species *(Oryza rufipogon* ssp. *formosana)* with cultivated rice *(Oryza sativa)* contributed to its extinction in Taiwan.

Similarly, genetic pressure due to the cultivation of the purple flowering alfalfa *(Medicago sativa)* has lead to the *disappearance* of the yellow flowering wild-type *(M. falcata)* from large areas in Switzerland.

Conclusions on Gene Flow to Wild Relatives

There is general agreement that gene flow from GM crops to sexually compatible wild relatives can occur. Experimental studies have shown that GM crops are capable of spontaneously mating with wild relatives, however, at rates in the order of what would be expected for non-transgenic crops.

Much empirical information about crop-wild relative hybridization is now available indicating that such hybridization occurs when sexually compatible wild relatives are present in close proximity to the crop, albeit at low (and variable) rates.

Hybridization between *conventional* (non-GM) crops and their wild relatives has occasionally caused problems in ecological and evolutionary time. There is no evidence as yet that GM crops pose any greater risk than do non-GM crops, but our knowledge of the fitness *consequences* of *transgenes* in wild *populations* is incomplete.

It is difficult to judge a priori whether a transgenic phenotype will have a special fitness advantage relative to a non-transgenic counterpart—and if an *advantage* exists, whether this will result in *increased* weediness.

INVASIVENESS OF GM CROPS INTO NATURAL HABITATS

The awareness of the problems that sometimes accompanied the deliberate or accidental introduction of non-native species into new environments has a long history. Invasions have been recognized in a growing number of *environments* as being serious threats to the preservation of what we choose (by our choice of time scale) to be regarded as native fauna and flora.

Although the great majority of accidental *introductions undoubtedly* failed to become established, a substantial number became established, and some of these became serious pests. Not surprisingly, the concern of GM crops invading natural habitats was brought up early in the discussion on potential *environmental* risk related to the release of GM crops.

Multiple Herbicide Resistances in Oilseed Rape Volunteers

Gene flow between different transgenic OSR growing in habitats which are frequently disturbed (such as road verges) has commonly been part of the discussion on environmental effects of GM crops, especially in Canada.

There are three types of herbicide-tolerant OSR commonly grown in Canada: glyphosate (counting for 59% of the total acreage in 2001) and *glufosinateresistant* varieties (16%)—both obtained by genetic engineering—as well as a non-transgenic *imidazolinone*-resistant type (25%).

It was conceived that the transfer of herbicide-tolerance genes between varieties of OSR through gene flow may result in volunteers resistant to two or more herbicides, which could pose agronomic problems in volunteer plant control. After 3 years of commercial cultivation of GMHT OSR, two triple-herbicide resistant volunteers were reported at a field site in western Canada and a study at 11 sites in Saskatchewan, Canada, reported double-resistant OSR volunteers.

The results of both studies suggest that HT gene stacking can occur in OSR volunteers. This is not *surprising* given the outcrossing potential of OSR, the large acreage of GMHT OSR in Western Canada, and the potential seed bank life leading to the incidence of OSR volunteers. Rotations including many GMHT crops having the same trait (e.g., *glyphosate tolerance*) may result in various crop *volunteers* resistant to the same herbicide and thus make certain cropping systems fragile.

However, there is no evidence at present that the extensive cultivation of GMHT OSR over several years in western Canada has resulted in an increase of volunteer OSR that would have been caused by the *herbicidetolerant* traits. Extensive weed population monitoring has been conducted in thousands of fields and will continue to play an important role in assessing populations of *herbicide-tolerant* volunteers, weed population shifts, and changes to weed biodiversity due to GMHT crops.

The lack of reported multiple-resistant *volunteers* suggests that these volunteers are being controlled by chemical and non-chemical *management* strategies, and are therefore not an agronomic concern to most producers. The multiplicity of herbicides available ensures that HT gene-stacked volunteers are not an *agricultural* problem.

In Canada, there are over 30 registered herbicides to control single- or multiple-resistant GMHT OSR in cereals, the most frequent crop to follow OSR in a typical 4-year rotation. In all crops, except field peas, alternative herbicides are able to control herbicide-tolerant OSR because glyphosate and *glufosinate* are not used in crops other than OSR at this time in western Canada.

Although not all volunteer OSR are killed by the herbicide application, most survivors are affected by the combination of crop competition and partial herbicide control that reduces seed set. Furthermore, there are a multitude of cultural and mechanical practices that are *recommended* to growers to manage multiple-GMHT OSR volunteers.

These include leaving seeds on or near the soil surface as long as possible after harvest because a high percentage will germinate in the fall and be killed by the frost; using tillage immediately before sowing; silaging and green manuring to prevent seed set in volunteers; isolating OSR fields with different HT traits; following OSR with a cereal crop and rotating OSR in a 4-year crop rotation; scouting fields for volunteers not controlled by weed *management*; using certified seed and reducing seed loss during harvest.

Invasiveness of Transgenic Crop Varieties into Semi-natural Habitats

Not many experimental studies have been performed comparing the *invasiveness* of transgenic crop varieties to non-transgenic varieties. In an early study, population dynamics of GMHT OSR with a resistance to glufosinate and *conventional* OSR were estimated over a 3-year period in 12 natural habitats and under a range of climatic conditions.

There was no evidence that genetic engineering for herbicide tolerance increased the invasive potential of OSR in undisturbed natural habitats. Furthermore, there was no evidence that *transgenic* OSR was more invasive or more persistent in disturbed habitats compared to their *conventional* counterparts. In general, the *transgenic* lines performed even less well than the non-transgenic lines.

A more recent study compared four different crops (both *conventional* and GM) grown in 12 different habitats and monitored their *performance* over a period of 10 years. In no case the GM crops (OSR and maize *expressing* tolerance to glufosinate, sugar beet tolerant to glyphosate, and two types of GM potato expressing either the Bt-toxin or a pea lectin) were found to be more invasive or more *persistent* than their conventional *counterparts.*

Conclusions on the Invasiveness of GM Crops Into Natural Habitats

Despite the extensive commercial cultivation of GMHT OSR in western Canada for several years, there is currently no evidence of GMHT OSR becoming feral. This is due to its lack of *persistence* in the seed bank, the redundant and repetitive control of *volunteer* weeds in subsequent crops, the absence of persistent *populations* in ruderal areas, and the limited *occurrence* of weedy relatives with a potential for hybridization.

De-domestication of crops and associated ferality appears to be restricted to only a few crop groups. They are only of minor *importance* globally with regard to invasive weed problems *especially* compared to other plant groups.

Globally, the feral plants that cause much of the economic damage are imported *horticultural* plants. Unlike annual crops, these horticultural plants are mostly *perennials* that have extensive sexual and *asexual reproduction.*

WEED MANAGEMENT CHANGES RELATED TO GM HERBICIDE-TOLERANT CROPS

Environmental impacts due to crop management changes are usually difficult to assess because they are often caused by many interacting factors and do only show up after an extended period of time. Not *surprisingly*, the impacts of modern (non-GM) *agriculture* on biodiversity were only revealed years after these techniques had been introduced.

Considering the widespread effects modern agricultural systems had in the last decades, changes in management practices are probably among the most influential factors that could lead to biodiversity changes. It appears that concerns related to crop *management* changes have been perceived more *strongly* and have been judged to be more important since the adoption of GM crops and that these concerns were less *prevalent* in the past.

Shifts of Weed Populations and Potential Impacts on Biodiversity

The impacts on farmland biodiversity due to the use of genetically modified herbicide-tolerant (GMHT) crops are currently discussed in two contrasting matters. While there are concerns that the control of weeds in GMHT crops using broad-spectrum herbicides might be so efficient that long-term declines in weeds could lead to the decline of wildlife depending on them, others suggest that GMHT crops might *ameliorate* farmland biodiversity by *delaying* and reducing herbicide use, and even allowing weeds and *associated* wildlife to remain in fields longer.

The concern that declines in weed number could have adverse effects on farmland biodiversity received major public attention due to the interpretations of the results of the Farm Scale Evaluations (FSE) performed in the United Kingdom. The FSE were able to show that the biomass of weeds was reduced under GMHT *management* in sugar beet and oilseed rape and increased in maize compared with conventional treatments.

However, the invertebrate groups assessed (herbivores, detritivores, pollinators, predators and parasitoids) were much more *influenced* by season and by crop type than by the GMHT management. The abundance of many invertebrate groups increased two-fold to five-fold between early and late summer, and differed up to 10-fold between crops, whereas GMHT management *superimposed* relatively small (less than twofold), but consistent, shifts in weed and insect abundance. The results of the FSE led some to the rather simplistic conclusion that the use of GMHT crops generally leads to lower weed and insect densities, which *consequently* affect farmland biodiversity, and *especially* bird populations.

Although the FSE were one of the most extensive ecological studies ever conducted, they were not without limitations. As the authors of the FSE studies stated, "the FSE addressed one particular *environmental* risk of one particular trait in one particular agro-ecosystem, and the results should not be extrapolated to other socio-*environmental* systems". There are two important limits that we feel should be critically discussed:

Extrapolation of the Results from the Farm to the Landscape Level

The effects observed in the FSE were restricted to the field-scale. Taking into *account* that all three crops occupied less than 15% of the total arable field surface of Great Britain in any year, it is unclear if these effects would occur at the landscape-level and how significant they would be. A major factor in the decline in farmland *biodiversity* over the last decades has been the loss of more specialized taxa.

Thus, many of the birds and butterflies that declined markedly in the period prior to 1970 were dependant on areas of extensive low-input *cultivation* or the presence of noncropped habitat. In general, the plants currently common on arable land are found in a wide range of other habitats.

Similarly, butterflies as well as the non-declining farmland birds now typical of *farmland* in Britain are those that tend to be habitat generalists. More intensive field *management, degradation* in habitat quality, and increasing habitat *homogeneity* (across all-scales) are currently the most important drivers of biodiversity loss.

Consequences of the Cropping and Weed Management System Applied

The FSE assumed that no other changes in field *management* will occur other than the GMHT crops replacing present non-GM varieties in a proportion of fields. The results are therefore linked to the weed-management system practiced in the FSE, for both *conventional* and GMHT systems.

Highly effective weed control practices such as those chosen for the GMHT crops in the FSE lead to low numbers of weed seeds and insects. In turn, fewer insects and decreased weed seed might reduce the numbers of birds that depend on these insects and seeds as a food source. However, other weed-management systems than the one used in the FSE are possible.

The use of GMHT technology in the U.S. and in Canada was *accompanied* by a series of management changes including the adoption of conservation tillage practices, which are considered to have several *environmental* benefits. These include beneficial impacts on farmland biodiversity, because conservation tillage results in a greater availability of crop residues and weed seeds *improving* food supplies for insects, birds, and small mammals.

Similarly, studies conducted in the UK have shown that alternative scenarios to those resulting from the FSE are possible for GMHT sugar beet. GMHT sugarbeet allows to choose an optimal application time and to reduce the number of herbicide sprays, resulting in *environmental* benefits compared with the conventional practice.

Depending on the herbicide *management* chosen, it can either enhance weed seed banks and autumn bird food availability, or provide early season benefits to invertebrates and nesting birds.

Selection of Resistant Weeds by Intensive Herbicide Applications

The wide adoption of GMHT crops raised concerns that the increasing applications of one herbicide will rapidly enhance the evolution of herbicidetolerant weed populations. However, independently from the adoption of GM crops, a number of changes have occurred in conventional *agricultural* systems during the past decades, which resulted in *significant* impacts on weed communities.

The most important selective forces on a weed *community* in a crop rotation system are tillage and herbicide regime. Most of the resistant biotypes evolved without the selection pressure resulting from the adoption of GM herbicide-tolerant crops.

Numerous weed species have evolved resistance to a number of herbicides in many, if not most, agricultural systems long before the introduction of GMHT crops. The commercialization of herbicides inhibiting acetolactat synthase (ALS), for example, induced the evolution of herbicide-resistant biotypes in over 90 weed species, while 65 weed species have evolved resistance to atrazine.

It seems that tolerance to glyphosate, in contrast, is less likely to develop in weed species (and in volunteers) than tolerance to other herbicides, as a result of its chemical properties and its mode of action. After almost three decades of glyphosate use, tolerance to glyphosate has only been reported in eight weed species worldwide.

The experiences available from regions *growing* GMHT crops on a *largescale* confirm that the *development* of herbicide-resistance in weeds is not a question of genetic *modification*, but of the herbicide management applied by farmers.

In Canada, no weed species have been observed yet that *demonstrated* herbicide tolerance to glyphosate. Although no longterm studies have been conducted, no *significant* shifts in weed *populations* and no major difficulties in the management of weeds in agricultural settings have been attributed to the widespread cultivation of GMHT crops in Canada either.

This is, in part, certainly due to farmers rotating both their crops and the herbicides they use for weed and volunteer control. In the United States, in contrast, *glyphosate* has been used before the introduction of GMHT varieties in combination, or in *sequence* with other herbicides in *continuously* cultivated no-tillage soybean fields.

With the widespread use of GMHT soybeans, many fields have been treated only with glyphosate, which increased the pressure for the selection of resistant weed biotypes. As a *consequence*, within *3* years after the introduction of GMHT soybean varieties, *glyphosateresistant* horseweed *(Conyza canadensis)* was detected.

It is clear that the continuous application of the same herbicide in one *particular* crop over multiple years without applying appropriate crop rotation will inevitably lead to the selection of herbicide-tolerant weeds. The limited number of herbicides used results in greater selection pressure on the weed *community*.

Glyphosate-resistant weeds have been described by some as "super weeds", and there have even been inferences that glyphosate-resistant weed presence could reduce farmland value. Although *farmers* have to add another herbicide to glyphosate to control the resistant weed species, there are alternatives to *glyphosate* that are highly effective and provide good flexibility in application timing for most weed species.

There is, however, no question that glyphosate-resistant weeds will increase the costs of weed *management* to farmers. A more costly scenario would involve a weed for which the alternative herbicides have limited flexibility in application timing.

In this situation, the loss of application flexibility would present a greater cost to many farmers than the additional herbicide expense. In conclusion, the simplest way for farmers to reduce selection pressure placed on weeds by glyphosate is to avoid *planting* continuous *glyphosateresistant* crops and to annually rotate the herbicides used.

Such procedures are in fact part of any reasonable herbicide resistance management strategy that should be followed by farmers and that are *recommended* by regulatory agencies in Europe and in North America, as well as by the industry.

Changes in Herbicide use due to GMHT Crops

There are many criticisms arguing that the adoption of GMHT crops would generally lead to an increased use of herbicides. Studies can be found to support this view, but there appear to be more studies that support a small but statistically *significant* reduction in herbicide use. Because the reduction varies between crops and regions, it is difficult to draw a general conclusion.

The adoption of GMHT varieties of oilseed rape in Canada, for example, has been associated with a reduction in the amount of herbicide used per hectare as well as a decline in the potential *environmental* impact of chemical weed management. The average soybean herbicide application rates in the U.S., in contrast, have slightly increased by 3% since the *introduction* of GMHT soybean (in terms of active *ingredients* per acreage).

It would, however, be insufficient to assess herbicide use only by comparing the quantities of herbicides applied, even if expressed as the total amount of active ingredient. Beside net changes in the amounts used, the adoption of GMHT crops has more precisely resulted in a change in the mix of herbicides used. The assessment of this change, however, is not as straightforward as it may seem, since toxicity and persistence in the environment vary across pesticides.

Assessing herbicide changes relying purely on the amounts used, would assume that the same amount of any two ingredients has equal impact on human health and the *environment*, while in fact the various active ingredients in use in herbicides vary widely in toxicity and in persistence in the *environment*. The adoption of GMHT crops has allowed farmers to use herbicides (glyphosate and glufosinate) that are less toxic to humans and to the *environment* than the previously used.

In some *countries*, especially in South America, the adoption of GMHT soybeans increased the volume of herbicides used relative to the amounts used before GMHT adoption. This is largely due to the fact that the GMHT technology has accelerated the switch from a conventional tillage system (where no or less *herbicides* were used because weeds were mainly ploughed into the soil) to a conservation tillage system.

The increase in the net volume of *herbicides* used should, however, be placed in the context of the *environmental* benefits of the new *conservation* tillage systems.

POSSIBLE ECOLOGICAL BENEFITS OF GM CROP CULTIVATION

Pesticide Reductions due to Insect-resistant Crops

Studies on the economic impacts of insect-resistant GM crops are revealing benefits for farmers, most of all where yields are hampered by high pest incidence or where the development of resistant pests impedes the use of pesticides. The benefits related to the adoption of Bt-crops may comprise both higher yields and *significant* reductions in pesticide use for some crops.

While the adoption of Bt-maize *expressing* the insecticidal protein Cry1Ab has resulted in only modest reductions in insecticide applications due to the small area of *conventional* maize treated with insecticides, the commercial cultivation of Bt-cotton has proven to have resulted both in a *significant* reduction in the quantity and in the number of insecticide applications.

Cotton is highly susceptible to several serious insect pests belonging to the budworm-bollworm complex, i.e., tobacco budworm *(Heliothis virescens)*, cotton *bollworm (Helicoverpa spp.)* and pink bollworm *(Pectinophora gossypiella)*. These insects constitute a major problem in most cotton-growing areas because they can cause *considerable* damage.

Conventional cotton cultivation therefore relies heavily on repeated insecticide *applications throughout* the growing season. Although estimates on pesticide use vary because pesticide use is depending on regional pest pressures, *management* practices and yearly variations, it appears that the adoption of Bt-cotton has significantly reduced the numbers of pesticide applications in every country where Bt-cotton has been grown.

Moreover, most studies estimate a reduction in the amount of pesticides used. Direct environmental benefits of reduced *insecticide* applications in Bt-cotton resulted in fewer non-target effects and in reduced pesticide inputs in water. In China, for example, the number of pesticide applications against lepidopteran pests in cotton has *considerably* dropped from nine in 1994 to four *applications* in 2001 following the adoption of Bt-cotton. Concerns have been raised that these environmental benefits maybe lowered by additional *spraying* against secondary pests that were formerly *controlled* by the broad spectrum pesticides. There is, however, no published evidence that Bt-cotton has resulted in a general change in the pest spectrum leading to an overall increase of pesticide applications.

In addition to direct environmental benefits, pesticide reductions related to the adoption of Bt-cotton have also shown to have reduced many *immediate* as well as longer-term risks to human health.

New Weed Control Strategies Offered by GM Herbicide-Tolerant Crops

The adoption of GMHT crop varieties has resulted in several weed management changes compared to conventionally managed crops. GMHT crop varieties allow the use of a single broad-spectrum herbicide that has a wider spectrum of activity and that may reduce the need for herbicide combinations or chemicals that require multiple applications.

The *herbicides* used in GMHT crops (glyphosate or glufosinate) are foliar-applied, postemergence herbicides, which usually allow using herbicides in a more *targeted* manner. They can be applied after weeds have emerged, i.e., areas with high weed densities can be *identified* and treated, while areas with low weed pressure can be treated with reduced *herbicide* amounts.

Post-emergence herbicides are thus generally applied at lower rates than soil-applied, preemergence herbicides, also because absorption by soil colloids and *degradation* are reduced. Glyphosate and *glufosinate* are considered being less toxic to human health and the *environment* than many of the *herbicides* they replace.

Both have relatively short soil half-lives and they persist almost half as long in the environment compared to the replaced herbicides. Neither moves readily to ground water, which results in fewer losses of chemicals by leaching and run-off from the field. Perhaps the most important *environmental* benefit of the adoption of GMHT crops is the *possibility* to use broad spectrum herbicides, which *encouraged* growers to adopt *conservation* tillage strategies.

Prior to the introduction of transgenic HT crop varieties, most *growers* used tillage to prepare the soil for planting. Excessive tillage, however, is known to cause soil structure changes, increase the susceptibility to soil erosion, and reduce soil moisture. Loss of topsoil due to tillage therefore causes *environmental* damage that can last for centuries.

Since the early 1990s, growers have been reducing their tillage *operations* for soil *conservation* benefits. According to USDA survey data, about 60% of the area planted with GMHT soybean was under conservation tillage in 1997, compared with only about 40% for conventional soybean. Gianessi cites a survey by the American Soybean Association, indicating that U.S. soybean growers reported making fewer tillage passes through their fields since 1995 when GMHT soybean was first *introduced*.

Because weed control can be done during the post-emergence phase, farmers can use direct-seeding techniques since there is no need for pre-seeding tillage. *Conservation* tillage leaves a layer of plant residues on the soil surface, preventing soil erosion, reducing *evaporation* and increasing the ability of the soil to absorb moisture.

A richer soil biota develops that can improve nutrient recycling and this may also help combat crop pests and diseases. Earthworm populations are generally higher in no-till fields than in conventionally tilled fields. In addition to a reduction in soil erosion and *degradation*, less frequent soil *cultivation* also results in a decrease in the emission of greenhouse gases, partly arising from a reduction in fuel use.

There is also evidence that *conservation* tillage can provide a wide range of benefits to farmland biodiversity by improving agricultural land as habitat for wildlife. The greater availability of crop residues and weed seeds can improve food supplies for insects, birds, and small mammals.

SCIENTIFIC DEBATES ON THE ECOLOGICAL IMPACT OF GM CROPS

The interpretation of collected scientific data is debated *controversially* by different stakeholders involved in the debate on potential impact of GM crops on biodiversity. Although some groups argue that experience and solid scientific knowledge are still lacking, the ongoing debate is generally not purely due to a lack of scientific data, but more to an ambiguous *interpretation* of what is considered an *ecologically* relevant effect of GM crops.

The interpretation of study results is thereby often challenged by the absence of a defined baseline for the evaluation of environmental effects of GM crops. Consequently, some consider any effect related to GM crops as being undesired, while others compare it to effects caused by modern agricultural practices *recognizing* that a multitude of factors involved cause *environmental* effects. The interpretation of study results is further often challenged by knowledge gaps on the natural variation *occurring* in any biological system. Rather than the GM crop alone being the influencing factor, environmental effects are caused by agricultural *production* systems where the GM crop is one factor among others.

Although science can help to assess these natural variations, it will most probably not be possible to elucidate all ecological interactions taking place in such systems. In practice, decision-making will thus have to be not purely based on scientific criteria, but will also be strongly influenced by political, social, economical and ethical factors.

Ecologically significant effects are only judged unacceptable (i.e., *representing* a *damage*) by the society if they are *perceived* as being linked to a *deterioration* in quality of a particular entity (e.g., biodiversity).

Valuation of scientific data is thus influenced by the individual and subjective perceptions of the terms safety, risk and uncertainty by the society and particularly by the persons involved in decision-making. The following list intends to highlight a number of issues, which mainly in Europe are currently debated *controversially* in the *discussion* on the safety of GM crops.

Effects of GM Crops on Non-target Organisms

- There is scientific controversy on the baseline that should be applied when assessing potential effects of insect-resistant GM crops. It is discussed whether this should be the most common agricultural practice used (e.g., integrated pest management), a practice like organic farming, which is only practiced by a low number of farmers, or a (hypothetical) practice that may represent the optimal system for the *environment*.

- There is a debate to what extent indirect toxic effects, i.e., effects on natural enemies that largely depend on the target pest, should be valuated considering that such effects are common for all pest control methods and not restricted to the use of insect-resistant GM crops.

Impacts of GM Crops on Soil Ecosystems

- A commonly accepted definition for soil quality has not yet been found.
- Population sizes and *community* structure of soil *microorganism* are subject to high *variation*, and the baseline comparison for ecological implication is still not clear. Standard indicator species have not been defined. Different studies use a range of different parameters and techniques.
- Is the presence of low percentages of activated transgenic Bt-toxin(s) from Bt-crops in soils a reason for concern, considering that Bt-toxins are naturally occurring in soils due to the soil bacteria *Bacillus thuringiensis,* and that Bt-spray formulations are commonly used for insect control in agriculture and forestry?

Gene Flow from GM Crops to Wild Relatives

- In most agricultural landscapes, there is usually a gradual transition from peri-agricultural to semi-natural habitats. Although "wild plants" can usually be distinguished from "agricultural weeds", a clear definition of what plant species are considered being truly wild plants is lacking.
- Should effects occurring within agricultural or peri-agricultural environments be given the same importance as those effects, which could occur in natural habitats?
- Should gene flow from GM crops to wild relatives be valuated in a different way than gene flow from conventional crops to wild relatives?

Invasiveness of GM Crops into Natural Habitats

- Is the presence of volunteer GMHT oilseed rape in habitats such as field borders or road verges an unwanted environmental effect, considering that non-transgenic oilseed rape is regularly occurring in such habitats and that HT is not considered to confer a selective advantage in natural habitats? Impacts of GM Crops on Pest and Weed Management and their Ecological Consequences
- Is it better to have a high biodiversity in-crop (i.e., to have weedy crops), or to enhance off-crop biodiversity (e.g., separate buffer strips outside the fields) providing food for insects and birds?
- Should herbicide-resistant weeds that have been caused by GMHT crops be valuated differently than herbicide-resistant weeds that have been caused by conventional (non-transgenic) weed management?

CONCLUSIONS

The risks of GM crops for the environment, and especially for biodiversity, have been *extensively* assessed worldwide over the past 10 years of commercial *cultivation* of GM crops. Consequently, substantial scientific data on *environmental* effects of the currently commercialized GM crops are *available* today, and will further be obtained given that several research programmes are underway in a number of countries.

The data available so far provide no scientific evidence that the *commercial* cultivation of GM crops has caused environmental impacts beyond the impacts that have been caused by *conventional agricultural management* practices.

Nevertheless, a number of issues related to the interpretation of scientific data on effects of GM crops on the environment are debated controversially. To a certain extent, this is due to the inherent fact that scientific data are always *characterized* by *uncertainties*, and that predictions on potential long-term or cumulative effects are difficult.

Uncertainties can either be related to the *circumstance* that there is not yet a sufficient data basis provided for an assessment of *consequences* (the "unknown"), or to the fact that the questions to solve are out of reach for scientific methods (the "unknowable").

There is thus a need to develop scientific criteria for the evaluation of effects of GM crops on the *environment* in order to assist regulatory authorities when deciding whether *environmental* effects of GM crops are considered to represent a relevant *environmental* impact. Agricultural production systems are complex and diverse.

As with the adoption of any new technology, the use of *agricultural biotechnology* might include positive and possibly less favourable *environmental* impacts. GM croping systems can help to reduce some *environmental* impacts associated with *conventional* agriculture, but they will also introduce new challenges that must be addressed.

When discussing the risks of GM crops, one has to recognize that the real choice for farmers and consumers is not between a GM *technology* that may have risks and a completely safe alternative. The real choice is between GM crops and current *conventional* pest and weed management practices, all possibly having positive and negative outcomes.

To ensure that a policy is truly *precautionary*, one should therefore compare the risk of adopting a *technology* against the risk of not adopting it. We thus believe that both benefits and risks of GM crop systems should be compared with those of current agricultural practices.

18 Chapter

IMPROVING LOW TEMPERATURE TOLERANCE IN PLANTS

Throughout their growth period, plants are exposed to abiotic and biotic stresses. This has led to plants' development of adaptive strategies to survive these stresses. Low temperature is one of the most important abiotic factors *limiting* growth, *productivity*, and *distribution* of plants.

Low temperature decreases biosynthetic activity of plants, inhibits normal function of physiological processes, and may cause *permanent* injuries leading to death. Plants vary widely in their ability to tolerate low temperature.

Chillingsensitive tropical species can be severely damaged even at *temperatures* significantly higher than freezing. *Chilling-tolerant* but freezing-sensitive plants are able to survive temperatures somewhat below 0°, but are damaged upon ice *formation* in the tissues.

On the other hand, freezing-tolerant plants are able to survive variable levels of freezing *temperatures*; the degree of *tolerance* depends on species, *developmental* stage, and duration of stress.

Chilling and freezing are stresses that affect the germination and seedling stages of the plants during early summer, as well as flowering, fruiting, and maturing of the crop during the growth period.

Furthermore, because the successful *minimization* of damage during *overwintering* is the prerequisite for efficient growth the next season, low-temperature stress tolerance during winter is important for *perennials*. Increasing low-temperature tolerance is not only important for securing crops against sudden periods of colder climate but also provides a possibility of *extending* the present geographical limits of cultivated varieties, and even species, to colder climates.

Another very important application is the increased cold *tolerance* extending the storage period of fruits and vegetables. Increased cold tolerance appears to be antagonistic to optimal growth, so it is *important* to analyze cost and benefits in crop plant breeding and find the perfect *combination* of preferred traits.

This can only be achieved by directly testing candidate genes. It also *underlines* the fact that molecular biology and especially *transformation* offer powerful tools for breeding programs. This chapter focuses on current knowledge obtained largely from transgenic *experiments* studying adaptive strategies used by plants to tolerate freezing stress and the genetic engineering *applications* that can be used to increase the tolerance.

FREEZING STRESS

Plants from *temperate* regions are commonly exposed to freezing *temperatures seasonally* and during their growth season. Plants encountering freezing *temperatures* have two general strategies to survive *freezing* stress: avoidance or *tolerance* of freezing. The former is mainly achieved by *supercooling* tissue water.

However, this mechanism has limited value because it mainly occurs in special organs such as seeds, *overwintering* buds, or parenchymal cells of *temperate* trees. Therefore, tolerance of freezing is the *dominant* mechanism by which plants survive *freezing* stress. Exposure of plants to subzero *temperatures* leads to freezing of tissue water.

Due to the higher freezing point and presence of more active ice nucleators in apoplastic solution compared to the cytoplasm, freezing invariably occurs extracellularly. Ice formation outside the cells reduces water potential of the apoplastic solution, which leads to withdrawal of water from the cells and *subsequent* cellular dehydration.

Therefore, on a cellular level, freezing stress also leads to dehydration stress; consequently, tolerance of freezing is correlated to tolerance of dehydration. Cellular membranes appear to be the main target for freezing injuries.

Freezeinduced dehydration can cause different types of structural perturbations on membranes. These include membrane fusions and lamellar to hexagonal II phase transitions. In addition to dehydration, other factors also contribute to the damage. Growing ice crystals can cause mechanical damage and low temperature per se can have direct effects on cellular processes due to denaturation of proteins and disruption of macromolecular complexes.

In addition, low temperature, especially in combination with high light intensities, generally leads to increased production of reactive oxygen species (ROS), which can damage different macromolecules in the cells. Reactive oxygen species (ROS) such as O_2, H_2O_2, and OH– are mainly formed in plastids, microsomes, and mitochondria and they damage macromolecules and membranes.

Plants have developed an elaborate repertoire of defense *mechanisms* to scavenge these and other radical compounds. These include specific enzymes such as catalase, superoxide dismutase (SOD), ascorbate peroxidase (APX), and glutathione reductase, as well as nonenzyme molecules such as ascorbate, glutathione, carotenoids, and anthocyanins. Osmolytes, proteins like dehydrin, phenolic *metabolites*, and isoprenoids also function as ROS scavengers.

Membranes are protected by a-tocopherol and specific glutathione peroxidases. Also, many sugars are active ROS scavengers; for example, mannitol is active specifically against hydroxyl radicals, the most dangerous form of activated oxygen species. However, a complex pattern of antioxidant *signaling* and redox homeostasis involved in cell death and *acclimation* responses is only beginning to be understood.

For example, the nature of ROS formation may be different under low *temperatures* compared to other stress types because the gene network (regulon) contains different genes or they are differentially expressed.

Cold Acclimation

Plants species native to temperate regions need to adjust to daily and seasonal *fluctuations* in temperature; the seasonal acclimation is important for overwintering herbaceous and woody plants. Several plant species have the ability to increase their level of freezing tolerance in response to low *nonfreezing* temperatures by a process known as cold acclimation.

These species utilize *environmental* signals to trigger processes that lead to increased freezing tolerance. In overwintering woody species, *acclimation* is a two-step process in which the first phase is triggered by shortening of the photoperiod below a critical length.

This leads to growth cessation and dormancy *development* and is accompanied by a moderate increase in freezing tolerance. The second stage of acclimation, which is also essential for obtaining full winter hardiness, is induced by subsequent exposure to low temperatures.In annual and in most *overwintering* herbaceous plants, freezing tolerance is not affected by the photoperiod but *acclimation* is triggered solely by low nonfreezing temperatures. In these species, cold acclimation is a rather rapid process; for example, in *Arabidopsis a* substantial increase in freezing tolerance can be achieved after 1-day exposure to low temperature, although full *acclimation* requires more than a week.

In addition to low *nonfreezing* temperatures, cold acclimation can be triggered by exposing plants to moderate water stress or by exogenously applied abscisic acid (ABA). The level of freezing tolerance obtained through cold acclimation is not static, but is rapidly lost upon return to warm nonacclimating temperature.

Cold acclimation is associated with several *physiological* and *biochemical* alterations in plants. The best characterized changes include changes in hormone levels; increases in soluble sugars, amino acids, and organic acids; and accumulation of osmoprotectants and protective proteins, as well as modification of membrane lipid composition.

Most of these changes are derived from altered gene expression and, although the causal relationship of many of these changes to increased freezing tolerance is still unclear, some of the genes and regulons involved in cold *acclimation* are being unraveled.

COLD SIGNALING IN PLANTS

Signal Transduction at Low Temperature

To respond to low temperature, plants must perceive the stress, *transduce* the signal to the nucleus, and activate expression of specific genes required for cold *acclimation* and metabolic *adjustments* needed for growth at low temperatures. The exact mechanisms by which this occurs are not clear, even though an increasing number of *components* involved in the signal processes have been characterized. However, the nature of the cold sensor still needs to be established. Calcium is a ubiquitous second messenger in plants and also mediates abiotic stress signaling.

The specificity of signaling is derived from specific Ca^{2+} signatures evoked by different types of stresses and *generated* by a combined action of Ca^{2+}-channels, -pumps, and -transporters as reviewed. Transient increase in cytosolic Ca^{2+}-concentration in the early stages of cold acclimation has been shown to be necessary for development of freezing tolerance.

The source of Ca^{2+}- and the specific channels for Ca^{2+}-influx are currently unknown; however, by using pharmacological approaches, it has been demonstrated that *rigidification* of membranes and cytoskeletal rearrangements are needed for the Ca^{2+}-influx in alfalfa and *Brassica napus*, indicating *involvement* of *mechanosensitive* channels in this process. Downstream signaling from the Ca^{2+}-signature is generally mediated by diverse types of Ca^{2+}-binding proteins, like calmodulin (CaM), calcineurin B-like proteins (CBLs), and Ca^{2+}-dependent protein kinases (CDPKs).

The proteins are activated by Ca^{2+}-binding and, in activated forms, they regulate activity of proteins involved in generation of signal-specific responses. The involvement of CaM and CDPKs in cold acclimation was initially demonstrated by Monroy et al., who showed that treatment of alfalfa suspension cultures with CaM or CDPK antagonists resulted in inhibition of low-temperature responsive gene expression and development of freezing tolerance. Genes encoding CaM and CaM-related proteins as well as genes encoding CDPKs have also been shown to be low temperature responsive, indicating a positive role in regulation of low-temperature tolerance.

However, Townley and Knight have shown that overexpression of the CaM gene in *Arabidopsis* leads to inhibition of *low-temperature* responsive gene *expression*, indicating that CaM can act as a negative regulator of cold acclimation. CDPKs have also been shown to be involved in *acquisition* of chilling tolerance.

Saijo et al. have *demonstrated* that overexpression of the *OsCDPK* gene leads to increased low-temperature tolerance in rice. CBLs are a family of Ca^{2+}-binding proteins that mediate the activation of protein kinases called CIPKs (CBL-interacting protein kinases).

A gene encoding a member of the CBL family, *CBL1*, has been shown to be responsive to abiotic stresses, including low temperature in *Arabidopsis*. However, cbl1 null mutant exhibits enhanced freezing tolerance and overexpression of *CBL1* leads to reduced level of tolerance, indicating that CBL1 acts as a negative regulator of cold responses.

A CIPK, CIPK3, has been demonstrated to be involved in activation of low-temperature responsive genes in *Arabidopsis*. *cipk3* mutant plants exhibited delayed induction of gene expression but no *differences* in the *maximum* level of induction, *indicating* that CIPK3 acts at the early stages of cold acclimation. Mitogen-activated protein kinases (MAPKs) are a family of proteins involved in transduction of diverse signals in eukaryotic cells.

Activation of MAPKs is mediated through a phosphorylation cascade where activated MAPKKKs phosphorylate MAPKKs, which then phosphorylate MAPKs. Activated MAPKs typically *phosphorylate* and *modulate* the activity of specific transcription factors, participating in generation of signal-specific transcription patterns.

Arabidopsis harbors about 60 putative MAPKKKs, 10 MAPKKs, and 20 MAPKs, which suggests that MAPKKs form a cross-talk node between different signals mediated through the cascade. However, very little information exists *concerning* the *components* involved in transmission of specific signals.

Cold-Regulated Gene Expression

Cold acclimation is associated with marked alterations in gene expression; several of the alterations are likely to be significant for development of freezing tolerance. The cold-responsive genes are often also induced by other environmental stimuli, like drought and salt, *indicating* common protective *mechanisms* in these stresses.

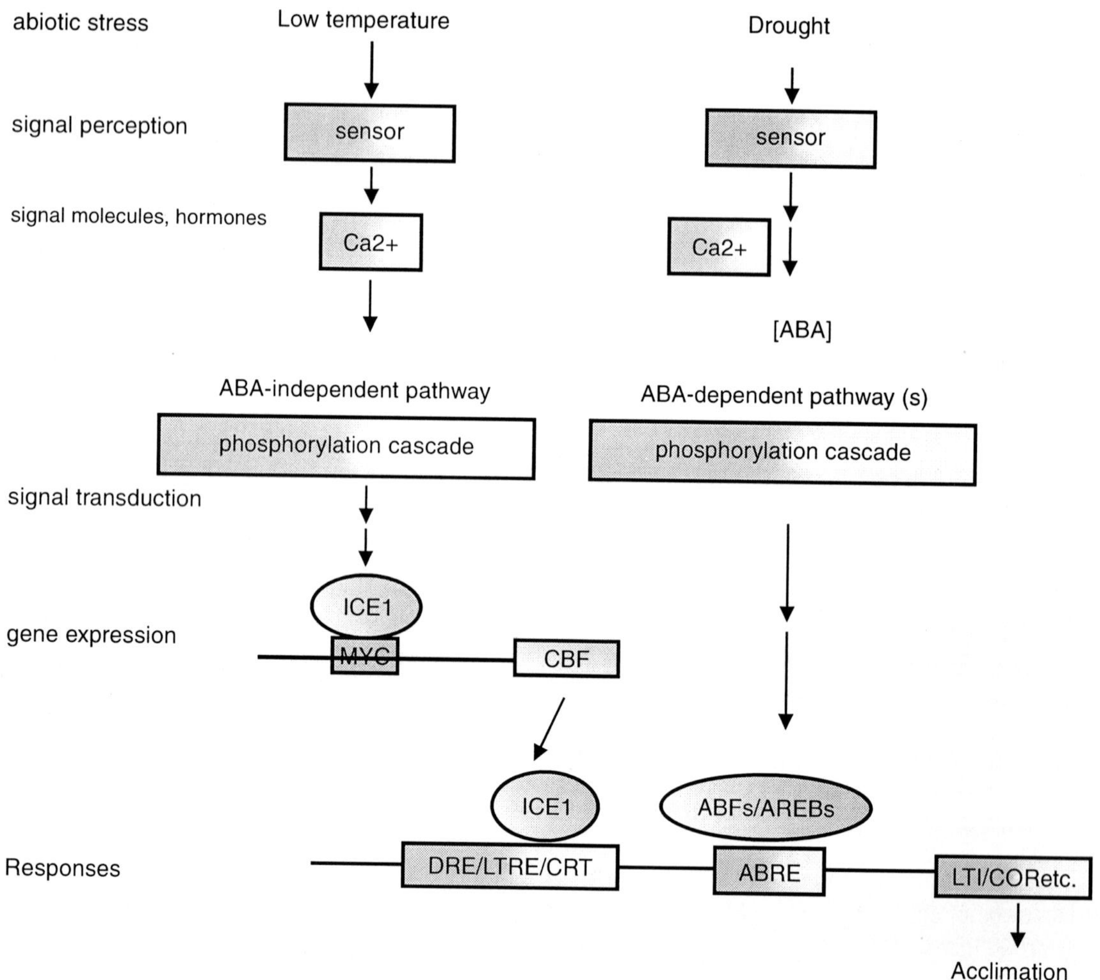

Figure 18.1: Simplified scheme of Arabidopsis thaliana signal transduction cascades involved in cold acclimation. Regulation and cross-talk are omitted for simplicity. (Picture based on Heino, P. and Palva, E.T., in Plant Responses to Abiotic Stress, vol. 4, Hirt, H. and Shinozaki, K., Eds., Springer-Verlag, Berlin, 2003, 151–186; and Shinozaki, K. et al., Curr. Opin. Plant Biol., 6, 410–417, 2003.)

Several, but not all, of the low-temperature responsive genes are also induced by exogenous ABA, suggesting ABA involvement in generation of stress responses. The effects of low temperature on *Arabidopsis* transcriptome have been analyzed in several different studies and the results indicate that up to 25% of the genes are responsive to cold.

The temporal patterns of low-temperature responsive gene expression are complex and the genes involved clearly belong to different regulons.

The CBF/DREBI Regulon

The emerging insight in cold acclimation is that this mechanism is complex, consisting of several distinct signal pathways that appear to interact with each other. Moreover, it is becoming evident that the low-temperature signal pathways are *converging* and interacting with other stress-induced *pathways*, such as those mediating *dehydration* and abscisic acid responses. Our earlier work *demonstrated* the presence of ABA-independent and ABA-mediated pathways in *low-temperatur*e signaling.

Interestingly, recent data indicate that there is cross-talk even between these two pathways of cold signaling. Work done mainly by the Thomashow and Shinozaki laboratories has established the central role of the CBF or DREB1 family of *transcription* factors (TF) in controlling ABA-independent responses to low *temperature*.

Identification of these AP2/EREBP-types of DNA-binding proteins was initiated by recognizing a common binding site in many promoters of the low-temperature responsive genes. We originally suggested the identity of such a low-temperature responsive element (LTRE) in the *LTI78/RD29A* promoter in *Arabidopsis*.

This 9-bp element, TACCGACAT, with a core sequence of CCGAC, was subsequently demonstrated by deletion analysis to confer responsiveness to low temperature, drought, and high salinity, but not to ABA. This dehydration-responsive element designated as DRE also occurs

Table 18.1: Expressed LEA Proteins Increasing Freezing Tolerance.

LEA group	*Origin*	*Model organism*
Group 2	CoCOR19—citrus	In tobacco, leads to a slight degrease in ion leakage during chilling and freezing stress
Group 2	CAP85—spinach	Small improvement in freezing tolerance of tobacco in time-course experiment
Group 2	Wcor410—wheat	Acidic dehydrin improves strawberry freezing tolerance
Group 2	COR15a—*A. thaliana*	Increases freezing tolerance in *Arabidopsis*
Group 3	HiC6—*C. vulgaris*	Significant suppression of chilling injury in tobacco
Group 3	WCS19—wheat	Group 3 chloroplast targeted protein increased freezing tolerance in *Arabidopsis*

in several other cold-responsive promoters and has been referred to as the C-repeat (CRT). The TF binding to the DRE/CRT/LTRE element and activating cold-induced gene expression was first identified by Stockinger et al. and designated CBF1 (C-repeat binding factor 1). Additional genes were subsequently isolated and shown to encode a small family of related TFs called CBF1, CBF2, and CBF3 or DREB 1B, DREB 1C, and DREB 1A (DRE-binding protein) in *Arabidopsis*.

An additional member of this TF family, CBF4, was isolated but may be more related to drought response. Interestingly, the *CBFI-3/DREBIA-C* genes are transiently regulated by low temperature. Rapid activation of *CBF* expression (within 15 to 30 min) is followed by cold-regulated target genes that define the CBF/DREB 1 regulon.

An efficient mutant screen by the J.-K. Zhu laboratory led to isolation of the first *ICE* (inducer of CBF) gene encoding an MYC-type bHLH transcription factor. As expected, expression of *ICE*I appears constitutive. Overexpression of *CBF/DREBI* leads to the constitutive expression of a number of target genes with promoters containing the DRE/CRT/LTRE element and to *improved* freezing, drought, and salt tolerance of nonacclimated plants.

In addition, overexpression of CBF3 leads to elevated levels of proline and sugars that are normally associated with cold acclimation. In several recent studies, transcriptome analysis has been used to identify genes of the CBF/DREB 1 regulon in *Arabidopsis*. Of the hundreds of cold-regulated genes identified, 85 were upregulated by CBF2 and, of the 25 most highly cold-induced genes, the majority were under CBF2 control.

These studies demonstrate that the CBF/DREB1-controlled genes constitute a low-temperature responsive regulon central to the plant cold acclimation response and development of plant freezing tolerance and could be employed for *engineering* plant cold tolerance. The conserved nature of the CBF/DREB 1 regulon in cold-tolerant plants further supports the notion that this regulon has an important role in the cold acclimation process.

For example, in wheat, the differences in Cbf expression were associated with variation in frost tolerance. Orthologs of CBF genes have been found in a number of herbaceous species, including *Brassica napus*, barley, wheat, rice, tomato, sour cherry and strawberry, sweet cherry, and even woody species such as silver birch.

ABA-Mediated Gene Expression

ABA is a phytohormone that regulates diverse aspects of plant development and growth, including stress responses. Genes' responsiveness to abiotic stresses is partly mediated by pathways that areABA dependent. ABA-deficient mutants of *Arabidopsis* are not able to increase their freezing tolerance to wild-type levels during cold acclimation and ABA deficiency also decreases cold-responsive gene expression.

However, the growth rate at low temperatures is not regulated by ABA but by gibberellic acid (GA) and salicylic acid (SA). Recently, Zhu et al. identified a gene encoding HOS 10, a MYB-type transcription factor needed for development of freezing tolerance *inArabidopsis*. HOS 10 appears to be required for stress induction of *NCED*, which encodes the rate-limiting enzyme in ABA biosynthesis.

This indicates a role for ABA in *generating* protection against freeze-induced dehydration. ABA-responsive gene *expression* has been shown to be mediated by ABFs/AREBPs, basic leucine zipper *transcription* factors binding to ABA response elements (ABREs) present in the promoter regions of ABA responsive genes.

Characteristic of ABREs is that more than one copy of the element is *necessary* for gene activation. Alternatively, a coupling element replaces one of the ABREs. A low-temperature and ABA-responsive gene encoding a C_2H_2-type zinc finger protein in soybean has been characterized.

The encoded protein, SCOF1, regulates low-temperature responsive gene expression and development of freezing tolerance. SCOF1 was found to enhance binding of the bZIP transcription factor SGBF1 to ABREs in stress-responsive genes, suggesting that SCOF1 regulates ABAmediated gene expression in low temperatures.

ENGINEERING TOLERANCE

There are many reports about genes that, when overproduced, give plants *enhanced* protection against low-temperature stress. However, definition of their roles as part of temperature stress tolerance *mechanisms* and possible *overlapping* functions needs to be elucidated.

Indeed, an obvious *explanation* for the wide range of different proteins in low-temperature stress is manifested in the many different forms of stress, each with its own specific protection mechanisms evolved.

This may also be the most important *motivation* for studying low-temperature stress for plant crop *improvement* purposes. In yeast, for example, the best selection strategy to obtain highly improved multiple-stress-resistant strains was found to be batch selection for freezing–thawing stress.

Target Genes

By 1985 it was *established* that altered gene expression at low, nonfreezing *temperatures* correlated with cold acclimation. Subsequently, a great number of coldinduced genes has been isolated and characterized from a variety of plant species.

These genes code for a number of different proteins, including enzymes involved in metabolic pathways, proteins with a protective role, and proteins affecting signaling pathways. Among these are fatty acid desaturases, chaperones, lipid transfer proteins, enzymes in *osmoprotectant* biosynthesis, antifreeze proteins, *transcription* factors, kinases, and phosphatases.

Furthermore, the functions of many cold-induced proteins are not clearly defined. However, in many cases, corresponding genes have been found in a number of different plant species, indicating that many proteins induced by low temperature are conserved. In addition to *specifically* induced target genes, a number of *regulation* mechanisms are only beginning to be unraveled.

These include signaling cascades leading to specific *transcription* factors, as well as more global regulation of whole genomes. Thus, in addition to well-characterized *regulatory* cascades, including CBF/DREB genes that may have a function at the level of histone acetylation, *chromosome* structure is regulated following low-temperature stress.

Lea Proteins

One of the most common categories of target genes includes a number of loosely related groups of genes called LEA (late embryogenesis abundant) proteins. Many of these genes are induced in response to any environmental influence that has a dehydration component (such as *drought*, low *temperature*, or *salinity*) by ABA or during the late stages of embryogenesis.

These proteins are thought to be involved in protecting cellular structures from effects of water loss— for example, by retaining water together with sugars or directly protecting other proteins or membranes including *renaturation* of unfolded proteins and sequestration of ions in a wide range of higher plants.

Table elsewhere in this chapter shows the transgenic LEA proteins expressed in plants. LEA proteins have been identified *primarily* from plants and comprise at least six different subgroups. These proteins do not seem to have a common origin; rather, they have adopted the same strategy for *protection* of cells from a common problem.

Group 1 family members are *unstructured* in solution. Their sequence is conserved especially within the hydrophobic internal 20-amino acid motif, which may be *repeated*. Group 1 proteins are induced by osmotic stress or ABA and they have been postulated to function as general water stress *protectants* in nonembryonic tissues.

Group 2 (also called dehydrins) is the largest group. Purified maize DHN1 proteins from this group have been shown to bind with phospholipids *in vitro*. The purified recombinant GmDHN1 exhibits a highly extended conformation at low *temperatures*, which could constitute the basis of the functional role in prevention of freezing, *desiccation*, ionic, or osmotic stress-related damage to macromolecular structures.

A member of group 3 has been shown to have *in vitro* antiaggregation activity due to water stress, which was synergistic with trehalose. This group also contains members outside plants, as referred in Goyal et al..

Group 4 has also been proposed to form *amphiphilic* a-helices that may interact with ions or membrane.

Group 5 proteins are embryogenesis specific.

Group 6 contains atypical hydrophopic LEA proteins.

Although LEA proteins have been known for quite some time, the functions of these proteins have remained somewhat unanswered. Despite some obvious enhancement in prediction tools, *overexpression* of genes in plants has not been conducted systematically.

Among the published reports, Hara et al. have recently shown that overproduction of a citrus dehydrin (CoCOR19) in tobacco leads to a slight decrease in ion leakage during chilling and freezing stress. Interestingly, the hydroxyl and peroxyl radical scavenging activity of CoCOR19 was found *in vitro* to be equal to serum albumin, a known antioxidant protein in mammals.

However, a hot-pepper protein, CaLEA6, tested in tobacco showed *enhanced* tolerance to dehydration and NaCl but not to chilling. Furthermore, a much-studied Group 3 barley HVA1 has not been reported to be tested for cold tolerance, although it is naturally cold inducible.

Lea Proteins and Yeast

The baker's yeast *Saccharomyces cerevisiae* has been a popular model organism in studying functions of many LEA group proteins, although yeast also has LEA-like proteins. Table elsewhere in this chapter depicts the LEA proteins expressed in yeast. Barley HVA1 (group 3) displayed a shortened lag period after transfer to high-NaCl or KCl media, whereas tomato le4 (group 2) increased tolerance only to KCl, maybe by stabilizing KCl-sensitive structures.

However, both increased freezing tolerance, supporting the idea of specialized functions of different LEA proteins during lowtemperature stress. Thus, different LEA proteins appear to have separate functions and protect cells against different stresses, even in yeast.

Functional Divergence of Lea Proteins

Many dehydrins are hydrophilic, containing random coil or α-helices, and remain soluble after boiling. However, some atypical LEA proteins are hydrophobic, suggesting a different function despite involvement in dehydration response.

Table 18.2: Plant LEA Genes Expressed in Yeast.

Group 1	Em—wheat	Enhanced osmotic tolerance	118
Group 2	le4—tomato	Enhanced freezing and KCl tolerance	128
Group 3	HVA1—barley	Enhanced freezing and salt tolerance	128
Group 3	hiC6—Chlorella *vulgaris*	Enhanced freezing tolerance	300
Group 4	le25—tomato	Increased salt and freezing tolerance	123

Even though the exact function of these proteins has not been established, their biochemical properties and accumulation patterns suggest that dehydrins could work in stabilizing cellular structures during dehydration stress, molecular *chaperones*, *sequesters* of iron and calcium, and *scavenging* oxygen radicals.

The genome of *Arabidopsis* has at least ten dehydrin genes, suggesting that each of the family members has specified functions. This specialization might be one reason why overexpression of an LEA protein does not increase tolerance to a particular type of stress—for example, *chilling* tolerance or when expression of three *different* LEA proteins did not increase tobacco's drought tolerance. Only a few *comparative* studies have been made between different plant *protective* assets.

One study compared dehydration, salt, and heat tolerance of bacterial otsA, a trehalose-6-phosphate synthase, the first *protein* in making of a nonreducing *disaccharide* of two glucose units called trehalose, and an atypical LEA protein, CaLEA. In this case, the LEA protein was found to be slightly better. Several transgenic plant lines overexpressing different low-temperature responsive genes have been created, but only a marginal effect on freezing tolerance has been *demonstrated*.

Similar results have been obtained in studies of water stress tolerance. Therefore, this type of target gene engineering has thus far met with limited success. The approach is most likely hampered by redundancy of the system, where an individual gene product makes a minor contribution to overall tolerance.

Thus, this approach would require *pyramiding* a number of target genes *providing* additive effects on tolerance. This is further *emphasized* by the fact that several LEA proteins are activated together by their common *transcription* factors and correlate with stress tolerance in transgenic plants Recent results from our group in expressing pairwise *combinations* of four different *endogenous* dehydrin genes *in Arabidopsis* was an attempt to test this.

Thus, RAB18, which *accumulates* in response to ABA, drought, and low *temperatures*, was put together with COR47, which accumulates primarily in response to low *temperature*, but also to ABA and salt stress. On the other hand, LTI29, responding primarily to low *temperature* but also to ABA and salt stress, was put together with LTI30, which *accumulates* mainly under cold stress.

Using both constructs, we were able to show enhanced *freezing* tolerance that we did not see with RAB18 *expressed* alone and without any detectable deleterious effect to the plants. These proteins have differing functions inside the cell, as witnessed by partitioning of LTI29 from being mainly cytoplasmic to mainly membrane localized following cold acclimation; LTI30 was not detected at the cytoplasm.

Thus, *pyramiding* protective proteins with differing functions is clearly one way of proceeding with research.

Membrane-Binding Proteins

In general, plant survival during freezing may be more limited by stability of cellular *membranes* rather than by soluble proteins. Indirect evidence for interactions with *membranes* or partially denatured proteins has been shown for the chloroplastlocated hydrophilic COR15a protein, which is not a dehydrin but is predicted to be largely *composed* of *amphipathic* α-helices.

Interaction between the protein and the plastidic inner envelope, which is thought to be mediated through amphipathic a-helices, is correlated with decrease in membrane leakage. Formation of the inverted hexagonal phase membrane structure can be prevented by the cold acclimation process and, in part, by overexpressing Cor15a. Moreover, two other reports about membrane binding proteins have been reported.

Osmotin-like protein from *bittersweet* nightshade (*Solanum dulcamara*) stabilizes kale (*Brassica oleracea*) protoplasts during freeze–thaw cycles. Cryoprotectin, a lipid transfer protein homolog, shows cryoprotective activity stabilizing isolated thylakoids from freeze–thaw cycles.

The protective function of the protein lies in its capability to bind and immobilize thylakoid lipids. Also, maize DHN1 binds to lipid vesicles, pointing to the possibility that the mode of action of some dehydrins is to support membranes.

Antifreeze Proteins

Antifreeze proteins (AFPs) were first identified from fish and found later from other species, including plants, as reviewed in Griffith and Yaish. Their function is to bind to the growing surface of ice crystals and prevent them from growing. Roughly, animal and insect AFPs exhibit a substantial thermal hysteresis activity that is a noncolligative depression of the freezing point of an ice-containing solution below its melting point—the freeze avoidance strategy.

AFP-producing plants and bacteria that cannot avoid *freezing* rely on another strategy by showing ice recrystallization inhibition. Thus, controlling growth of an ice crystal during freeze–

thaw cycles instead of *preventing* their formation is the freeze-tolerant strategy. Transgenic attempts have been made with limited success in plant, synthetic, insect, and fish genes to express AFPs in frost-susceptible crops to increase their freezing tolerance. In plants, the additional effect of these proteins is to function as pathogenesis-related proteins.

Thus, plants are acquired with systemic, nonspecific, pre-emptive defense against *psychrophilic* pathogens that would otherwise prosper under snow cover at subzero *temperatures*.

Antioxidants and Detoxification

The importance of reactive oxygen species (ROS) scavenging proteins is that they have been shown to increase success rates not only in controlled experiments but also in overwintering plants in field trials, like the expression of superoxide dismutase within chloroplast, which did not affect freezing tolerance but rather enhanced recovery from stress.

Reactive oxygen species control many different processes in plants, so transgenic approaches may not always produce clear *improvement*, although it might just reflect a problem in expression or *localization*.

For example, using SODs creates enhanced hydrogen peroxide production, which may be alleviated in plants with upregulation of H_2O_2 scavenging enzymes. ROS scavenging pathways include the water–water cycle, ascorbate–glutathione cycle, *glutathione peroxidase* cycle, and catalase, as reviewed in Mittler et al. and Mittler.

The ascorbate–glutathione cycle plays an important role in regulating cellular ROS levels. In this cycle, ascorbate peroxidase (APX) reduce H_2O_2 using ascorbic acid (AsA) as an electron donor generating monodehydroascorbate (MDA), which can be reduced back to AsA by MDA reductase using NAD(P)H. MDA can also spontaneously produce dehydroascorbate (DHA), which is reduced back to AsA by DHA reductase with the help of glutathione, GSH, oxidized to GSSG (the oxidized form of glutathione).

The cycle closes with glutathione reductase converting GSSG back to GSH with NAD(P)H. Plants contain a family of ascorbate peroxidases and overexpression of thylakoidal APX (tAPX) in tobacco gives chilling tolerance.

Antisense lines were not obtained, suggesting an essential function. However, tAPX *overexpression* in *Arabidopsis* did not increase resistance to low *temperatures* but rather to *paraquatinduced* oxidative stress and nitric oxide. Furthermore, antisense constructs with 50% tAPX activity left showed no symptoms under normal conditions. Expression of cytosolic cAPX has been reported to confer tolerance to *chilling* in tomato.

However, in soybean, the cAPX deficiency is associated with chilling tolerance in cultivated species. Also, downregulating cAPX activity in tobacco, BY-2 cell lines showed increased *tolerance* to heat and salt but cells grew more slowly.

The APX activity in BY-2 cells is much higher than in *Arabidopsis*, the residual activity resulting as marginal increase in cellular ROS levels triggering *tolerance mechanisms* was discussed as an explanation for increased tolerance. It has been suggested that excessive levels of cAPX scavenge ROS too actively, thus hindering expression of defense genes, which need a certain level of stress for signaling.

Membranes

Membrane fluidity depends on composition of lipid molecular species, degree of lipid *saturation* where increase in the level of *unsaturation* increases fluidity, and *temperature* environments. Thus, temperature-induced changes in membrane fluidity represent a potential site for cold perception, as also discussed in Sung et al..

The proportion of unsaturated fatty acids in the lipid acyl chains is particularly high in chloroplast membranes. Several genetic loci involved in fatty acid desaturation of lipids in chloroplast or microsomal membranes in *Arabidopsis* have been identified and the genetic engineering of plant membrane lipids has been recently reviewed in Iba.

It seems that increase of the content of unsaturated lipids gives better chilling *tolerance* in tobacco. A decrease in synthesis of unsaturated trienoic fatty acid increases high-temperature tolerance. Glycerol-3-phosphate acyltransferase (GPAT) from *Arabidopsis* does not change proportions of individual lipid classes but increases the level of *unsaturation*, leading to increased chilling tolerance in tobacco and rice, whereas overexpression of squash GPAT in tobacco and rice leads to increase of *saturated* species of phosphatidylglycerol, which results in plants more sensitive to chilling.

Thus, it is possible to engineer tolerance to low or high *temperature*, but not both at the same time. In addition to membrane unsaturation, it appears that lipid *asymmetry* in the membrane also *contributes* to low-temperature tolerance.

Internalization of phosphatidylserine from the outer leaflet of plasma membrane by an *Arabidopsis* ALA1, a putative aminophospholipid translocase, in a yeast dsr1 mutant was tightly linked to rescue in cold.

Enzyme Engineering

A completely different approach for achieving low-temperature tolerance is to engineer protein structure instead of engineering expression pattern, the main topic of this chapter. Pyruvate orthophosphate dikinase, a key enzyme in C4 pathway in maize, loses its activity under 12°C due to dissociation. Expressing engineered genes from *F. brownii* in maize that does not dissociate as readily gives a small improvement, which may be enhanced if the endogenous gene can be downregulated or engineered.

Nevertheless, it represents a potentially very *interesting* approach in trying to enhance the *photosynthetic* rate at low *temperatures*.

METABOLIC ENGINEERING

Compared to engineering expression of protective proteins, metabolic *engineering* of osmoprotectants is another way of improving plant stress tolerance. A group of target genes that have been successfully modified for increasing low-temperature tolerance in plants are those participating in producing certain small organic molecules called compatible and *counteracting* solutes, compensatory solutes, chemical *chaperones*, or osmoprotectants. Induction of osmoprotectant biosynthesis is part of the plant response to drought, salinity, and low temperatures.

Compatible solutes occur in all organisms from archaebacteria to higher plants and animals.

These are highly soluble compounds that carry no net charge at *physiological* pH and do not perturb macromolecules such as proteins. Some of these molecules are already present in unstressed tissues. Synthesis is often only increased or *degradation* decreased during stress.

The primary function of these compatible solutes is understood to maintain cell turgor and thus the driving gradient for water uptake. For this purpose, by definition they should be able to exist at high concentrations in cells without any deleterious effects. It seems that *compatible* solutes also function as free-radical *scavengers* or chemical chaperones and directly stabilize membranes and/or proteins.

Furthermore, the biosynthetic flux of the compatible solute may help to maintain redox balance and affected sugar levels may provide a signal for adaptive *regulation* throughout the plant. Compatible solutes fall into several major groups: amino acids (e.g. proline), quaternary amines (e.g., betaines), tertiary sulfoniums (e.g., dimethylsulfoniopropionate), and polyol/sugars (e.g., mannitol, trehalose, sucrose, etc.).

However, out of many potentially interesting compounds, relatively few have ever been tested by genetic engineering. Of the few compounds that have been tested, in a number of publications the increase in cold tolerance was obtained by *introducing* simple metabolic traits from other organisms into plants that are not natural *accumulators.*

However, some of the compounds may not be compatible any more in species that do not naturally accumulate them, as discussed later. The other way is to try to increase and maintain a higher concentration level of the metabolite in species where it has earlier been shown to elevate naturally following stress response.

The way to achieve this in the latter case is to establish a new pathway or to increase the synthesis rate of the metabolite by increasing the gene dosage (and gene *expression*) of the ratelimiting enzyme or by decreasing the degradation rate of the metabolite by downregulating the *degrading* enzyme-encoding gene. Table elsewhere in this chapter lists transgenic *experiments* giving enhanced low-temperature tolerance.

Betaines

Betaines are amino acid derivatives in which the nitrogen atom is fully *methylated.* In plants, a representative member of this group is glycine betaine (GB), which is a well studied subject in salt stress; more than 15 articles on transgenic plants have been published.

In GB-accumulating plants, it is synthesized in the chloroplast through an oxidation reaction from choline to glycine betaine via betaine aldehyde *intermediate.* In higher plants, two enzymes—choline *monoxygenase* (CMO; in mammals and some bacteria, CDH) and betaine aldehyde dehydrogenase (BADH)—are responsible for these reactions.

In certain bacteria, both reactions are catalyzed by one enzyme, choline oxidase (COD), as reviewed in Sakamoto and Murata. Transgenic plants *expressing* betaines are more resistant to high salt concentrations, osmotic stress, and cold and warm temperatures.

Improved lowtemperature tolerance has been reported when expressing the *Arthrobacter globiformis codA* (coding for choline oxidase, which synthesizes glycine betaine in one step) gene in *Brassica juncea*, tobacco, and tomato, as well as rice and *Arabidopsis.*

Table 18.3: Transgenic Plants Showing Enhanced Low-Temperature Tolerance.

Protein and origin	*Model plant*	*Remarks*
		Chilling stress
desC—*S. vulcanus*	Tobacco	Thermophilic bacterium acyl-lipid Δ9-desaturase giving chilling tolerance
acyl-lipid Δ9-desatu-rase—*A. nidulans*	Tobacco	Broad specificity Δ9 desaturase "fluidizing" membrane bound lipids 305 CvFAD2 and 3—*C. vulgaris* Tobacco Two microsomal desaturases increasing and decreasing freezing tolerance
FAD7—A. *thaliana*	Tobacco	Chloroplast Co3 desaturase increases trienoic fatty acid (TA) amount and confers chilling tolerance
GPAT—*A. thaliana,*	spinach Tobacco, rice	Increases proportion but not amount of unsaturated phosphatidylglycerol
Glycerol-3-P-acyl transferase (GPAT)—squash and *A. thaliana*	Tobacco, rice	Causes changes in the unsaturation of fatty acids and chilling tolerance levels
ALA1—A. *thaliana*	*A. thaliana*	Aminophospholipid translocase involved in generating membrane lipid asymmetry
Glutamine synthetase—rice	Rice	Faster recovery from chilling stress due to increase in glutamine levels; increase in photorespiration capacity
Glutathione peroxidase—*Chlamydomonas*	Tobacco	Cytosolic and chloroplast versions increased chilling tolerance
MnSOD and Fe-SOD—tobacco and *A. thaliana*	Tobacco	Fe-SOD binds to membranes and protects PSII; stromal Mn-SOD less effective
Cu/Zn-SOD—pea	Tobacco	Chloroplast targeted SOD
Nt107—tobacco	Tobacco	Glutathione S-transferase/glutathione peroxidase combination
DHAR—human	Tobacco	Dehydroascorbate dehydrogenase reduces DHA to ascorbate
APX—P. *sativum*	Tomato	Cytosolic expression of ascorbate oxidase enhancing chilling tolerance
Ipt—*A. tumefaciens*	*F. arundinacea*	Isopentenyl transferase resulted in increased cold tolerance

(Table Contd.)

Protein and origin	***Model plant***	***Remarks***
ProDH—*A. thaliana*	*A. thaliana*	Antisense suppression of proline degradation improves tolerance to freezing
Invertase—*S. cerevisiae*	Potato	Apoplast-localized invertase inhibits export of sugars and thus leaves retain higher sugar content
otsA-otsB *E. coli*	Rice	Fusion of two *E. coli* trehalose biosynthetic genes allowing enhanced protection and recovery without stunting growth
TpS 1 and TpS2-*S. cerevisiae*	*A. thaliana*	Trehalose synthases *TPSl* alone or together with *TPS2* gives pleiotrophic effects and enhanced stress tolerance
mtlD—*E. coli*	Eggplant	Mannitol production enhancing chilling tolerance in a crop plant
SacB—*B. subtilis*	Tobacco	Bacterial levansucrase for fructan biosynthesis gives low temperature tolerance
OsCDPK 7 and 13-rice	Rice	Signaling; calcium-dependent protein kinase confers tolerance; number 7 has separate pathways for cold and salt
OSISAPl—rice	Tobacco	Signaling; zinc finger protein confers tolerance at germination stage
Bcl-xL–human and Ced-9–*C. elegans*	Tobacco	Plants transgenic to animal cell-death suppressors germinate at lower temperatures than wild-type
Ppdk–*F bidentis/E brownii*	Maize	Chimeric enzyme dissociates at lower temperature than native
		Freezing stress
Fe-SOD–*A. thaliana*	Alfalfa	Enhanced recovery from stress after resuming growth
Mn-SOD—tobacco	Alfalfa	Increased winter survival
AAPT1–canola	*A. thaliana*	Phospholipid synthesis; increased resistance to damage at low growth temperatures
Phospholipase D–*Arubidopsis*	*A. thaliana*	PLDS overexpression and PLDcc downregulation increases freezing tolerance; involved in hydrolyzation of phospholipids
Spermidine synthase (SPDS) *C. ficifolia*	*A. thaliana*	Increase in polyamine content gives abiotic stress tolerance and rise in DREB levels
Galactosidase *L. esculentum*	Petunia	Downregulation of hydrolytic enzyme increases raffinose concentration and freezing tolerance
SEX1–*A. thaliana*	*A. thaliana*	Involved in regulation of starch hydrolysis in early cold response
Wftl, W112–T *aestivum*	*L. perenne*	Fructan (sugar polyol) biosynthesis genes increase

(Table Contd.)

Protein and origin	Model plant	Remarks
		fructan levels likely in the vacuole
P5C–*Arubidopsis, Vigna*	Tobacco	Proline, fructan, and betaine biosynthesis give freezing tolerance to tobacco
codA–*A. globiformis*	Tomato	Betaine production protects flowers and seeds (repor-ted)
codA–*A. globiformis*	*A. thaliana*, rice, *Brassica*, tomato	Biosynthesis of glycine betaine enhances germination and cold tolerance of plants
Cox–*A. pascens*	*A. thaliana*	Choline oxidase giving modest freezing tolerance, but not to canola or tobacco
betA, betB—*E. coli*	Tobacco	Improved tolerance to photoinhibition under low temperature in leaf discs
GSMT, DMT—*A. halophytica*	Cyanobacterium, *A. thaliana*	Germination yield retained high despite cold imbibition-treatment of seeds
Antifreeze protein—carrot	Tobacco	Increased freezing tolerance
MKK2—*A. thaliana*	*A. thaliana*	Signaling; MAPKK especially activated by cold
Osmyb4—rice	*A. thaliana*	Rice transcription factor showing significantly increased freezing tolerance in *Arabidopsis*
OsMAPK5—rice	Rice	Signaling; affects adversely between abiotic and pathogen tolerance
SCOF-1—soybean	*A. thaliana*, tobacco	Zinc finger protein improves freezing and chilling tolerance
Cryophyte/Los4—*A. thaliana*	*A. thaliana*	RNA helicase involved in mRNA export affects CBF and ABA signaling
Fiery1/Hos2—*A. thaliana*	*A. thaliana*	IP_3 turnover; mutation gives cold tolerance due to increased inositol concentration
NPK1—tobacco	Maize	Signaling; MAPKKK enhances freezing resistance in maize
ABF3—*A. thaliana*	*A. thaliana*, rice	ABA-signaling component gives increased low temperature tolerance
ABI3—*A. thaliana*	*A. thaliana*	Signaling; transcription factor in ABA mediated processes
CaPF1— *C. annuum*	*A .thaliana*	Overexpression of ERF/AP2-type transcription factor allowed slightly better protection
ICE1—*A. thaliana*	*A. thaliana*	CBF master regulator can be overexpressed without pleiotrophic effects, giving better freezing tolerance
CBF/DREB—*A. thaliana, P. avium*	*A. thaliana, B. napus*, maize, tomato	Constitutive overexpression of AP2-type confers low temperature resistance, according to several papers, but causes pleiotropic side effects

(Table Contd.)

Protein and origin	Model plant	Remarks
CBF/DREB—*A. thaliana*	Tomato, tobacco	Use of regulatable promoter confers stress tolera-nce without affecting yield
CBF/DREB—*A. thaliana*	Rice	Increased cold tolerance without detrimental side effects

However, in the case of codA, one must consider the role of the by-product of the GB synthesis, H_2O_2, which is a signaling component inducing the ROS-response and thus gives chilling tolerance. Expressing CDH alone or together with BADH in tobacco leaf discs also improved tolerance to photoinhibition under low temperature.

However, the main theme in all reported cases has been that the levels of GB produced are very modest compared to plants that *accumulate* it naturally. It is thought that this occurs because of limited supplies of precursors in *nonaccumulators*.

However, this problem seems to be possible to circumvent by using *extensive* engineering for precursor production. Moreover, a novel pathway from extreme halophile bacteria for producing GB by direct methylation of glycine also gives improved *osmotolerance* in *E. coli*. Using closely related *enzymes* in transgenic *Arabidopsis* gave much higher (10×) concentration of GB in *Arabidopsis* and *Synechococcus* than with codA.

In this case, the precursor is not choline but glycine, the levels of which are only somewhat limiting. Thus, it seems that the protective effect of GB is independent of species or mode of synthesis in natural accumulators. However, there are also reports about GB in non-natural accumulators giving only modest or even deleterious

Furthermore, even in natural accumulators, glycine betaine is not degraded once the stress is over. Thus, GB cannot be utilized once growth is resumed.

BADH and S-adenosyl-L-methionine-dependent N-methyltransferase (NMTase) are enzymes able to synthesize another betaine, β-ala-betaine, which reportedly accumulates to high levels in transgenic plants; however, low-temperature tolerance was not tested.

The levels of several other betaines (proline betaine, hydroxyproline betaine, sulfonium betaine DMSP, and choline-o-sulfate) are known to respond to cold but have not been assayed for engineering cold tolerance.

Amino Acids

Two amino acids are strongly upregulated following cold in *Arabidopsis:* proline and glutamine. Glutamine is an amide form of glutamate synthesized by the *glutamine* synthetase GS1. *Overexpression* in rice allows faster recovery from chilling stress, which may be due to increase in photorespiration capacity.

Proline is *synthesized* from glutamate via glutamic-y-semialdehyde (GSA) and A^1-pyrroline-5-carboxylate (P5C). P5C synthase (P5CS) catalyzes the conversion of glutamate to P5C, followed by P5C reductase (P5CR), which reduces P5C to proline.

In the reverse reaction, proline is metabolized to glutamate in a feedback manner via P5C and GSA with the aid of proline dehydrogenase (ProDH) followed by P5C *dehydrogenase* (P5CDH). It has been proposed that proline would not function as a *compatible* solute per se, but rather by regulating NADP+/NADH ratios by cycling between proline and its precursors.

The flux would be an important homeostatic mechanism and potentiate activity of the oxidative pentose phosphate pathway. Following relief from the stress, oxidation of proline would also provide an important energy source for ADP phosphorylation.

Concentration of proline in *Arabidopsis* is actively regulated by osmotic stress and drought. Cold regulates proline levels timewise much more slowly. In rice, the proline amount is cold inducible, and the proline synthesis *knockout* mutant is sensitive to cold. Proline application to *low-temperature-stressed* chickpea improved floral retention and pod set and the concentration of proline was higher in retained vs. aborted flowers.

Moreover, when proline catabolism was depressed in *the Arabidopsis* antisense line, it improved tolerance to freezing. However, further addition of external proline caused hypersensitivity.

Sugars

Intracellular concentration of soluble sugars has been shown to increase in several frost-hardy plant species upon exposure to low *temperatures*. These include fructans, fructose, galactinol, glucose, raffinose, stachyose, sucrose, and "sugar alcohols" (mannitol, trehalose, myo-inositol, and sorbitol).

Many sugars like mannitol, sorbitol, D-ononitol, and D-pinitol are also active ROS scavengers. Many soluble sugars need to be synthesized upon exposure to cold. However, the simplest way to achieve soluble sugar (mannitol, sucrose, raffinose, and stachyose) *accumulation* inside the cell following cold sensing is to degrade starch.

This was noted a long time ago and also shown with populus and recently with moss *Physcomitrella patens* and joint *Arabidopsis* and pea experiments. Sugar *metabolism* seems to be involved in a delicate balance affecting many different signaling pathways in plants; *pleiotropic* effects when *engineering* sugar synthesis have been reported.

Undesirable phenotypes have been associated with trehalose, as discussed in Bae and Avonce, and accumulation of sorbitol in transgenic tobacco transformed with *stpd1* (a cDNA encoding sorbitol6-phosphate dehydrogenase) from apple caused necrotic lesions assumed to have resulted from disturbance in carbohydrate transport and allocation.

Also, bacterial SacB encoding for fructan synthesis gene exhibited symptoms like stunting, necrosis, reduction in starch accumulation, and chloroplast agglutination in many plant species, although no *Arabidopsis* experiment is reported. Lists of examples can be found in Cairns and Nuccio et al.. Furthermore, there may be species-specific differences in the importance of different sugars.

The transgenic approach and mutant analyses in *Arabidopsis* clearly proved that raffinose is not essential for basic freezing tolerance. However, in petunia, there seems to be a correlation with *freezing* tolerance and raffinose. It was discussed that α-galactosidase engineered in petunia might have some other role that might explain some of the discrepancy, but it may also argue for the possible explanation that the amount of a single sugar is not important if the overall concentration of sugars remains the same. However, there are also examples of improved low-temperature tolerance using genetic engineering: transgenic fructan *production* showed increased tolerance to freezing in ryegrass using wheat *fructosyltransferase* directed to vacuole.

Localization was suggested to explain why there were no negative effects noticed, unlike with fructan synthesis using bacterial SacB.

Trehalose, *disaccharide* of glucose, can protect membranes and transgenic rice, tobacco, and *Arabidopsis* plants from cold and dehydration; small amounts of trehalose accumulate in *Arabidopsis* following cold signaling.

The phosphorylated precursor, trehalose-6-phosphate, is considered to have an important role in sugar signaling and the photosynthesis rate in *Arabidopsis*. However, pathogens also secrete trehalose in trying to redirect plant *carbohydrate* metabolism.

Thus, it seems that trehalose induces detoxification and stress response proteins involved in pathogen attack and oxidative stress in *Arabidopsis* and further induces degradation of trehalose. Mutations in the sugar metabolism genes have also provided fruitful *information*.

Arabidopsis gly1 (coding for glycerol kinase) mutant, which is unable to utilize glycerol and thus transiently accumulates glycerol, exhibits *enhanced* freezing tolerance. Furthermore, a mutation at a starch-related a-glucan/water dikinase encoded by *STARCH EXCESS 1* (*SEX1*) in *Arabidopsis* (hypothesized to regulate starch degradation in plastids by phosphorylating starch to ensure better accessibility for the *degrading enzymes*) is unable to *accumulate malto-oligosaccharides*, glucose, and fructose during the first day of cold acclimation and shows impaired freezing tolerance.

However, when low-temperature treatment is continued, the situation is normalized. Even though the cold-induced starch degradation activity was not linked to this enzyme, it enabled faster *mobilization*. Thus, starch is important during the very early phase of cold *acclimation*.

Sugars seem to be important during the first week of acclimation according to an *Arabidopsis* growth room experiment, after which other metabolites, among them proline, accumulate and sugar concentration starts to decline.

Other Metabolites

Analyses of low-temperature induced metabolites have only begun. Thus, analysis of polar metabolites from *Arabidopsis* identified 114 metabolites, out of 434 monitored, where the pool sizes were substantially (>5×) increased in response to low temperature.

Identity of roughly 30 was determined; among them, trehalose, putrescine, and ascorbate were reported *from Arabidopsis* for the first time.

However, the structure of most of the *coldinduced* metabolites *remains* to be determined. This is in accordance with results obtained in birch, where we have been able to identify only a few of the cold-induced metabolites of the sugar fraction (G. Brader, A. Welling, I. Tsitko, and T. Palva, personal *communication*).

Thus, there is a good possibility for obtaining new and even better suited metabolites for freezing protection than the few tested thus far. Many of them were *originally* identified when a stress type other than low *temperature* was studied (sucrose is a notable exception).

REGULON ENGINEERING

Stress Signaling

Engineering signaling cascades opens a possibility for recruiting many more target genes under the control of one signaling pathway. However, a delicate adjustment for proper expression pattern is needed to balance *minimizing* the negative effects. *Nicotiana* protein kinase (NPK1) is the uppermost signaling component in a MAP-kinase cascade.

Low level of expression was found to be enough for lowering freezing tolerance points by 2°C in maize without deleterious effects; higher production caused detrimental eff. HSPs are known to be involved in chilling *resistance* of fruits and GSTs are involved in oxidative stress protection. An MAPK cascade consisting of MEKK (MAPKKK), MKK2 (MAPKK), and MPK4/MPK6 (MAPKs) has been recently shown to mediate cold responses in *Arabidopsis*

Overexpression of MKK2, the second kinase in the MAP kinase cascade, increases cold and salt tolerance. Overexpression resulted in increase in the transcript levels of an MAP kinase cascade, up- or *downregulating* 152 genes at least threefold. Increased cold tolerance is achieved with overexpressing calcium-dependent protein kinases 7 and 13 of rice.

The potential functions of these proteins are to enable cross-talk between multiple *signaling pathways*. The first gene was shown to cause induction of genes encoding salt/drought specific LEA proteins. OsWRKY72 and 77 are ABA-inducible rice *transcription* factors; their transient expression leads to induction of HVA22 reporter construct in rice and, together with ABA, they *synergistically* induce HVA22 promoter.

However, no data on low temperature tolerance are yet reported. Early response to dehydration 15 (ERD15) is a signaling component encoded by a gene induced within 30 min from onset of biotic or abiotic stress. ERD 15 presumably affects the cross-talk between ABA signaling and pathogen signaling.

Overexpression of ERD 15 gives insensitivity to ABA signaling and RNAi silencing leads to improved freezing tolerance of transgenic *Arabidopsis* (Kariola et al., manuscript in preparation).

Cold-Tolerant Mutations

In some cases, silencing a gene or a mutation in a gene leads to increased *lowtemperature* tolerance instead of overexpression. Thus, T -DNA insertion *mutation* of a vacuolar Caz+/H+ antiporter, *CAXl*, leads to *improved* cold acclimation.

However, long-term freezing tolerance is normal. Genes encoding CBFs have been shown to be upregulated in *a CAXI* mutant that normally may play a role in reducing cytosolic Ca^{2+}concentration to resting levels. CBF transcription was also found to be dependent on Ca^{2+} [270]. CRYOPHYTE/LOS4 is a DEAD box RNA helicase regulating mRNA export from the nucleus and affecting the CBF pathway. Mutations in the gene render plants more sensitive (*los4-1*) or resistant (*los4-2*) to freezing and chilling.

Constitutive *overaccumulation* of proline amino acid is caused by a mutation in ESKIMO 1, *eskl*, which conferred freezing tolerance to *nonacclimatedArabidopsis*. Because soluble sugars and genes tested did not show a clear difference with wildtype plants, it was suggested that proline accumulation alone could be responsible for a large proportion of *Arabidopsis* freezing tolerance.

However, only a small increase in total freezing tolerance of the acclimated plants was reported. Antisense downregulation of phosphatase PP2CA of *A. thaliana*, also involved in signaling, showed accelerated development of freezing tolerance but no increase in basal tolerance.

CONCLUSIONS

Resistance to abiotic stress such as low *temperature* is a very complex *phenomenon* in plants. In addition to the actual protective mechanisms, there is a distinct role in the repair mechanisms after the stress.

Furthermore, *maintenance* of energy metabolism and pH stability promoting these two mechanisms is a factor *contributing* to both types of resistance ability. However, increasing knowledge of those pathways is offering insights as to how and where to direct research. These, for example, include targeting *detoxification* pathways for obtaining plants that can be sustained under true field conditions or engineering CBF/DREB and ZAT12 regulons.

Modification of a single gene, like CBF/DREB, resulted in significant *improvements* in stress tolerance in several cases. However, changes more upstream in the pathway often lead to activation of a larger set of genes, including other than stress related. Because resistance to abiotic stress is a polygenic trait, *engineering* signaling pathways offers a potent way to hit the relevant genetic target by engineering a single gene or a small number of genes.

It is important to remember that, during stress, protection mechanisms are induced and growth-related genes are repressed. Thus, growth and stress resistance are inversely correlated. Possibly, stress mechanisms are expensive to build and maintain and growth-related metabolism may be sensitive to stress. The solution for the problem would be careful regulation of the engineered trait.

However, the constitutive overexpression of the CBF master regulator, ICE1, in transgenic plants did not exhibit obvious growth or developmental abnormalities. Useful for all interested in genetic engineering is the article about fructan biosynthesis and the most usual problems encountered in expression of foreign genes in plants and a recent list of chloroplast targeting articles.

Also, pyramiding several protective genes into the same organism is the next step in research now that several interesting candidates have emerged. As important as *transforming* individual genes is to exposing their functions, it is also at the same time very labor intensive and time *consuming* (as well as expensive). New methods have recently emerged that offer tools for speeding up the research.

Thus, a method called tilling consists of making up point *mutations* in the genome with chemicals, combined with PCR-based screening of the region of interest. Amplified region harboring mutation is *hybridized* with respective wildtype regions and heteroduplex is cleaved by CEL I, after which the products are resolved using electrophoresis.

The method enables one to form allelic series that provide a range of phenotypic severities, which is important if the gene is essential, for example. Another very *interesting* method is transforming large chromosomal fragments instead of individual genes. These can be based on

Agrobacterium or particle bombardment. *Importantly,* these methods can be used even if the *whole* genome is not sequenced.

 PERSPECTIVE

It is clear that some of the acclimation mechanisms needed for acquired lowtemperature tolerance are different between annuals and perennials, and active growth phase and overwintering phase. For example, shortening day length under a critical *photoperiod* (so-called short-day [SD] signal) in birch tree *Betula pendula* potentiates low temperature-induced dehydrine expression up to five times higher that that of cold alone; in *Arabidopsis* only cold induces the same birch gene.

However, in many cases the molecular basis for cold acclimation is remarkably conserved, allowing us to appreciate different variations of the theme and to learn more about how the acclimation process is done and how the seasonal low *temperature* causes *characteristic* changes in the induction pattern of transcripts and metabolites in many plant species.

The recurring theme in seasonal acclimation is the constant change at levels of metabolites and "division of labor" among them. Differences in low-temperature-resistance mechanisms lie within the plant also. For example, leaves accumulate sugars different from those of roots following acclimation *inArabidopsis,* thus signifying that, when a decision about the transgenic approach must be made, choosing the correct promoter may have a bigger effect in the phenotype than traditionally has been thought.

Choosing the right compartment for targeting the gene, whether it is to be cytoplasmic or organellar, is another important factor to consider in an attempt to achieve a useful addition in the resistance mechanisms. One key problem to address in crop improvement is lack of well-defined *biochemical* indicators for tolerance that would enhance *breeding* programs, with or without a transgenic component.

An attempt to solve this for salinity stress has been reported; this would also be applicable to low *temperatures.* However, as pointed out by the authors, the plant physiology is so complex that, in addition to variation among species, in many cases physiological responses to stress vary from cultivar to cultivar within a single species.

This fact stresses that *biochemical* indicators would need to be specified for individual species rather than generalized for all. Finally, it is worth remembering that many of the genetically modified *stresstolerant* plants generated to date are nonagronomic plants. The stress resistance, however useful for the plant, is important only if it results in higher crop yield.

This is exemplified in the case of glycine betaine accumulators, which are more prone to fungal diseases in field trials, thus negating the effect of drought tolerance. The effects of engineered traits on *overwintering,* flowering, or seed production are only *sometimes* reported, although flowers are the parts most susceptible to abiotic stress. Securing the crop is, after all, one of the most used arguments for *motivating* plant stress research in general.

19

Chapter

PROTEIN EXTRACTION

Extracting the proteins from seeds is generally performed without much difficulty. However, to be successful, this first step of proteomic analysis requires special care because the seed is not a homogeneous tissue. Seed composition and tissue can vary considerably between species. Soon after fertilization, cell division results in different tissues such as the endosperm, embryo, scutellum, cotyledon, aleurone layer, and envelopes, each of which has a different biochemical composition.

Like most plant tissues, seeds may contain different components that can seriously reduce protein extraction or modify the protein diversity revealed using two-dimensional electrophoresis (2-DE). The peripheric layers of the seeds are often composed of hemicellulose, lignans, polyphenols, and arabinoxylans. In many species, the cell wall material is composed of arabinoxylans and arabinogalactans.

The seed is often a reservoir of components, and some tissues can be rich in polysaccharides and lipids as well as many secondary metabolites. These tissues are generally poor in protein but often rich in proteases.

To extract the seed proteins satisfactorily, it is necessary to take certain criteria into consideration in solubilizing protein for electrophoretic analyses and to avoid sources of variation that could seriously interfere with 2-DE separation such as vertical streaking, smearing, reduction in the number of spots revealed, and so on.

For cereal kernels, the main storage components are starch and complex carbohydrates, which may prevent easy extraction of the proteins. The many proteins present in the seed are usually classified into four groups according to their solubility in specific solvents used successively to extract the proteins.

In finely ground seed, albumins are water-soluble proteins, whereas globulins have to be extracted subsequently with an NaCl solution. Both these proteins are soluble, in contrast to the storage proteins found in cereal kernels. Albumins and globulins each represent about 10% of the total proteins of cereal seeds and more than *85%* of the total proteins of leguminous seeds. Storage proteins were initially classified as prolamins and glutelins.

They are both hydrophobic and specifically accumulate in small vacuoles or protein bodies. Prolamins such as gliadins, hordeins, zeins, avenins, and rizines (in wheat, barley, maize, oat, and rice, respectively), are monomeric, and they are typically soluble in 70% ethanol. Glutelins (glutenins in wheat) are generally polymerized and extracted with an acidic solvent including a reducing agent.

As the two classes of storage proteins (prolamins and glutenins) are rich in both prolin and glutamine, they were included in the prolamin class and other specific solvents are currently used to extract storage proteins. Depending on the species, it is possible that not all seed proteins will be fully extracted.

Several criteria should be taken into consideration when a method of extraction is chosen. Because the proteins are not the major component in seed, they are often aggregated or linked to other components such as cell wall material or starch granules, or they may be not readily soluble owing to the coarse fragmentation of the seed resulting from milling or grounding.

The latter phenomenon is crucial in the case of cereals in which genetic factors may influence the kernel hardness of the endosperm and hence the granulometry of the flour. The regularity of the granulometry of the crushed or milled seeds will influence the reproducibility of the protein extraction. The water content of the seed also influences the granulometry, and all material should be kept at constant moisture before sampling.

Furthermore, even when seeds are harvested from a pure homozygous genotype, they may not be of identical age depending on their position on the spike, the pod, the capitulum, and so forth. For example 2 or 3 d may be required for the fertilization of the ovaries of all the flowers located between the medium and distal part of the wheat spike.

The resulting kernels are often of different size, and the quantitative composition of the proteins present in some of their tissues may be different. Several classical procedures used to extract seed proteins are described in the following section.

They can be divided into two types: those considered as general procedures in which the major proteins present in seed can be revealed using appropriate extracting solutions, and procedures better suited to cereal proteins, in which four classes can be revealed, plus one specific to starch granules.

MATERIALS

All chemicals should be of analytical grade.

General Procedures for Extracting the Whole Seed Proteins

1. Extracting solution: 10% (v/v) trichloroacetic acid (TCA) diluted in glacial acetone containing 0.07% (v/v) of 2-mercaptoethanol and 0.4% (v/v) of plant cocktail inhibitor proteases. This

solution, called TCA/acetone extracting solution, should be stored at –20°C.

2. Washing solution: the pelleted proteins are washed in glacial acetone solution with the same ingredients as above but without TCA, and stored at –20°C.
3. Solubilization solution: *7 M* urea, *2 M* thiourea, 4% (w/v) 3[3-cholaminopropyl diethylammonio]-1-propane sulfonate (CHAPS), 2% (w/v) dithiothreitol (DTT), 0.4% (v/v) protease inhibitor cocktail (Sigma), 1% (v/v) carrier ampholytes 3 to 10 and 1% (v/v) of carrier ampholytes 6 to 9.5 (or 4–7 or 6–11 depending on the IPG strip gradient used in the isoelectric focusing (IEF) step.
4. Alkylation solution: 4-vinylpyridine
5. Glycerol solution: 60% (v/v) glycerol diluted in water with bromophenol blue traces.
6. Protein determination: use the Bradford assay or a 2D Quant kit with bovine serum albumin (BSA) as the protein standard.

Specific Protein Extraction

Albumins and Globulins

1. Sodium-phosphate buffer: 50 mM sodium phosphate buffer, pH 7.8, 0.1 M NaCl containing 0.4% (v/v) protease inhibitor cocktail (Sigma). This extracting buffer can be stored at 4°C for up to 4 wk before use.
2. Dialysis: the dialysis is performed using the slide-A-lyzer® dialysis cassette 7K MWCO, 0.1 to 0.5 mL capacity.

Amphiphilic Proteins

1. Tris-HCl buffer: 0.1 *M* Tris, 5 mM EDTA, 0.25 *M* NaCl brought to pH 7.8 with HCl. This Tris-HCl buffer can be stored at 4°C for several weeks.
2. Triton X-114 solution: add 2% (v/v) Triton X-114 and 0.4% (v/v) of protease inhibitor cocktail (Sigma) to the above Tris-HCl buffer. This Triton solution should be prepared just before use.
3. Precipitation solution: 1 vol diethylether and 3 vol ethanol prepared under the fume hood before use.

Starch Granule Proteins

Deionized water should be used throughout the procedure.

1. Density gradient: 90% (v/v) cesium chloride (CsCl; Prolabo).
2. Washing solution: 4% (w/v) CHAPS and 2% (w/v) DTT.

METHODS

General Procedure for Whole Seed Proteins

The purpose of the general procedure is to extract proteins from the finely crushed whole seed without considering which specific protein families could be revealed. The procedure proposed by Damerval et al. and Granier, which is presented elsewhere in this book, can be used for all seeds.

It is particularly suitable for the extraction of proteins from any green mature seed but also for the early stages of cereal kernel formation either for envelope tissues, embryo or the developing endosperm, which can be expelled through the cut end by pressing the kernel. Specific tissues such as the aleurone layer, embryo, and endosperm can be isolated from the developing kernel and the mature kernel.

In contrast to the embryo, which is easily isolated, the aleurone layer requires time and experience to be able to dissect under the microscope sufficient material for protein extraction and separation using 2-DE. Given possible variation between the seeds harvested on one individual plant, it is advisable to collect the green seeds from representative or known parts of the ear, capitulum, pod, etc.

Depending on the procedure used, precipitation before solubilization or direct solubilization, some differences may appear in the quantity of proteins extracted or in changes in the protein profile revealed on the 2-DE gels. In any case, once a procedure has been adopted, the same procedure should be used throughout the experiment.

Precipitation before Solubilization

After collection, the green material from the ear, pod, capitulum, etc., should immediately be weighed. The green seed material is frozen in liquid nitrogen before being crushed with a mortar and pestle.

1. The powder (100 mg) is immediately added with 1 mL of TCA/acetone glacial extracting solution. The proteins are left to precipitate overnight and then centrifuged at 15,000g, at 4°C, for 15 min.
2. The pellet is washed twice with 1 mL of the washing solution centrifuged at 15,000g, at 4°C for 15 min, and the supernatant is discarded.
3. The pellet obtained from 100 mg is air-dried to remove residual acetone and then stored at –80°C. This procedure allows the proteins to be concentrated before resolubilization with 1250 µL of the solubilization solution or with an IEF buffer containing specific solvents such as chaotropes and detergents.

Direct Resolubilization

Seed proteins can also be extracted directly from crushed kernels without previous TCA/ acetone extraction and precipitation. Detergents and chaotropic agents are often more efficient in extracting the proteins directly using the native tissue than using aggregated and precipitated forms, and this procedure also prevents protein loss caused by incomplete precipitation and/or resolubilization. The procedure described here does not include organic precipitation using glacial acetone, which is useful to concentrate proteins and remove salts and other organic compounds.

This acetone precipitation procedure was proposed only recently. Another extracting procedure was recently reported in which proteins soluble in KCl were extracted from developing wheat kernels.

In barley the proteins were first extracted using 5 mM Tris-HCl, pH 7.5, 1 mM CaCl2. Thiourea/

urea lysis buffer containing protease inhibitor cocktail, Dnase I, Rnase , Triton X-100, and DTT was used for *Arabidopsis thaliana* seeds.

The procedure described here is mainly oriented to cereal endosperm proteins that are mainly composed of storage proteins (prolamins and glutelins). It does not eliminate some other proteins; in particular many albumins and globulins will also be extracted together with storage proteins.

1. The material should be weighed immediately after collection and then crushed or milled.
2. Add 500 tL of the solubilization solution to 40 mg of wholemeal flour in an Eppendorf tube, mix on a vortex, and incubate at room temperature for 1 1/2 h.
3. After sonication (20 W, 20 s), the slurry is let to rest 30 min and centrifuged (9000g, 5 min, 20°C). Then 250 tL of the supernatant is collected. The main content of the supernatant is the storage protein fraction.
4. The protein concentration in the extract can then be estimated using either the Bradford assay (Sigma) or the 2D Quant kit (Amersham).
5. Add to 250 tL of the supernatant 20 tL of carrier ampholytes (according to the IPG strip gradient used in the IEF step) and 4 μL 4-vinylpyridine. After a contact of 15 min and vortexing, 254 tL of the glycerol solution is added. The protein extract can be stored at –80°C until use or analyzed directly in 2-DE.

SPECIFIC PROTEIN EXTRACTION

Albumins and Globulins

The simultaneous extraction of the two proteins classes (i.e., water-soluble albumins and salt-soluble globulins) has been optimized for the IEF. Thus, after being extracted with the sodium-phosphate buffer as described elsewhere, the protein extract is desalted and the proteins are then precipitated and solubilized in a buffer compatible with the IEF.

Albumins and globulins of wheat kernel were recently revealed on 2-DE using this procedure. Whole grains (including envelopes and with or without the embryo depending on the objective) are crushed or milled following the procedure described elsewhere in this chapter. Extraction is performed as follows:

1. 100 mg of wholemeal flour is added to 1 mL of sodium phosphate buffer, and continuously stirred at 4°C for 2 h. After centrifugation (8000g, 10 min, 4°C), 500 tL of supernatant is collected.
2. Supernatant is dialyzed against cold water at 4°C for 24 h according to the manufacturer's instructions.
3. The desalted sample is left to precipitate with 1 mL of acetone at –20°C overnight and then centrifuged (8000g, 4°C, 5 min).
4. The supernatant is removed and the pelleted proteins are rinsed three times with glacial acetone and centrifuged (8000g, 4°C, 5 min). The pellet is finally air-dried to remove residual acetone.
5. The recovered pellet is solubilized in 250 μL of solubilization buffer with occasional

vortexing. After 1 1/2 h at room temperature, the solubilized pelled is sonicated (20 W, 20 s), and the slurry is left to rest 30 min and centrifuged (9000g, 5 min, 20°C). The supernatant is collected.

6. The supernatant containing the protein extract is collected and supplemented with 20 µL carrier ampholytes and 4 µL of 4-vinylpyridine. The solution is vortexed and left to rest for 15 min.
7. Then 254 µL of the glycerol solution is added. The solution can be stored at –80°C until use or directly analyzed in 2-DE.

Amphiphilic Proteins

These proteins are composed of two types of amino acid sequences, one that is rich in hydrophilic amino acids (mostly Lys, Arg, and His) and the other in hydrophobic amino acids (such as Val, Leu, and Ile). Most, if not all, of the membrane proteins are amphiphilic.

The extraction procedure described here was based on the sequential procedure described elsewhere, with some modifications for 2-DE of amphiphilic proteins of wheat seed.

1. Kernels should be crushed as described.
2. The proteins are extracted by stirring 250 mg of flour in 7.5 mL of Triton X-114 solution at 4°C for 1 h and centrifuged at 10,000g, at 4°C, for 30 min.
3. The supernatant is heated at 37°C for 45 min for the phase partitioning and then centrifuged at 5000g, at 22°C for 10 min. The upper light phase should be removed with care.
4. Five volumes (approximately 10 mL) of the precipitation solution are added to the lower detergent-rich phase containing the amphiphilic proteins. The proteins are left to precipitate at –20°C overnight.
5. After centrifugation at 2000g, at –8°C, for 10 min, the pellet is washed three times with 10 mL of diethylether-ethanol solution and centrifuged at 2000g, at –8°C, for 10 min.
6. Finally the pellet is washed with 5 mL of diethylether, centrifuged, and dried under vacuum at room temperature. The dry pellet can be stored at –80°C until further use. For isofocussing, the solubilization of the dry pellet is obtained by adding 250 µL of the solubilization solution.

Starch Granule Proteins

Starch is the major component (70–75% dry base) of cereal kernel endosperm. The starch granules, which come from amyloplasts, develop during grain formation and in the mature endosperm. A multimodal distribution of starch granule size is generally observed in cereal seeds.

The procedure below describes the extraction of the proteins strongly attached to and/or present within the starch granules of the cereal kernel. This procedure was developed from previous studies on wheat granule binding starch synthase with some modifications.

1. One or two half-kernels are crushed with a mortar and pestle at room temperature, and the floury material is manually separated from the envelope tissue.

2. Soak 40 to 60 mg of flour in 1 mL of deionized water at 4°C overnight. The slurry is centrifuged at 10,000g, 4°C, for 2 min.
3. Then 300 μL of cold water is added to the pellet and the mixture is vortexed.
4. The slurry is layered with 1 mL of 90% (v/v) CsCl, left to rest at 4°C for 5 min, and then centrifuged at 14,000g, at 4 °C, for 5 min. The supernatant is carefully pipeted off.
5. Then 1 mL of the washing solution containing CHAPS and DTT is added to the pellet. The mixture is vortexed and then heated at 37°C for 15 min with vortexing every 5 min. The slurry is centrifuged at 14,000g, at 4°C, for 3 min, then the supernatant is gently pipeted off.
6. The starch granule pellet is centrifuged (using the same parameters) and washed three times with water as follows: 1 mL of water is added to the pellet, and the slurry is vortexed, left to rest for 5 min at ambient temperature, and centrifuged at 14,000g, at 4°C, for 3 min. The supernatant is carefully pipeted off each time.
7. The pellet is then washed one last time with 1 mL of glacial acetone for 5 min, vortexed, and centrifuged. The starch granule pellet can be air-dried and weighed and stored at –20°C if needed.
8. The starch granule pellet is resuspended using the washing solution at a 1:5 (w/v) ratio. Usually 40 mg of dried starch granules are suspended by vortexing with 200 μL of a freshly made solution of 4% (w/v) CHAPS and 2% (w/v) DTT at room temperature. The suspension is left to rest for 5 min and then heated at 100°C for 5 min, which causes the starch granules to release their content.
9. The slurry is cooled on ice for 10 min and then centrifuged at 17,000g, at 4°C, for 15 min. The supernatant containing the proteins strongly attached or present within the starch granules is collected and stored at –80°C or used directly for 2-DE. For isofocusing, add 150 μL of the solubilization solution to 100 μL of supernatant.

Notes

1. The most commonly used reducing agent is DTT, but the choice of the reducing agent is primarily sample specific, and tributyl phosphine (TBP) can also be used.
2. The solution should be prepared before use or can also be aliquoted and stored at –80°C.
3. TCA, which strongly influences folding and precipitation of proteins, may prevent their complete resolubilization. TCA can thus be omitted from the extraction solution.
4. DTT at 20 mM can be used instead of 0.07% 2-mercaptoethanol as the reducing agent.
5. The use of plant protease inhibitor is recommended in all cases, since resolubilization, which for some material requires successive vortexing and sonication (20 w, 20 s), is generally performed at positive temperatures.
6. Although the TCA/acetone procedure allows the proteins to be concentrated, it should be noted that some low-molecular-weight proteins may require centrifugation with higher parameters (for example at 30,000g, at 4°C, for 30 min) to be pelleted.

7. The protein pellet can be air-dried then stored at –80°C or directly resolubilized without storage.
8. When green material or immature kernels are used, the green seeds can be frozen (using nitrogen) and then finely crushed under liquid nitrogen using a mortar and pestle.
9. Material can also be lyophilized and stored at –20°C until analysis.
10. When the sample is made of mature cereal kernels, the grains are often milled using for example, a Cyclotec 14920 mill with a 0.75-mm mesh sieve. The wholemeal flour must then be extracted immediately.
11. Alkylation of the free SH can be performed with iodo-acetamide instead of 4-vinyl pyridine. Alkylation is usually performed only after the IEF step during the equilibration step of the IPG gel strips. The subunits of storage proteins are usually better separated when the alkylation is performed after isofocusing.
12. The glycerol solution was first adopted for cup loading and maintained when proteins were added to IPG strips by passive rehydration. This solution can be removed for some IEF separations, like albumin and globulin separation.
13. Albumins or water-soluble proteins can be directly extracted in chilled distilled water as performed for *Arabidopsis thaliana* seeds.
14. Since acetone precipitation allows partial removal of salts, the dialysis step can be left out, particularly when small quantities of protein extract have to be loaded on IEF. When large quantities (>150 µg) of protein extract have to be loaded, dialysis can reduce horizontal streaking caused by interfering substances in the extracting solution.
15. The phase partitioning enables the amphiphilic proteins to be collected in the lower dense phase. The light phase should be carefully removed with a pipete, as many proteins have been observed at the frontier between the light and dense phase.
16. Starch granules can be isolated from one, two, or more embryo-less kernels. Alternatively, the seeds can be cut in half and the remaining embryo part used for seedling purposes. The amount of starch granules to be used to extract the proteins present within or strongly attached to the granules can be higher than 40 mg. This amount was sufficient to detect on silver-stained 2-DE gels the majority of the wheat starch granule proteins. A similar approach was recently used on barley.

PROTEIN EXTRACTION FROM XYLEM AND PHLOEM SAP

Higher plants contain vascular bundles that permit nutrient distribution as well as communication between even the most distant plant parts. These bundles contain two types of transport units, the xylem and the phloem.

The main function of the xylem is to transport water and nutrients to the aerial tissues; the phloem allocates organic assimilates, like sugars and amino acids, from the site of production to all other plant parts.

Proteins have also been found in xylem and phloem saps of different plants. Although xylem elements are dead cells, xylem sap of healthy and pathogeninfected plants contains proteins at low concentrations that nevertheless appear to have specific functions, for instance, in the maintenance, reorganization, or reinforcement of cell walls or in defence against pathogens (1–5 and references therein). The transporting tubes that build the phloem are called sieve elements (SEs).

SEs are highly specialized cells lacking nuclei and ribosomes and are thus not equipped for transcription and translation. The transport fluid in these tubes is normally designated as phloem sap. In this sap, more than a hundred proteins have been detected in different species, and a reasonable number of these proteins has been identified and characterized.

They are likely to be imported from the tightly associated companion cells (CCs) through specialized plasmodesmata. In contrast to xylem fluid, protein concentrations in phloem sap can reach quite high levels (up to 60 mg/mL in cucurbits).

It is believed that these proteins could play a role in phloem maintenance and defence, but some may also be crucial for long-distance communication. This chapter describes sampling procedures for xylem and phloem sap and outlines how the proteins can be extracted and purified so that they are suitable for downstream proteomic analyses.

MATERIALS

Collection of Xylem Sap

1. Razor blade.
2. Screw-capped tubes.
3. Containers (e.g., pots) and ice to collect xylem sap.

Concentration of Xylem Sap Proteins

1. Amicon Centriprep YM-3 and/or Amicon Centricon Plus-20 filter units for concentration and partial purification of xylem sap proteins.
2. 12.5% TCA in 100% acetone supplemented with 0.0875% β-mercaptoethanol added just prior to use (35 μL β-mercaptoethanol per 40 mL) or 80% acetone for protein precipitation.

Collection of Phloem Sap

1. Sterile razor blade or hypodermic needle.
2. Filter paper.
3. Pipet, reaction tubes, and ice to collect phloem sap.

Purification of Phloem Sap Proteins

1. 2 M HCl.
2. 2 M NaOH (analytical grade).
3. Acetone/methanol/dithiothreitol (DTT) (90% [v/v] /10 % [v/v] /10 mM). 100% acetone (analytical grade)

METHODS

Collection of Xylem Sap

Xylem sap is a part of the extracellular space of plants. It has a unique composition, including specific proteins, the presence and concentration of which can vary depending on the condition of the plant. Because pure xylem sap is easy to obtain from most plants, the tools of proteomics can be readily applied to identify xylem sap proteins.

For preparation of protein samples for separation on one-dimensional electrophoresis (1-DE) or 2-DE gels, issues to take into account are the low protein concentration and the presence of oligosaccharides (and glycosylated proteins). There are basically two steps in the application of a xylem sap protein sample on a 1-DE or 2-DE gel: collection of xylem sap and concentration of xylem sap proteins.

1. Xylem sap can be obtained by cutting the stems with a razor blade and collecting the sap exuded spontaneously (driven by root pressure) from the remaining stem on the root side.

   The stems can be cut at any height, but, in general, the closer the cut is to the base of the stem, the higher the yield of sap. However, enough of the stem (around 10 cm) should remain to connect to a tube on ice.

2. Sap collection
   a. The remaining stem segment is placed horizontally, and a tube is taped to the stem segment. The tube is surrounded by ice in a container, and sap is collected for up to 6 h (the ice container needs to be refilled several times during sap collection).
   b. Alternatively, the exuding xylem sap can be collected repeatedly every few minutes with a pipet into a reaction tube placed on ice.

3. In any case, it is important to wash the cut surface before sample collection to remove the content from cut cells and the phloem sap that exudes directly after cutting.

4. Before concentrating proteins, it is advisable to remove any particulate matter like soil particles, microbial cells, or tissue remnants by centrifugation.

CONCENTRATION OF XYLEM SAP PROTEINS

Xylem sap contains proteins but also carbohydrates and other compounds like amino acids, salts, and (in pathogen-infected plants) polyphenols.

For 1-DE analysis, simple precipitation of proteins suffices, even when using ethanol (4 parts of 95% EtOH/5% 0.1 M NaAc to 1 part of protein sample), which also precipitates poly- and oligosaccharides.

To prepare samples for isoelectric focusing, the sap should be first partially purified and concentrated using Amicon filter units and then precipitated with trichloracetic acid (TCA)/acetone.

Protein Concentration and Partial Purification with Amicon Filter Units

Either Amicon Centriprep YM-3 (at most 15 ml, cutoff: 3 kD) or Amicon Centricon Plus-20 (larger volumes, cutoff: 10 kD) filter units can be used to concentrate and partially purify xylem sap proteins.

1. After centrifugation to remove particulate matter, add at most 15 mL (Centriprep YM-3) or 19 mL (Centricon Plus-20) xylem sap to the sample container.
2. Spin Centriprep YM-3 for approx 75 min at 4°C at 3000g until equilibrium is reached (between fluid levels inside and outside the filtrate collector).
3. Spin Centricon Plus-20 for 15 min at 4°C at 4000g. Decant filtrate. To the Centricon Plus-20, another 19 mL xylem sap can now be added to sample filter cup.
4. Spin for another 15 min.
5. Decant filtrate again and repeat spin and decant steps if further concentration is desired.
6. Collect concentrate (at least 500 μL) directly from Centriprep YM-3.
7. Collect concentrate (at least 200 μL) from Centricon Plus-20 by spinning the inverted unit for 5 min at 1000g.

Protein Precipitation with TCA/Acetone

1. Add 4 parts of either 12.5% TCA in 100% acetone with 0.0875% (3-mercaptoethanol to 1 part of protein sample and mix.
2. Incubate for at least 45 min at –20°C (or 1–4 h at 0°C for 80% acetone), and then centrifuge tubes for 30 min in a centrifuge at maximum speed (refrigeration not required).
3. Discard supernatant and wash the pellet three times with ice-cold 100% acetone. 4. Remove remaining liquid with a pipet, and dry the pellet at room temperature.

The pellet can be solubilized in rehydration buffer *(2 M* thiourea, *7 M* urea, 4% 3β-cholaminopropyl diethylammonio]-propane sulfonate (CHAPS), 10 mM DTT) for isoelectric focusing or store dry at –20°C.

Collection of Phloem Sap

Phloem sap is much more difficult to obtain from most plant species than xylem sap, and the major challenge of phloem sap proteomics is therefore to obtain enough material to perform proteomic studies. However, several different methods to obtain phloem samples can be applied, their feasibility largely depending on the plant species of interest. In a few species (e.g., *Ricinus,* Cucurbitaceae, *Yucca*), phloem sap can be collected after applying small incisions or excising whole organs.

Plants not suitable for this procedure can be sampled by EDTA-facilitated exudation. In many plant species, the aphid stylet technique can also yield phloem sap of high purity but only in small amounts. The established plant model species, like thale cress *(Arabidopsis thaliana)* or rice *(Oryza sativa),* hardly allow the collection of sufficient amounts of SE exudate for proteomic analysis.

In Arabidopsis, the sample amounts obtainable are not sufficient for proteomic approaches, whereas in rice, only some highly abundant phloem sap proteins have been identified from planthopper stylet exudate. Most current information about the identity of phloem polypeptides comes from cucurbits *Ricinus,* and recently also from oilseed rape, in which sap collection by exudation is relatively easy. Two variants of the exudation technique are described below.

1. Variant 1.
   a. Cut the main stem or petiole with a razor blade.
   b. Alternatively, hypodermic needles can be used to puncture the plant.
2. Variant 2.
   a. Proceed with the shoot side and dry the cut surface with a filter paper.
   b. Remove the first droplet exuding from the incision with filter paper.

Collect the subsequently exuding sap with a pipet in a reaction tube that is kept on ice.

Purification of Phloem Sap Proteins

1. When separating phloem proteins in 1-DE or 2-DE gels, the high concentrations of sugars and other organic materials present in this transport fluid have to be taken into account. In addition, plants possess mechanisms to respond to wounding events that include the polymerization of proteins.
2. For 1-DE, phloem samples can be directly expelled into 1-DE sample buffer, heated, and applied to a gel at room temperature.
3. When performing subsequent 2-DE, proteins should be purified by precipitation before the samples can be applied to the isoelectric focusing gels or strips.

Depletion of the Major Phloem Proteins 1 (PP1) and 2 (PP2)

The two major phloem proteins, phloem filament protein PP1 and phloem lectin PP2, occur in all dicots and can make up more than 50% of total phloem proteins in certain species (e.g., *Cucurbitaceae).* Under oxidative conditions, these two proteins form insoluble polymers linked by disulfide bridges that can result in streaking and bad resolution on 1-DE and 2-DE gels.

To remove these proteins, acidification followed by neutralization may be used (28). All the following steps can be performed at room temperature.

1. Adjust sample to pH 2.0 with 2 *M HCl.*
2. Neutralize to pH 7.5 with 2 *M* NaOH.
3. Centrifuge at 15,000g for 15 min.
4. Collect supernatant and discard the copious white pellet that contains PP1 and PP2.

Precipitation of Total Phloem Sap Proteins by Acetone/Methanol/DTT

To remove carbohydrates and other disturbing components, proteins can be precipitated by treatment with acetone/methanol/DTT.

1. Add 3 volumes of ice-cold sample precipitation solution.
2. Precipitate at –20°C overnight.
3. Centrifuge for 5 min at 6800g and 4°C and discard supernatant.

4. Wash precipitate twice with 100% cold acetone, and centrifuge at 6800g and 4°C for 5 min.
5. Discard supernatant and air-dry pellet for 5–10 min at room temperature.
6. Dissolve the pellet in buffer for either 1-DE or for 2-DE.

Notes

1. Since xylem sap contains proteases, care has to be taken that samples are kept cool all the time; protease inhibitors can be used to reduce the risk of protease digest.
2. Sap yields after 6 h of bleeding of tomato plants vary widely. From healthy, 6- to 7-wk-old plants, more than 10 mL can be obtained from an individual plant, but occasionally a plant will yield nothing or very little. The conditions of plants will obviously influence sap yield, but we have not found specific conditions that reproducibly affect yield. Diseased plants, such as those infected with the vascular wilt fungus *Fusarium oxysporum,* have much lower sap yields.
3. Protein or sugar concentration can be used as a measure for phloem contamination; low concentrations of both substances indicate a high purity of xylem sap samples.
4. Poly- and oligosaccharides react with common reagents to measure protein concentration, like Bradford and bicinchoninic acid (BCA; Sigma). Their presence in xylem sap leads to an overestimation of protein content.
5. Due to turgor pressure that is highly positive in SEs and negative in xylem elements of living plants, only phloem sap will exude from such incisions.
6. It is important to keep in mind that phloem sap is obtained from the shoot side, whereas xylem sap can be obtained from the other side (the root containing part) of the divided stem.
7. Since phloem sap usually contains protease inhibitors at high concentrations, the addition of chemical protease inhibitors is normally not required.
8. It is important to check the protein composition (e.g. by analysing the protein composition of the pellet by 1-DE) after this precipitation step, because usually not exclusively PP1 and PP2, but also other proteins can precipitate during the procedure.
9. Do not precipitate for extended periods since proteins might become insoluble.
10. Centrifugation at higher speed leads to solubilization problems.
11. Do not dry by vacuum centrifugation since this results in poor solubility.
12. If the pellet does not dissolve, incubation for longer times, sonication, or incubation at higher temperatures might be useful. If some insoluble particles remain, centrifuge samples before applying the samples to gels.

PROTEIN ETRACTION FROM WOODY PLANTS

In perennial plants, the successive addition of secondary xylem tissue differentiated from the vascular cambium gives rise to a unique tissue called wood. Wood is composed of nonconducting and conducting elements implicated in the long-distance transport of water and nutrients in trees. In gymnosperms, wood is comprised of two main cell types: tracheids and ray parenchyma. In angiosperms it also contains vessels and fibers. This simplicity hides the fact that it is also a highly variable material.

The activity of the vascular cambium and the differentiation of newly divided cells are genetically controlled and also affected by environmental and ontogenic effects that ultimately influence wood and end-use properties. Given the role wood plays both in the biosphere in terms of sinks for excess atmospheric CO_2 and in our daily life as a raw material for thousand of products and an endlessly renewable source of energy, it is surprising that our understanding of how wood develops is far from complete.

Wood formation is a complex phenomenon driven by the coordinate expression of numerous genes especially involved in the biosynthesis and the assembly of polysaccharides, lignins, and cell wall proteins.

Up to now, the study of molecular mechanisms involved in the development of wood has mainly taken a transcriptomic approach, combining expressed sequence tag (EST) sequencing and transcript profiling.

Only one large-scale project has attempted to identify proteins from the differentiating secondary xylem of maritime pine. In this chapter we describe a protocol optimized to extract proteins from wood-forming tissue in three forest tree species: pine, poplar, and oak.

The protocol was successfully extended to other organs, namely, root, leaf, pollen, bud, flower, cambium, and phloem.

MATERIALS

Tissue Sampling and Storage

Wood Forming Tissue

1. The rough outer bark is first removed using a bark shaver with a 30-cm blade.
2. The phloem and cambium are levered off the stem together by making incisions (two vertical cuts between two horizontal cuts) using a sharp knife into the exposed tissue.
3. Differentiating xylem (wood-forming tissue) is collected from the exposed log surface using a vegetable peeler or a knife, immediately frozen in liquid nitrogen and stored at –80°C until used for protein extraction.
4. Samples are always taken from adult trees during the active growing season. Different types of wood (early and late wood, juvenile and mature wood, opposite and compression wood; 1), differing in their chemical, anatomical, and physical properties, can be sampled within a single individual.

Other Tissues

For mapping the proteomes of different tissues/organs of the tree, leaves, roots, vegetative and sexual buds, pollen, phloem, and cambium are taken during the active growing phase of seedlings or adult trees.

Total Protein Precipitation

1. Polycarbonate 10 mL oak ridge centrifuge tube.
2. Precipitation buffer (make fresh as required and store at –20°C): prepare a solution with 10% Trichloroacetic acid (TCA) a very effective protein precipitant, and 0.07% 2-mercaptoethanol in acetone.
3. Rinsing buffer (make fresh as required and store at –20°C): 0.07% 2-mercaptoethanol in acetone.

Protein Solubilization

1. Solubilization buffer: *7 M* urea, *2 M* thiourea, 0.4% Triton X-100, 4% 3-β-cholamidopropyl dimethylammonio]-1-propane sulfonate (CHAPS), 10 mM dithiothreitol (DTT), 1% immobilized ph gradient (IPG) buffer (Amersham Biosciences, Uppsala, Sweden). Store at –20°C.

METHODS

Total Protein Etraction

1. Weigh an empty 10-mL centrifuge tube without the sealing cap. We used polycarbonate Oak Ridge centrifuge tubes for their physical strength.
2. Cell disruption: 500 mg fresh tissue (stored –80°C) is finely powdered in liquid nitrogen using a mortar and pestle.
3. Resuspend the powder in 8 mL of ice-cold precipitation buffer.
4. Transfer the resulting mix to the weighed centrifuge tube.

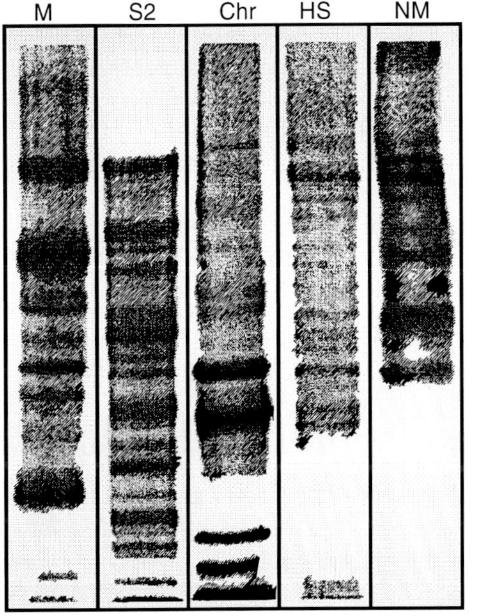

Figure 19.1: Nuclear protein fractions obtained from onion root meristematic cells, separated by SDS-PAGE, and stained with Coomassie Brilliant Blue. A total of 10 μg of proteins was loaded in each well. Lane M, initial fraction containing membranes and remnants of the cytoskeleton. Lane S2, soluble ribonucleoprotein fraction, obtained by extraction in a low ionic strength EDTA buffer. Lane Chr, chromatin fraction, released after digestion with DNase I. Lane HS, first nuclear matrix fraction, soluble in a high ionic strength (high salt) buffer. Lane NM, insoluble part of the nuclear matrix fractions. kDa, molecular weight markers, in kilodaltons. Some major bands are identified, corresponding to characterized proteins, such as the nucleolin-like proteins NopA100 (N1) and NopA64 (N2), fibrillarin (F), histone H1 (H1), and histones of the core nucleosome (HC).

5. Rinse the mortar with 2 mL of ice-cold precipitation buffer.
6. Transfer the resulting mix to the same centrifuge tube.
7. Mix the tube contents by gently inverting the tube for 15 s, and then let the proteins precipitate for 1 h at –20°C.
8. Centrifuge the tube at 16,000g for 15 min.
9. Remove the supernatant by gently pouring down the sides of the tube.
10. Rinse the pellet (remove residual TCA) by adding 10 mL ice-cold rinsing buffer in the tube and let the tube sit for 1 h at –20°C.
11. Centrifuge the tube at 16,000g for 10 min.
12. Dry the pellet under vacuum for about 2 h.
13. Powder the pellet using a glass stick.
14. Weigh the centrifuge tube containing the dry pellet.

Protein Solubilization

1. Resuspend the powder in the solubilization buffer. We use between 10 and 30 µL of buffer per mg of powder. This buffer contains a mixture of chaotropes (urea, thiourea), detergents (Triton-X 100, CHAPS), reductants (DTT), and carrier ampholytes (IPG buffer).
2. Centrifuge the tube at 400g for 4 min at room temperature to precipitate any undisolved material (e.g., cellular fragments).
3. Pour the supernatant into a clean tube.
4. Centrifuge at 400g for 4 min at room temperature, and pour the supernatant into a clean tube.
5. Store the supernatant at –80°C.
6. Protein concentration is quantified over six replicated assays, using the protocol described by Ramagli et al. (8). The mean concentration is then calculated and used to load 300 µg of proteins on an IPG-strip.

Notes

1. Caution: Because this buffer uses toxic compounds and generates unpleasant smell in the lab, it should be prepared under the hood.
2. It takes about 30 min to dissolve urea and thiourea. It is absolutely prohibited to heat the buffer to accelerate its solubilization. MilliQ water (18.2 MΩ-cm resistivity) is used to prepare the buffer.
3. A 20% working Triton X-100 solution is first prepared and stored at 4°C.
4. IPG buffer is to be used according to the chosen IPG strip pH gradient of the isoelectric focusing step.
5. Although the protocol is described for one replicated sample, three extractions are usually completed in parallel for each sample and pooled at the very end of the protocol to

provide enough proteins to perform five replicated 2D gels.

6. Allow the temperature of the centrifuge to drop to 0°C before starting the centrifuge.

EXTRACTION OF NUCLEAR PROTEINS FROM ROOT MERISTEMATIC CELLS

The identification and characterization of large amounts of proteins in plants by proteomic methods currently faces the frequent problem of insufficient available data on plant genome sequences. Only two plant species, namely, *Arabidopsis* and rice, are fully sequenced, which means that only in very few cases has the mass spectrometry (MS) approach been used exclusively for protein identification, always with *Arabidopsis* as the biological model.

In other cases, MS sequencing was accompanied by amino-terminal sequencing by the Edman reaction. Another strategy consisted of the identification of proteins after obtaining tag sequences by spectrometry, which could be then compared with the catalogue of known sequenced genes.

In general, plant proteomics was largely facilitated by the existence of sequenced genomes for the biological models that were the object of the studies. The method we describe here was designed to avoid, to some extent, the necessity of possessing the genome sequence of the considered plant species.

The objective is to concentrate on a limited number of proteins that are enriched in different fractions known to have functional significance. Therefore, we will deal with the proteome of a subcellular organelle, in this case the cell nucleus, and we will divide it into functional subproteomes. The first step is, obviously, to obtain the biological material for the study. Since we were interested in studying nuclear proteins related to, or involved in, cell proliferation events, we chose the root meristematic cell population.

This material was homogenized and the organelles of interest (in our case nuclei) were purified. Nuclei isolation from meristematic cells is facilitated by the maximum relative cellular volume occupied by the nucleus in this cell type. From these purified nuclei, a set of subproteomes was obtained after a stepwise procedure of protein fractionation based on protein solubility in buffers of increasing ionic strength.

The procedure yields an initial washing fraction containing proteins of the nuclear envelope and remnants of the cytoskeleton. In the following fraction, which is soluble in a low ionic strength buffer containing EDTA, and is called S2, we obtain the most soluble nuclear proteins, which are ribonucleoproteins.

In a third step, we extract the proteins of the chromatin, after incubation in DNase. Finally, the last two fractions contain proteins of the nuclear matrix, first by solubilization in a high salt buffer and then by recovering the insoluble pellet.

These insoluble proteins are associated with the network of filaments that contain RNA. After sequential protein extraction, each fraction is suspended in an appropriate buffer in order to separate proteins either in monodimensional sodium dodecyl sulfate-polyacrylamide gel electrophoresis (SDS-PAGE) or in bidimensional gels.

In fact, the bidimensional gels constitute expression patterns that can be used for various purposes by comparing patterns obtained from cells in different physiological states, or extracted from certain mutants or genetic constructions, or subjected to drug treatments, or affected by diverse stimuli.

In particular, we have used this approach to characterize nucleolar proteins involved in cellular proliferation events, as well as to determine expression changes induced by microgravity on board the International Space Station.

MATERIALS

Plant Material and Extraction Medium

1. Germination: for germination of onion *(Allium cepa L.)* bulbs, cylindrical glass receptacles containing filtered water (milli-RO4 water; Millipore, Bedford MA) are used.
2. Extraction medium: excised plant material is deposited in extraction medium, a blend of reagents intended to provide stability to subcellular fractions. The composition of this medium, which is a modification of the medium described by Greimers and Deltour (13), is as follows: 2% arabic gum (Sigma), 1.25% Ficoll (Sigma), 2.5% dextran sulfate (Fluka), 25 mM Tris-HCl, pH 7.4, 0.5 mM EDTA, 2.5 mM MgCl2, 4 mM n-octanol, 8 mM β-mercaptoethanol (Sigma), 6.8 mM diethyl pyrocarbonate (DEPC; Sigma), 30% glycerol and a cocktail of protease inhibitors containing 1 tg/mL aprotinin, 1 μg/mL pepstatin, 1μg/mL leupeptin and 0.1 mM phenylmethylsulfonyl fluoride (PMSF), all from Sigma. *Caution*: Because two of the components of the medium, DEPC and (β-mercaptoethanol, are toxic products, it is advisable to work in a fume hood and to wear chemical-resistant gloves.

Purification of Nuclei

1. Sample homogenization: performed in a high-speed Ultraturrax blender (IKA, Labortechnik, Staufen, Germany) and filtered through three layers of nylon cloth, with pores of 100, 50, and 30 μm, respectively.
2. Storage of purified nuclei: once nuclei are purified, they are stored in nuclei stock buffer (NSB), which is 10 mM Tris-HCl, pH 7.4, 10 mM HEPES, 10 mM KCl, 2 mM MgCl2, 4 mM n-octanol, 0.1 mM CaCl2, *0.24 M* sucrose, 0.5 mM spermidine (Sigma), 0.15 mM spermine (Sigma), 0.02% sodium azide (Sigma), plus the cocktail of protease inhibitors.
3. This buffer can be stored at 4°C for several months, although care must be taken to avoid fungal contamination. The cocktail of protease inhibitors must be added at the moment of use, not when preparing the solution.

Nuclear Protein Fractionation and Extraction

Throughout all these steps, the cocktail of protease inhibitors must supplement all solutions.

1. Fraction of membranes and remnants of cytoskeleton: the first fraction is extracted by adding to NSB a solution of 1% (v/v) Nonidet NP-40 (Roche) and 0.5% (v/v) sodium deoxycholate (Sigma).
2. Soluble fraction (S2): the second fraction is extracted with the low ionic strength buffer, which is 10 mM Tris-HCl, pH 8.0, and 1 mM EDTA.

3. Chromatin fraction (lane Chr): for extraction of the third fraction, the buffer used is composed of NSB to which 100 µg/mL RNase-free DNase I (Sigma) and 0.5% Triton X-100 are added. After DNA digestion, 0.25 M ammonium sulfate is incorporated.
4. High salt fraction (lane HS): extracted with NSB containing 2 M NaCl.
5. Insoluble fraction or nuclear matrix fraction (lane NM); can only be solubilized in urea buffer, which is 20 mM MES, pH 6.6, 1 mM EGTA, 0.1 mM MgCl2, 1% (β-mercaptoethanol, 0.02% sodium azide, 0.5% Triton X-100, 8 M urea, 2 M thiourea. This buffer is stable during several months at 4°C, but, since urea may form crystals in cold, it is advisable to transfer it to room temperature some time before its use, or, alternatively, to warm it up slightly, not exceeding 37°C, at the moment of use.

Protein Preparation for SDS-PAGE and for 2D-Electrophoresis

1. Precipitation step: proteins from each fraction are precipitated with 7% trichloroacetic acid (TCA). The pellet is washed in ethanol/ether 3:1 (v/v).
2. Preparation for SDS-PAGE: if proteins are to be separated by SDS-PAGE, dry pellets of nuclear protein fractions are resuspended in Laemmli buffer, which is 10% glycerol, 0.2 M Tris-HCl, pH 6.8, 0.002% bromophenol blue (Bio-Rad), 4% SDS, 5% (β-mercaptoethanol.
3. Preparation for 2D-electrophoresis: dry pellets of nuclear protein fractions are resuspended in rehydration buffer, which is 40 mM Tris-HCl, *2 M* thiourea, *7 M* urea, 4% Triton X-100, 100 mM dithiothreitol (DTT), 2% carrier ampholytes (BioRad) (pH 7–4 carrier ampholytes were mixed with pH 3–10 ampholytes at a 2:1 ratio), and 0.001% bromophenol blue (Bio-Rad). The buffer can be stored at room temperature, without DTT and the ampholytes, which should be added at the moment of protein loading onto the gel.
4. Quantitative assessment of the protein concentration. For this purpose, the Bradford Protein Assay reagent (Bio-Rad) is used. The optical density of the reaction is measured in a spectrophotometer, at a wavelength of 595 nm.

   The machine is calibrated to zero with a blank containing 750 µL of water, 250 µL of the Bradford reagent, and 1 µL of electrophoresis buffer (Laemmli or rehydration) without proteins and bromophenol blue. The value obtained is compared with a standard graphic, previously calculated, composed from known concentrations of BSA, ranging from 1 to 140 µg/mL.

METHODS

Plant Material

1. Peel the onion *(Allium cepa L.)* bulbs, removing the brown dry shell, wash them with tap water, and place each one on top of a cylindrical glass tube containing approx 90 mL of filtered water, so that only the base remains submerged in the water. The water should be continuously aerated by bubbling air at 10 to 20 mL/min. Renew water every 24 *h*.
2. Two or 3 d after initiation of the culture, many roots have sprouted from most bulbs; a normal germination process produces more than 40 roots per bulb, of at least 2 cm in length, in 95% of bulbs, after 3 d of culture. They are ready for collection.

3. With the aid of a scalpel or a razor blade, remove the root cap and, with a pair of forceps, dissect the first 3 mm of the root tip; this portion is the root meristem. Take approx 500 mg of meristems.
4. Deposit samples in a glass Petri dish, 4 cm in diameter, containing 6 mL of Extraction medium, to which the protease inhibitor PMSF has been added just before use.
5. Collect root meristems up to an amount of 1 g of sample.
6. The Petri dish must be placed on ice.
7. *Caution*: the work should be performed under a fume hood.
8. With the help of a vacuum pump, degas the collected sample for 10 min, to facilitate the infiltration of the medium within the sample.

Purification of Nuclei

1. After incubation of root meristems in extraction medium (may be extended from 15 min to overnight, at 4°C), homogenize them with the Ultraturrax blender and filter the homogenate through three nylon cloth layers with pores of 100, 50, and 30 μm, respectively.
2. Collect the remaining material retained in the nylon with a spatula, resuspend this material in extraction medium, and repeat the filtration procedure twice more. Each homogenization step, involving the operation of the blender, consists of the introduction of the rotating stick of the blender into the tube containing the sample up to its bottom and the activation of the blender motor, at 16,000 rpm, in three strokes of 5 s each, separated by 5-s intervals.
3. Collect and unify the filtrates and wash the resulting sample by centrifugation at 800g, for 10 min at 4°C.
4. Suspend the pellet again in 1 mL of extraction medium. Facilitate good suspension with the help of pipet, and then centrifuge twice more. At the end of this procedure, the pellet must contain clean isolated nuclei.
5. Transfer the pellet to an 1.5-mL Eppendorff tube containing 1 mL of nuclei stock buffer (NSB). Check the identity of the nuclear fraction and the abundance and purity of nuclei under the light microscope. Phase contrast may be used for examination, but a simple staining agent, such as methyl green/pyronin, or toluidine blue, or 4,6-diamidino-2-phenylindole (DAPI), can be of help in identifying nuclei.

PROTEIN EXTRACTION BY NUCLEAR FRACTIONATION

For the design of this procedure, we used the procedure described by Penman and coworkers and adapted it to our requirements. The most important modification was the introduction of a step of extraction of the most soluble proteins, because it was reported in the literature that the nuclear protein fraction soluble in a low ionic strength buffer was functionally significant because it was enriched in ribonucleoproteins active in the nuclear RNA metabolism.

In general, the procedure consists of a sequential fractionation of proteins using solubility as the fundamental criterion. The sample is transferred through successive buffers of increasing astringency or ionic strength. The successive steps are as follows:

1. Fraction of membranes and remnants of cytoskeleton:
   a. The first step is the incubation of purified nuclei, contained in NSB, in a buffer rich in detergents.
   b. Add 1% (v/v) NP-40 and 0.5% (v/v) sodium deoxycholate to the nuclei sample and incubate for 10 min at 4°C in an orbital shaker; then, shake the tube with a vortex in two strokes, 20 s each.
   c. Centrifuge the sample at 1000g for 10 min, at 4°C and collect the supernatant, which is the first fraction (membranes and remnants of the cytoskeleton).
2. Soluble fraction (S2): Resuspend the pellet in 1 mL of the low ionic strength buffer with a vortex, incubate for 1 h, at 4°C in the orbital shaker, and then centrifuge at 1000g, for 10 min at 4°C. The supernatant is the second fraction, called the S2 extract, containing ribonucleoproteins.
3. Chromatin fraction:
   a. Suspend the pellet again in 400 μL of NSB supplemented with 100 μg/mL RNase-free DNase I and 0.5% Triton X-100 with a vortex, and incubate for 30 min at room temperature; this will digest DNA.
   b. Extract digested DNA by adding ammonium sulfate (400 μL) and incubating for 5 min at room temperature. As in previous steps, incubations are made under stirring in an orbital shaker.
   c. Centrifuge at 2000g for 10 min to obtain in the supernatant the fraction of proteins associated with chromatin.
4. High salt fraction:
   a. Add 400 μL of NSB to the pellet, resuspend it with a vortex, and increase the ionic strength of the buffer gradually with NaCl to a final concentration of 2 M.
   b. Leave the sample in this buffer for 5 min in the orbital shaker, at room temperature, and centrifuge at 10,000g for 10 min.
   c. The supernatant is the fourth nuclear protein fraction, corresponding to a first nuclear matrix extract, called high salt fraction.
5. Insoluble fraction or nuclear matrix fraction: the remaining pellet contains the insoluble proteins of the nuclear matrix. However, in order to make this pellet soluble, incubate it in 1 mL of the urea buffer, after vigorous vortexing, for 45 min at room temperature in the orbital shaker, followed by additional vortexing in two strokes and sonication for 30 s.

Protein Preparation for 1D- or 2D-Electrophoresis

1. Protein precipitation.:

a. For each protein fraction,obtained in the supernatant in each step of the fractionation procedure, precipitate proteins with 7% TCA for 2 h, at 0°C.

b. Centrifuge at 10,000g for 30 min, and discard the supernatant.

c. Wash the pellet, to eliminating the rest of the TCA, in precooled ethanol-ether at –20°C for a minimum of 2 h, although it can be extended to overnight.

2. Resuspension in the electrophoresis buffer:

a. Collect proteins by centrifugation at 20,000g for 30 min and dry the pellet under vacuum.

b. Add to the dry pellet 60 µL of either Laemmli buffer (if SDS-PAGE is to be performed) or rehydration buffer in the case of 2D-electrophoresis.

c. To facilitate protein dissolution in rehydration buffer, it is advisable to sonicate three times, 2 s each, on ice.

3. Assessment of protein concentration:

a. Quantify protein concentration by the Bradford reaction. Take 1 µL of the sample contained in the buffer (without bromophenol blue) and add 749 µL of water and 250 µL of the Bradford Protein Assay reagent.

b. Mix well with a vortex and leave for 15 min to develop colour.

c. Measure optical density in the spectrophotometer and compare the value obtained with the standard graphic.

An example of the results of the nuclear protein fractionation procedure and further electrophoretic separation of proteins in one dimension by SDS-PAGE is shown in Figure elsewhere in this chapter.

Notes

1. Extraction medium can be prepared the day before use, but PMSF should not be added until the moment before you begin. The medium is stored in the refrigerator, conveniently closed and labeled.
2. To prepare PMSF, add 0.3484 g of PMSF to 20 mL of isopropanol. The solution must be kept in the refrigerator; it is quickly degraded at room temperature. Under storage, it tends to precipitate, but it is easily dissolved again by gentle shaking.
3. The dry brown shell of the onion bulbs must be totally removed, and the bottom crown from which roots sprout out must be carefully cleaned to remove dry root remnants. Washing of clean bulbs is carried out under tap water flow for a minimum of 30 min. Onions have a seasonal germination rhythm; the optimal seasons for root growth are autumn and winter. Commercial onions, purchased in a market or greengrocery, are usually suitable for research, but the possibility that the bulbs have received a physical or chemical treatment to inhibit root growth should be considered.
4. Continuous aeration can be obtained by means of a simple air pump (for example, the type used in aquaria) connected to a system of rubber tubes, each one directed to a water-filled bulb receptacle, in which it is immersed by means of a glass tip, conveniently bent.

5. Root cap removal and meristem dissection can be obtained simultaneously by using a system of two razor blades assembled with Parafilm, so they leave a space of 3 to 5 mm between them.
6. When data from meristematic (proliferating) cells are to be compared with a non meristematic (nonproliferating) cell population, differentiated root cells can be obtained at the same time of the meristem dissection, by discarding a root fragment of 3 mm immediately next to the meristem and collecting the rest of the root.
7. The degassing procedure of extraction medium containing root samples should be at a pressure such that bubbles begin to appear from the medium. As for the rest of the nuclei purification procedure, this step must be carried out in a cold environment (i.e., on ice).
8. When different samples are to be compared (e.g., from different treatments or conditions), the number of nuclei is the factor of data normalization, allowing comparisons. Nuclei are counted under the light microscope (toluidine blue staining is helpful for this purpose) using a graticule.
9. If flow cytometry is to be used as a method of analysis, the extraction medium must be especially crystal clear, to eliminate possible precipitates that could interfere with the analysis. For this purpose, an additional centrifugation at 1200g for 30 min could be helpful.
10. A stock 0.5 *M* solution of ammonium sulfate should be prepared in advance. This solution is very stable, even at room temperature, for years. From this solution, small amounts are added to the sample (four times) to reach a final concentration of 0.25 *M*. Each addition is followed by vigorous shaking of the tube.
11. As in the previous case, the final 2 *M* concentration of NaCl is obtained from an initial 4 *M* stock solution, which is also very stable at room temperature. The addition, in this case, is practically dropwise, since it is done eight times. A total of 400 µL of NaCl is used.
12. Protein concentration is evaluated on an aliquot not containing bromophenol blue. In any case, a yellowish tonality of the sample, once the buffer is added, is indicative of incomplete elimination of TCA. To overcome this, 2 to 3 µL of Tris-HCl saturated in distilled water are added.
13. Alternatives to TCA for precipitating proteins exist, such as ammonium sulfate and alcohols. Furthermore, precipitation can be suppressed by mixing the sample directly with the buffer in a proportion of 1:1. The usefulness of precipitation is the possibility of concentrating proteins and of evaluating their concentration.
14. In the standard graphic used to evaluate protein concentration, the range selected (1–140 µgr/mL of BSA) is the interval in which a linear relationship exists between optical density and protein concentration. If the value measured is above the limits of this graphic, dilute the protein before the measurement, and then multiply the result by the dilution factor.

ISOLATION OF CELL WALL PROTEINS FROM MEDICAGO SATIVA STEMS

As in all subcellular proteomics, a critical factor in isolating the cell wall proteome is the extraction of a protein fraction uncontaminated by proteins from other cellular locales. Generally, two approaches have been utilized to isolate cell wall proteins: nondisruptive and disruptive protein extraction.

Both methods have advantages and drawbacks, especially concerning issues of contamination and to the development of the current method. A second important factor for cell wall proteomic efforts that include two-dimensional electrophoresis (2-DE) is the removal of polysaccharide and polyphenolic contaminants that cause problems during electrophoresis.

In the past, cell cultures have provided a source of homogeneous and relatively "clean" tissue for isolating cell wall proteins. Differentiated plant tissue, although often more biologically relevant,

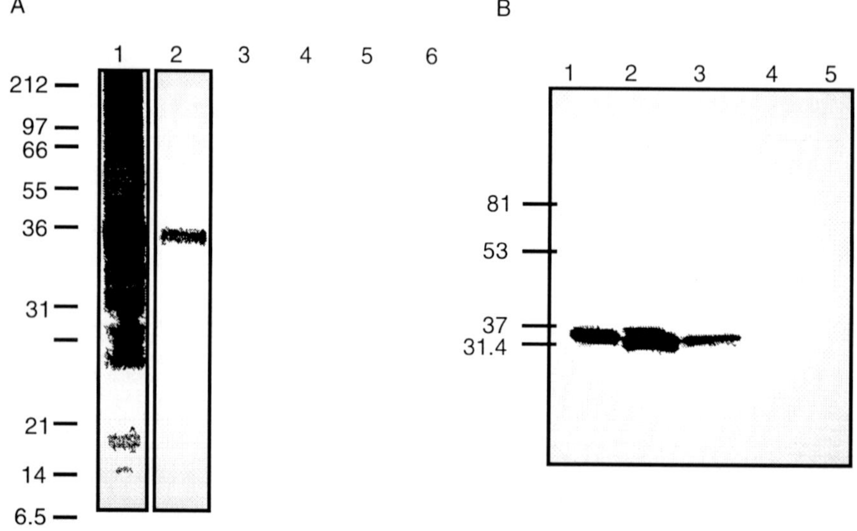

Figure 19.2: (A) SDS-PAGE and (B) CCoAOMT western blot analysis of sequential wash steps in a cell wall preparation. (A) Lane 1, grinding buffer (soluble fraction), Subheading 3.1.6.; lane 2, wash buffer 1 (NaCl wash), Subheading 3.1.7.; lane 3, first water wash, Subheading 3.1.8.; lane 4, acetone wash, Subheading 3.1.9.; lane 5, second water wash, Subheading 3.1.10.; lane 6, wash buffer 2 (Na-acetate wash), Subheading 3.1.11. Lane 1 contains 25 μg of protein as determined by Bio-Rad protein concentration assay, lane 2 contains 0.2% of the wash, lane 3 contains 0.4% of the wash, and all other lanes contain 1% of their respective washes precipitated with TCA. Proteins were electrophoresed on a 10 to 20% acrylamide gel and stained with Coomassie. (B) Lane 1, positive control, recombinant CCoAOMT, a known cytosolic protein; lane 2, grinding buffer (soluble fraction), Subheading 3.1.6.; lane 3, wash buffer 1 (NaCl wash), Subheading 3.1.7.; lane 4, first water wash, Subheading 3.1.8.; lane 5, wash buffer 2 (Na-acetate wash), Subheading 3.1.11. Lane 1 contains 0.25 μg of recombinant CCoAOMT, and lane 2 contains 0.2% (15 μg) of the soluble fraction; other lanes contain 1% of their respective washes precipitated with TCA. The proteins were transferred to PVDF from a 10 to 20% acrylamide gel, probed with antiCCoAOMT antibody, diluted 1:10,000, and anti-horseradishperoxidase (HRP), diluted 1:10,000. Detection was by chemiluminescence (Amersham ECL).

is more complex and difficult to work with, and large-scale proteomic efforts are relatively new for these tissues.

This introduction includes a short review of current cell wall protein extraction methods followed by the description of a specific method for the extraction of cell wall proteins from *Medicago sativa* stems. Perhaps the oldest and gentlest method of isolating cell wall proteins involves the direct extraction from intact cultured cells by suspending or washing the cells in an appropriate solution.

Smith et al. used $CaCl_2$ gradients to elute extensin precursors from tomato suspension cultures poured into small columns, and Scott and O'Neil extracted extracellular proteins from carrot suspension cells by suspending them in different concentrations of CaCl2 and Triton X-100 as well as in 0.1 *M* LiCl.

Carrot suspension cultures extracted with 0.1% Triton X-100 or 0.1 M $CaCl_2$ could then be returned to culture medium with little change in their growth patterns. One of the first attempts to isolate and identify large numbers of cell wall– associated proteins involved extractions of live suspension cultures containing only primary walls from five plant species.

The cells were harvested by filtration, and proteins were extracted by stirring the cells in five different buffers. The buffers included 0.2 M $CaCl_2$, 50 mM cyclohexane diaminotetra-acetic acid (CDTA) in 50 mM sodium acetate, pH 6.5, 2 mM dithiothreitol, 1 M NaCl, and 0.2 M borate, pH 7.5, and were used in both sequential and nonsequential extraction regimes.

Blee et al. employed a suspension culture of transformed tobacco cells that contained both primary and secondary walls as the source of cell wall proteins extracted directly from living cells. Proteins were extracted with 0.2 M $CaCl_2$ or 50 mM CDTA. A modification of this method uses vacuum infiltration of protoplasts or whole plant tissues to elute apoplastic and cell wall proteins.

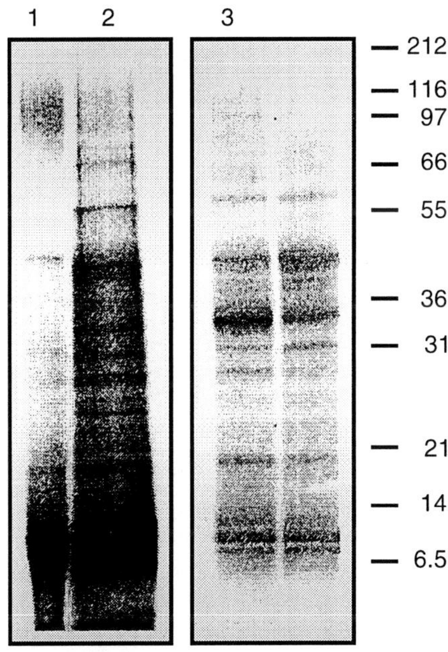

Figure 19.3: SDS-PAGE of cell wall proteins. Lanes 1 and 2 are protein extracts before treatment, and lanes 3 and 4 are protein extracts after treatment with the ReadyPrep 2-D Cleanup kit. Lanes 1 and 3 contain CaCl2extracted proteins (extraction buffer 1), and lanes 2 and 4 contain LiCl-extracted proteins (extraction buffer 2). Twenty five micrograms of protein in each lane were electrophoresed on a 10 to 20% acrylamide gel and stained with Coomassie.

This method involves an infusion step whereby a solution of salts or other solutions enters the intercellular space by the use of gentle reduced pressure. Roger et al. used a solution of 1 M NaCl and 0.4 M $CaCl_2$ to infiltrate immobilized protoplasts derived from hypocotyls of flax plants, and harvested the apoplastic proteins by centrifugation and filtration. Apoplastic fluids from potato tubers were harvested by infiltrating the tissue with a buffer containing 0.6 M NaCl, then centrifuging to collect the extract apoplastic fluid from leaves has been collected using this method with a solution of 20 mM ascorbic acid, 20 mM $CaCl_2$.

Root apoplastic fluid was collected by simply cutting and centrifuging the tissue to harvest the exudate. A major disadvantage of the nondisruptive methods is that the yield of cell wall proteins is usually low.

The current genomic-based assessments predict many hundreds of secreted proteins; however, only a fraction of this number is found in the nondisruptive studies of plant cell wall proteins. A

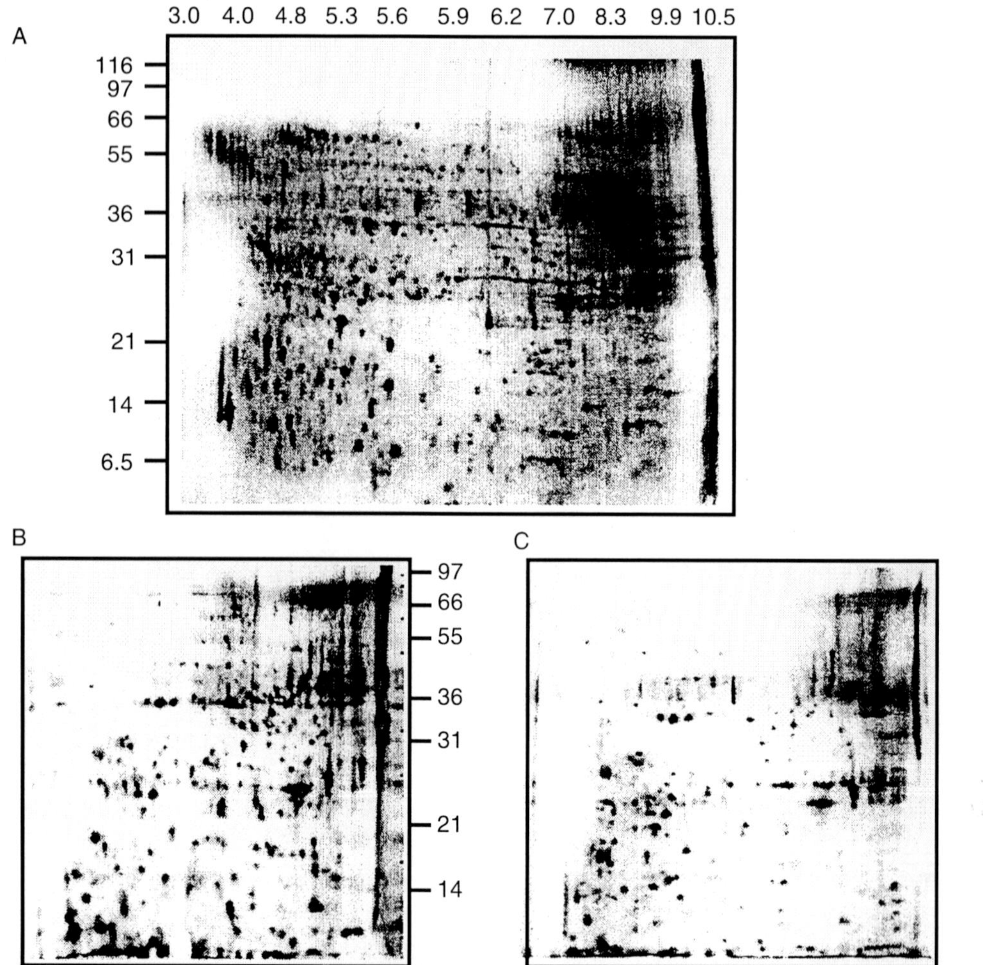

Figure 19.4: 2-DE of (A) combined CaCl2 and LiCl extracted (extraction buffers 1 and 2), (B) CaCl2 (extraction buffer 1) extracted, and (C) LiCl (extraction buffer 2) extracted cell wall proteins. (A) Five hundred micrograms of protein were focused by IEF to 64,000 Vh on a pI 3 to 10 NL, 24-cm strip. Molecular weight markers are listed on the side of the gel, and pI markers are noted at the top. Two-hundred-fifty micrograms protein (B) and 150 µg protein (C) were focused by IEF to 30,000 Vh on pI 3 to 10 NL, 11-cm strips. The MW markers are the same as in (A). Twelve percent acrylamide gels were used for the second dimension; all gels were silver stained.

second disadvantage is the possibility of rupturing the plasma membrane, which would lead to contamination of the cell wall fraction with cytosolic and membrane proteins.

Because contamination is a formidable obstacle, methods of ensuring cell wall purity, such as assays for marker enzyme activities or Western blots for typical contaminant proteins, should be included. Another method to elute cell wall proteins from live cells utilizes plasmolysis of the plasma membrane to shrink it away from the cell wall.

Borderies et al. used live *Arabidopsis* suspension culture cells to extract loosely bound cell wall proteins. The cultures were first plasmolyzed with 50% glycerol and then extracted sequentially with various buffers. Two different extraction regimes using NaCl, EDTA, and 0.2 *M* $CaCl_2$ or NaCl, EDTA, and 2 *M* LiCl were utilized to optimize the method and decrease the problem of membrane permeability caused by the extraction treatments.

Several of these treatments resulted in contamination of the cell wall proteins with intracellular proteins, so transmission electron microscopy was employed to verify an intact plasma membrane. Disruptive methods are the second major approach to cell wall protein extractions, and plasmolysis has also been used with this method.

After treating live *Arabidopsis* suspension cells with a solution containing glycerol and mannitol, the cells were passed through an N_2 disruption bomb. The wall fraction was than recovered and examined by microscopy. Proteins were extracted from the cell wall preparations with 2% sodium dodecyl sulfate (SDS) and analyzed for contaminating intracellular proteins by Western blots.

As with the nondisruptive methods, contamination is a significant problem, and a means of ensuring cell wall purity is necessary. Homogenized *Arabidopsis* suspension cells were also used as a source for cell wall proteins in two papers from the same group.

In both cases, cells were washed, filtered, and passed through a cell disrupter. The homogenate was layered on a glycerol solution, and after sedimentation by gravity the cell wall fraction was collected and washed. The purified cell walls were examined by electron microscopy and checked for contaminating intracellular or plasma membrane proteins by immunofluorescence and immunoblots.

The results supported the authors' claim that the cell wall fractions were free of contaminating proteins. In both papers, proteins were extracted from the cell wall fraction first with 0.2 *M* $CaCl_2$ and then with a urea buffer. Cell wall proteins have been extracted from live and homogenized ligninproducing suspension cultures of Norway spruce.

Ionically bound cell wall proteins were eluted from washed and filtered cells by incubating them in a 1 *M* NaCl buffer. Separated cells were homogenized, and proteins that were liberated, but ionically bound to the cell walls, were extracted with the same 1 *M* NaCl buffer and then discarded. The cell walls were isolated, washed, homogenized, and suspended in extraction buffer.

These walls were then lyophilized and treated with a mixture of cellulase/macerozyme to digest cell wall carbohydrates and release covalently bound proteins. Traditionally, protein mixtures extracted from the cell walls of plant tissues are used as the source for isolating single proteins or classes of proteins. For example, 0.2 *M* $CaCl_2$ was used to extract a hydroxyproline-rich cell wall glycoprotein (HPRG) from the seed coat of soybean seeds.

Similarly, a prolinerich cell wall protein was isolated from the cell walls of soybean seedlings.

The protein was detected in the supernatant remaining after the cell wall proteins were precipitated by 10% trichloroacetic acid (TCA). Cell wall proteins involved in extension were purified by McQueen-Mason et al. from salt-extractable cell wall proteins found in cucumber seedlings.

McDougall used a single tissue, xylem, to isolate differentially expressed oxidases from cell walls of the wood of compression and noncompression branches of spruce. Large-scale cell wall proteomics has been used less frequently with differentiated plant tissues, primarily owing to limitations imposed by protein, polysaccharide, and polyphenolic contaminants.

A method is described here that was developed as a large-scale approach for comparative cell wall proteomics of plant tissues and that addresses the major contaminant issues. The method involves cell disruption, a series of stringent washes to remove contaminating proteins, and extraction of cell wall proteins with $CaCl_2$ and LiCl.

The steps are monitored for purity by Bradford assays and SDS-polyacrylamide gel electrophoresis (PAGE) gels. After treatment with a clean-up kit, the proteins are ready to separate by 2-DE. The method has been used to obtain reproducible separations by 2-DE of a large and varied population of proteins from the isolated cell walls of lignified alfalfa (*Medicago sativa*) stems.

The difficulties associated with removing polysaccharides and polyphenolics that interfere with focusing in the first dimension and cause streaking and background staining in the second dimension have been minimized, resulting in protein preparations that are reasonably free of contaminating materials and that contain several hundred proteins.

The protein spots can easily be identified by matrix-assisted laser desorption ionization-time of flight mass spectrometry (MALDI-TOF MS) or by liquid chromatography (LC)/MS/MS. One drawback of the method is the apparent lack of cell wall proteins often observed in other types of cell wall preparations. These include highly glycosylated proteins and proteins associated with the plasma membrane (PM).

The glycosylated proteins are more soluble than other wall proteins and are therefore likely to be lost during the stringent washes necessary for removing cytosolic proteins. The PM-associated proteins are not as tightly bound to the cell wall as other proteins and are similarly lost in the stringent washes. It is probable that these proteins could be concentrated and separated by 2-DE, or a complementary, nondisruptive technique could be used to isolate them.

As with other cell wall protein extraction methods, a requirement of this method is the need to show that the isolated cell walls are free of contaminating proteins. SDS-PAGE or immunoblots of marker enzymes should be done on the washes to ascertain protein extract purity. The extraction salts chosen in this method have been commonly used for eluting cell wall proteins.

Calcium chloride is thought to release charged molecules through ion exchange, has been predicted to be a more efficient ion exchanger than NaCl, has been shown to release more proteins from the cell wall than *0.1%* Triton X-100 in live cultures and has been used extensively to extract cell wall protein from plant cell walls.

Membrane integrity is known to be interrupted by 0.2 *M* $CaCl_2$; thus we chose 0.2 *M* $CaCl_2$ for extracting cell wall proteins from disrupted tissue. The method reported here also utilizes LiCl, a common cell wall protein extractant. Voight used concentrations of LiCl ranging from *0.1 M* to 8

M on *Chlamydomonas* cells and found that the optimal concentration to extract cell wall proteins from all cell-cycle stages was at least 2 *M,* with no additional proteins extracted at concentrations above 4 *M* LiCl.

As the concentration of LiCl increased, greater amounts of carbohydrates were extracted along with the proteins. Our method uses *3 M* LiCl for extractions to harvest the greatest amount of protein without coextracting an excess of carbohydrates. Although the washes preceding the cell wall protein fractions isolated using this method appear to be clean by 1D SDS-PAGE and by Western blot, only approx *50%* of the identified proteins have a signal peptide.

This proportion of classically secreted proteins seems reasonable compared with other proteomic studies of cell wall proteins and may reflect the inherent difficulties in purifying a subset of proteins from an "organelle" without a surrounding membrane. It may also suggest a nonclassical pathway(s) for protein secretion.

MATERIALS

Tissue Disruption, Washes, and Gel or Western Assay for Purity

1. Liquid N_2.
2. Mortar and pestle, chilled to 4°C.
3. Buchner funnel, side arm flask, and vacuum tubing.
4. House vacuum or vacuum pump.
5. Nylon mesh membrane (nitex, 47 μm^2), cut to fit the Buchner funnel.
6. Spatula.
7. 1 M Na acetate, pH 5.5, stock.
8. 1 M NaCl, stock.
9. 1 M Ascorbic acid (store in dark bottle), stock.
10. Grinding buffer: 50 mM Na acetate, pH 5.5, 50 mM NaCl, 30 mM ascorbic acid in Milli Q water, 4°C.
11. Wash buffer 1: 100 mM NaCl in Milli Q water, 4°C.
12. Milli Q water, 4°C.
13. Acetone stored at –20°C.
14. Wash buffer 2: 10 mM Na acetate, pH 5.5, in Milli Q water, 4°C.
15. 25% TCA.
16. Bio-Rad Criterion 10 to 20% acrylamide gel or other commercial SDS-PAGE gel.
17. Coomassie Blue R-250 stain, 1 g/L in 40% methanol, 5% acetic acid in Milli Q water, or other suitable stain.
18. Destain: 40% methanol, 5% acetic acid in Milli Q water or other suitable destain.
19. Millipore Immobilon-P or other membrane for Western blots.

Table 19.1: Homogenization Buffera		
Component	**Mixture**	**Final concentration (mM)**
TRIZMA base	6.05 g	50
Sucrose	167 g	500
Glycerol	125.7 g	10% (w/v)
EDTA-Na_2	100 mL of 0.2 M stock solution	20
EGTA	100 mL of 0.2 M stock solution	20
NaF	100 mL of 0.5 M stock solution	50
(3-glycerophosphate	1.08 g	5
Phenantroline	0.198 g	1
PVP [b]	6 g	0.6% (w/v)
Ascorbic acid	1.76 g	10 H_2O make to1 L

20. Transfer solution for Western blotting: 25 mM Tris-HCl, 192 mM glycine, 20% methanol or other suitable transfer buffer.
21. Antibody to known cytosolic protein such as caffeoyl-CoA-O-methyl transferase (CCoAOMT).
22. Amersham ECL kit or other commercial detection kit for Western blots.

Protein Extraction from Cell Walls

1. 1 M CaCl2, stock.
2. 5 M LiCl, stock.
3. 1 M Na-acetate, pH 5.5, stock.
4. Extraction buffer 1: 200 mM $CaCl_2$, 50 mM Na-acetate, pH 5.5, in Milli Q water, 4°C.
5. Extraction buffer 2: 3 M LiCl, 50 mM Na-acetate, pH 5.5, in Milli Q water , 4°C.

Protein Concentration and Desalting

1. Amicon Ultra-15 centrifugal filtration devices or other concentration devices.
2. Distilled or Milli Q water, 4°C.

Determination of Concentration

Protein Clean-up, and Rehydration of Sample

1. Bio-Rad protein determination or other protein concentration determination method.
2. Bovine serum albumin (BSA) for a standard.
3. Distilled or Milli Q water.

Table 19.2: Microsome Resuspension Buffer

Component	*Mixture*	*Final concentration (mM)*
Phosphate buffer, pH 7.8	12.5 mL of 0.2 M stock solution	5
Sucrose	56 g	330
DTT	154 mg	2
NaF	10 mL of 0.5 M stock solution	10
H_2O, make to	500 mL	

Table 19.3: Composition of the Two-Phase System Used for PM Purification

Component	*Mixture*	*Final concentration (mM)*
Dextran T-500 20% (w/w)	11.82 g	6.4%
PEG-3350 40% (w/w)	5.76 g	6.4%
Phosphate buffer 0.2 M, pH 7.8	0.9 mL	5
KCl, 2 M	0.09 mL	5
Sucrose 1.6 M	6.74 mL	300
H_2O make to 27 g		

Table 19.4: Composition of the Plasma Membrane (PM) Washing Buffera

Components	*Mixture*	*Final concentration (mM)*
TRIZMA base	1.21 g	10
Boric acid	0.61 g	10
Sucrose	102 g	300
KCl	0.67 g	9
EDTA-Na_2	25 mL of 0.2 M stock solution	5
EGTA	25 mL of 0.2 M stock solution	5
NaF	100 mL of 0.5 M stock solution	50
H_2O make to	1 L	

Table 19.5: Composition of Buffer Aa

Components	*Mixture*	*Final concentration (mM)*
TRIZMA base	1 mL of 1 M stock solution pH 9.5	5
EDTA-Na_2	5 mL of 0.2 M stock solution	5
EGTA	5 mL of 0.2 M stock solution	5
Urea	48 g 4 H_2O make to	200 mL

Table 19.6: Composition of Buffer Ba

Components	Mixture	Final concentration (mM)
TRIZMA base	1 mL of 1 M stock solution, pH 8.0	5
EDTA-Na2	2 mL of 0.2 M stock solution	2
EGTA	2 mL of 0.2 M stock solution	2
H_2O make to	200 mL	

Table 19.7: Composition of Sample Buffer 2X (SB 2X)

Components	Mixture	Final concentration
TRIZMA base	1.52 g	0.125 mM
Glycerol	20 g	20% (w/v)
DTT	3 g	0.2 M
SDS	20 mL of 20% stock solution	4% (w/v)
Bromophenol blue	1 mg	1% (w/v)
H_2O make to	100 mL	

4. Bio-Rad ReadyPrep 2-D Cleanup Kit.
5. Resuspension buffer: 8 M urea, 4% 3[3-cholaminopropyl diethylammonio]-1-propane sulfonate (CHAPS), 20 mM dithiothieitol (DTT), 0.2% ampholytes in Milli Q water; SDS sample buffer; or other appropriate buffer.

METHODS

Tissue Disruption, Washes, and Gel to Assay for Purity

1. Harvest 7 to 8 g of mature (internodes four to six) alfalfa stems. The yield of cell wall protein for that amount of mature stem tissue should be more than 1 mg. Store at –80°C after harvest or process immediately.
2. Keep all solutions on ice.
3. Break stems into small pieces approximately 1 to 2 cm in length to make grinding easier.
4. Thaw frozen tissue.
5. Grind with mortar and pestle until the tissue is foamy. Make sure the tissue is ground well. First grind without buffer, then add 10 mL of grinding buffer, and grind again.
6. Pour ground tissue onto the nylon mesh filter in the Buchner funnel and vacuum filter. Use a spatula to spread the tissue evenly over the filter. Rinse the mortar and pestle with 15 mL more of grinding buffer and use it to wash/filter over cell debris. Rinse debris pellet three times more with 25 mL of buffer each time for a total of 100 mL per 7 to 8 g

(approx 14 mL buffer/g) of starting tissue. Remove the washes by applying a vacuum. Save a portion of the wash to assay for purity. SDS-PAGE or Western blots with an antibody to a known cytosolic protein are appropriate methods for purity assays.

7. Wash the debris with 50 mL of wash buffer 1 (NaCl wash). Pour it over the cell debris on the nylon filter and remove by vacuum filtration. Turn off the vacuum while adding washes and make sure the washes are in contact with all the debris. Save a portion of the wash to assay for purity.
8. Repeat the washes with 2 × 50 mL of distilled water.
9. Wash with 5 × 50 mL of ice cold acetone.
10. Wash a final time with 50 mL of wash buffer 2 (10 mM Na-acetate).

Extraction of Cell Wall Proteins

1. Place the cell debris in a 50-mL tube on ice and add 7.5 mL extraction buffer 1 ($CaCl_2$ buffer). Lay the tube on its side to increase the surface area of debris in contact with the extraction buffer. Set on a shaker and shake gently for 30 to 45 min.
2. Remove the protein extraction solution and save on ice. Repeat the extraction with a second aliquot of extraction buffer 1 for 30 to 45 min.
3. Remove the second protein extract and combine with the first extract. Add 15 mL of extraction buffer 2 (LiCl buffer) and extract for at least 45 min on ice or overnight in a cold box.
4. Centrifuge gently (approx 1000g), at 4°C to remove particulate matter before placing extracts in concentrators.

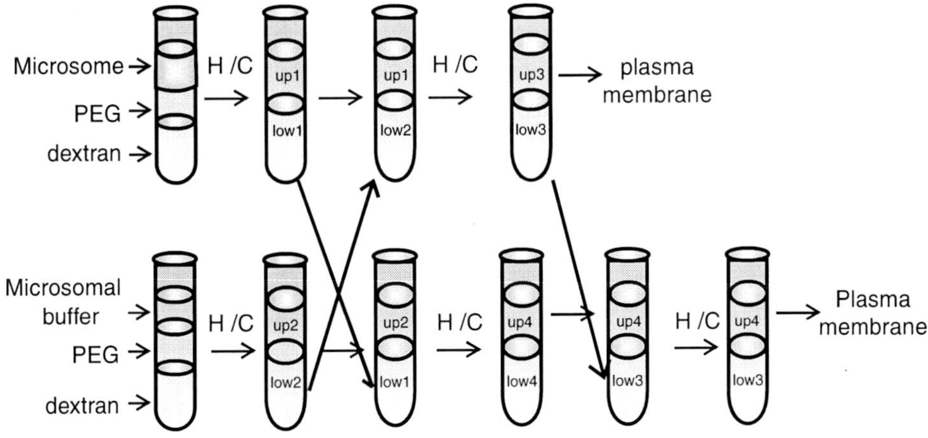

Figure 19.5: Schematic representation of PM purification by two-phase partitioning. The microsomes are mixed with the two-phase partitioning system (Table 3) composed of PEG 3350 and Dextran T-500 (see Subheading 3.1.2.). After homogenization and centrifugation (H/C), the upper and lower phases become enriched in PM and endomembranes, respectively. Each phase (up1 and low1) is enriched once again using complementary fresh phases (up2 and low2). The upper phase up3 is collected. The upper phase up4 is washed before being collected.

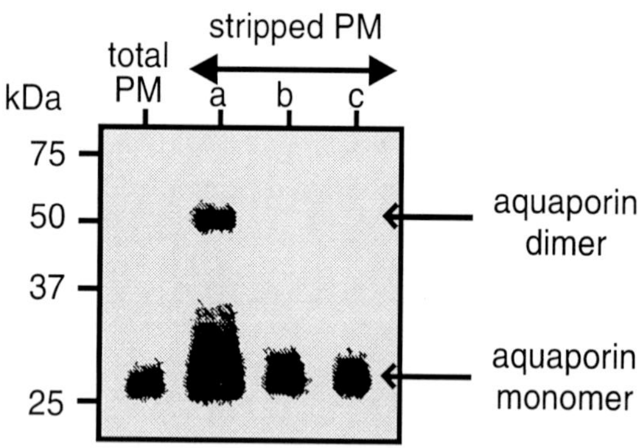

Figure 19.6: Detection of aquaporin PIPs in the plasma membrane of Arabidopsis roots. Total plasma membrane (PM) and PM stripped with a urea-NaOH treatment (lane a), carbonate washing (lane b), and 0.2% (w/v) Triton X-100 (lane c) were separated by SDS-PAGE (11% acrylamide gel) and probed with antibodies raised against PIP2;1. Ten micrograms of protein were loaded per lane. The immunodetected signal at 28 kDa corresponds to the monomer form of aquaporin. The signal at 50 kDa corresponds to the dimer of aquaporin. The urea-NaOH treatment strongly enhances the immunodetected signal.

Protein Concentration and Desalting

1. Concentrate with a centrifugal concentrator according to the manufacturer's directions. We like the 15-mL Amicon Ultra Centrifugal Filter Device. The extracts can be kept separate or combined in this step. Concentrate to a volume of 100 to 150 µL.
2. The ReadyPrep 2-D Cleanup kit from Bio-Rad accomodates salt concentrations up to 1 *M*. Since the LiCl extracts are in 3 *M* LiCl, samples are desalted by adding 2 vol of distilled water to the concentrated extract and concentrating again. Remove the protein solution to a microfuge tube. To remove the sample from the concentrator, it may help to cut the end off a 200-µL pipet tip. Rinse the membrane of the concentrator with a small volume (approx 100 µL) of distilled water or buffer and combine with the concentrated proteins.

Protein Clean-up, Rehydration of Sample, and Determination of Concentration

1. Determine protein concentration using the Bradford method or equivalent.
2. Cell wall preps at this stage can be used for SDS-PAGE without any further cleanup, but the protein bands will not be as sharp as those processed with a commercial clean-up kit and resuspended in SDS sample buffer.
3. For 2-DE ($CaCl_2$ and LiCl extracts combined; $CaCl_2$ extract; LiCl extract), use The ReadyPrep 2-D Cleanup kit from Bio-Rad or another commercial clean-up kit and then resolubilize in rehydration buffer. The Bio-Rad kit works for 1 to 500 µg of protein in a volume of 100 µL.

Notes

1. The acidic pH mimics the pH of the cell wall and reduces protease activity, the NaCl helps prevent cytoplasmic proteins from associating with the cell walls, and the ascorbic acid helps inactivate polyphenol oxidases.
2. Approximately 3 g of young stems (intern-odes one to three) yield a similar amount of protein
3. Stems that are ground after they are frozen and thawed will probably show a slightly different profile of proteins than those that are ground fresh or those that are ground while frozen. Decide which method suits you best and then stick with it. Consistency while

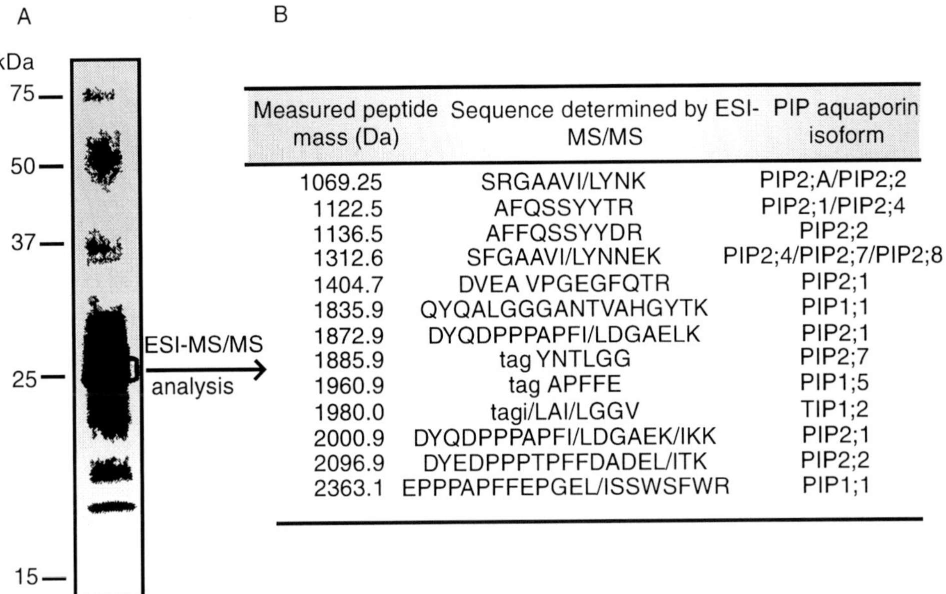

Measured peptide mass (Da)	Sequence determined by ESI-MS/MS	PIP aquaporin isoform
1069.25	SRGAAVI/LYNK	PIP2;A/PIP2;2
1122.5	AFQSSYYTR	PIP2;1/PIP2;4
1136.5	AFFQSSYYDR	PIP2;2
1312.6	SFGAAVI/LYNNEK	PIP2;4/PIP2;7/PIP2;8
1404.7	DVEA VPGEGFQTR	PIP2;1
1835.9	QYQALGGGANTVAHGYTK	PIP1;1
1872.9	DYQDPPPAPFI/LDGAELK	PIP2;1
1885.9	tag YNTLGG	PIP2;7
1960.9	tag APFFE	PIP1;5
1980.0	tagi/LAI/LGGV	TIP1;2
2000.9	DYQDPPPAPFI/LDGAEK/IKK	PIP2;1
2096.9	DYEDPPPTPFFDADEL/ITK	PIP2;2
2363.1	EPPPAPFFEPGEL/ISSWSFWR	PIP1;1

Figure 19.7: Mass spectrometry (MS) analysis of trypsin-cleaved 28-kDa band immunodetected by anti-PIP aquaporin antibody in the root PM . (A) SDS-PAGE of PM stripped with urea and NaOH. Two hundred micrograms were loaded on the gel, electrophoresed, and revealed by Coomassie G-250 staining. The bracket indicates the excised band. (B) Electrospray ionization (ESI)-MS/MS analysis of SDS-PAGE band immunodetected by anti-plasma membrane intrinsic membrane (PIP) antibody. Different aquaporin PIP isoforms are present in the 28-kDa band.

grinding is important.

4. Grinding with a mortar and pestle rather than disrupting with a glass homogenizer has yielded more reproducible results in our hands.
5. Filtration has several advantages over centrifugation. The nylon mesh 47-μm^2 nitex used in filtering allows starch grains to pass through but retains cell walls, and low-speed centrifugation does not pellet the debris well. Higher speed centrifugation would form a

Table 19.8: Composition of 2D Solution.

Components	Mixture	Final concentration
Detergent	1 g	2% (w/v)
Urea	21 g	7 M
Thiourea	7.6 g	2 M
Triton X-100	0.25 g	0.5% (w/v)
Pharmalytes (3-10)	0.6 mL	1.2% (w/v)
DTT	0.16 g	20 mM
H_2O make to	50 mL	

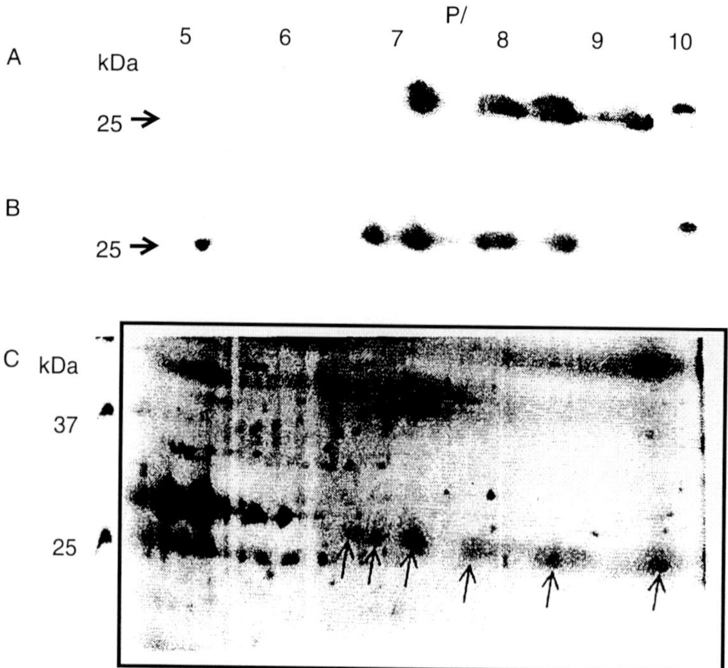

Figure 19.8: Protein separation by 2D gel electrophoresis reveals multiple forms of aquaporins expressed in the PM of Arabidopsis root. Protein solubilization was carried out as described in Subheading 3.3.1. 2D gel electrophoresis was carried out as described in Subheading 3.3.2. using 3 to 10 linear IPG gels. (A) The antibody raised against the PIP1;1 aquaporin isoform can recognize four PIP1 homologs but surprisingly immunodetected at least seven spots. (B) A similar result was obtained with the anti-PIP2;2 antibody, which can recognize three PIP2 homologs and yet revealed at least six distinct spots. These results suggest that modified forms of PIP1 and PIP2 homologs, in addition to unmodified ones, are present in the root PM sample. (C) Several of the immunodetected spots could be assigned to proteins revealed by silver staining gel and are shown by an arrow. MALDI-TOF-MS analysis of these spots has confirmed the presence of PIP aquaporins in these spots .

firmer pellet, but it would also pull proteins out of the supernatant.

6. Use sufficient volume and sufficient number of washes to ensure clean cell walls. Recommended ratios are approx 6.7–7.0 mL/g fresh weight for salt and sodium acetate, twice (14 mL/g) that for each H_2O wash, and five times that (35 mL/g) for acetone wash. Monitor the prep steps (by SDS-PAGE, Bradford, Western blot or chosen method) to ensure that the washes become progressively cleaner.
7. Twenty-five micrograms of the soluble proteins and 1% of each wash precipitated with TCA is enough to assess purity by SDS-PAGE stained with Coomassie Blue. If you are using Western blots to assess purity, either less protein can be used or an equivalent amount of protein will yield a higher assurance of purity.
8. This is a short, moderate salt concentration wash to remove membrane associated proteins or cytosolic proteins stuck to the cell wall. Higher salt concentration or a prolonged exposure will extract cell wall proteins.

9. Acetone disrupts membranes and allows the removal of membrane proteins, chlorophyll, and other contaminating substances.
10. Use a pipet to compress the cell debris against the side of the tube and squeeze out the extraction buffer. Filtration could also be used to separate the debris from the extracted proteins, but this could entail a loss of proteins. We recommend extraction with at least 2 mL of each extraction buffer per gram of starting tissue.
11. Extract twice with $CaCl_2$ in case the first extraction is diluted by residual wash.
12. Protein yield is higher if the cell walls are extracted overnight in the cold, but a reasonable protein yield can still be obtained with a shorter extraction (45 min).
13. Several other extraction procedures have been tried but have yielded lower quality data:
    a. The $CaCl_2$ extraction was followed by a urea extraction. Although both extracts contained proteins visible on SDS-PAGE and 2-DE gels, the 1D gels of the urea extracts were smeary, and the 2-DE gels from both samples were very streaky and ugly.
    b. TCA/acetone or phenol/EtOH was used to precipitate the samples. Samples precipitated with TCA/acetone were difficult to focus using isoelectric focusing (IEF) and yielded 2-DE gels streaked owing to cell wall polysaccharides or other contaminants. The phenol/ETOH-precipitated samples were easier to focus, and the gels were not as streaky, but there was a great loss of protein.
    c. Extracts were also treated with cellulose and pectinase, with and without protease inhibitors, to remove polysaccharides and other substances. This helped a little in focusing the CaCl2 samples, but the gels were still ugly, and the proteins extracted with urea were almost completely lost after treatment with cellulose and/or pectinase.
    d. The cell wall residue was boiled in SDS and separated on SDS-PAGE gels; this yielded

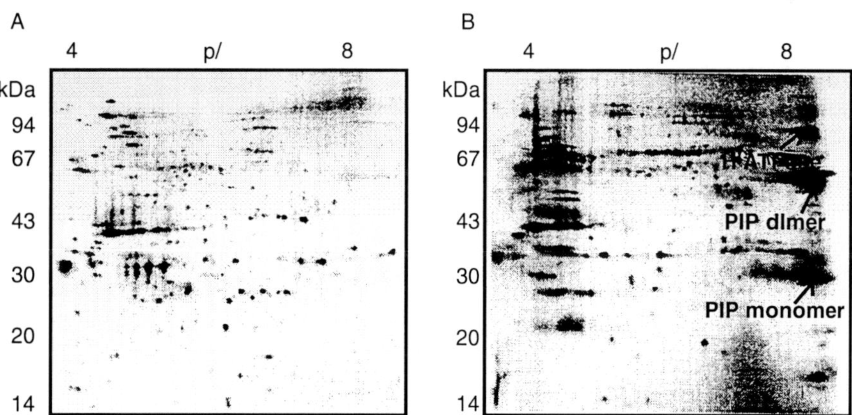

Figure 19.9: 2D gel electrophoresis of total PM proteins (A) and urea-NaOH treated PM proteins (B) of Arabidopsis leaf Protein solubilization was carried out as described in Subheading 3.3.1. 2D gel electrophoresis was carried out as described in Subheading 3.3.2. using 3 to 10 nonlinear IPG gels. Gels were stained with colloidal Coomassie G-250. Arrows indicate strong enrichment in aquaporins (PIP monomer and PIP dimer) and ATPase (H+-ATPase) after urea-NaOH treatment of membrane. Proteins were identified based on immunological detection and MS analysis.

a few protein bands that were overwhelmed by streaks and smears. e. Additionally, a high-speed centrifugation of the protein solution to remove polysaccharides yielded little benefit.

14. Other methods of concentrating the proteins were attempted and include precipitations and Amicon Centricons; however, the Amicon Ultra-15s have worked best for us.
15. Without using the 2-D Clean-up kit, the first dimension gels were hard (often impossible) to focus, and the second dimension gels were streaky, smeary, and ugly unless the protein loads (and therefore contaminant loads) were very low (<50 μg). Also, when the concentration of proteins loaded onto the gel was increased, the number of proteins visible on the gel did not increase proportionally, probably owing to the streaks and smears.
16. We have only tried the Bio-Rad kit and have had good experiences with it. Only once have we had problems, with a kit that had been on the shelf too long.

PLANT PLASMA MEMBRANE PROTEIN EXTRACTION AND SOLUBILIZATION FOR PROTEOMIC ANALYSIS

The plant plasma membrane (PM) regulates the exchange of information and substances between the cell and its environment. This interfacial position gives to PM proteins critical roles in cellular processes such as signal transduction, metabolite and ion transport, and endocytosis, as well as response to pathogens and cell wall assembly, which are specific plant functions.

The differences in physicochemical properties of cellular membranes are the basis for their separation. Plasma membranes can be purified according to three major procedures:

1. Differences in size and density between PM and other membranes is one feature used to isolate PM. This protocol requires centrifugation of a microsomal fraction through a continuous or discontinuous density gradient.
2. The free-flow electrophoresis procedure separate cellular membranes according to their charge. The PM is more negatively charged than other membranes and thus can be efficiently separated from other membranes. However this approach requires a specific free flow electrophoresis instrument.
3. The isolation of PM fraction by two-phase partition relies on differences in surface properties between membrane vesicles of different origins. The underlying principle of this technique is that numerous water-soluble, high-molecularweight polymers do not mix above a certain concentration but will form separate phases, each composed of more than 85% water. This makes the polymer-containing phases suitable for biological material. Added membranes separate between the aqueous polymer phases according to differences in surface properties. Originally described by Larsson et al., this technique is now widely used in the scientific plant community since it gives rise to a high yield of PM proteins with few endomembrane contaminations. In addition, it is a simple procedure that does not require specific equipment.

Membrane proteins can be classified into two groups: those that span the lipid bilayer are defined as intrinsic or integral proteins, and the others are associated with membranes. Associations are mediated by posttranslational modifications such as a glycolipid anchor, by the grafting of a fatty acid, or by protein–protein interaction. This suggests the occurrence of dynamics of protein association with the PM. In a PM-enriched fraction, a large proportion (60–80%) of proteins are soluble, either extrinsic proteins functionally associated with the PM or cytosolic contaminants. Thus, direct solubilization of a PM fraction, even with the most efficient detergent, which is sodium dodecyl sulfate (SDS), may be inefficient in recovering intrinsic proteins, owing to their low representation in the PM fraction. Methods based on the use of detergents, organic solvents, or alkaline treatments of membranes are used to categorize intrinsic proteins. Among them, alkaline extraction has gained widespread popularity as an easy and efficient method for selectively stripping extrinsic proteins off membranes without affecting the disposition of integral components. A procedure based on alkaline-urea treatment of the PM is described in this chapter, allowing the recovery of very hydrophobic proteins such as aquaporins.

Increasing data show that function and subcellular localization of membrane proteins are regulated by posttranslational modifications. 2D gel electrophoresis constitutes one of the more general methods able to separate modified forms of proteins posttranslationally.

Thus glycosylation, carbamylation, and deamidation appear as trains of spots that differ in isoelectric point (pI) and/or apparent molecular mass; phosphorylation and Na-acetylation shift the pI of proteins toward acidic pH and basic pH, respectively, without modification in the apparent molecular mass. More generally, any covalent modification of charged residues may modify the net charge of the protein, which in turns shifts its apparent pI.

The limitations in 2D gel electrophoresis analysis of intrinsic proteins occur through their high hydrophobicity, which requires use of particular solubilization protocols and have generally low abundance. This chapter describes procedures for purifying PM from root, leaf, and suspension cells from the model plant *Arabidopsis thaliana* and for solubilizing PM proteins for proteomic purposes. The plasma membrane intrinsic protein (PIP) aquaporins, which are 26 to 35-kDa hydrophobic proteins with six transmembrane α-helices, are used as pilot proteins to assess the relevance of extraction and solubilization procedures.

MATERIALS

Biological Material

1. *Arabidopsis thaliana L.* (Heynh.) plants (ecotype Wassilewskija or Columbia) are cultivated in hydroponic conditions as described in Santoni et al..
2. *Arabidopsis thaliana L.* (Heynh.), ecotype Columbia, suspension cells are cultured at 24°C under continuous light as described in Gerbeau et al..

Equipment

1. Ultrapure water (double-distilled, deionized) is used for all reagent preparations.
2. Reagent grades should be the highest quality as appropriate for intended use (cell culture,

ultrapure electrophoretic).

3. Waring blender: to disrupt plant material mechanically (leaf and root) and to pregrind suspension cells.
4. Cell disrupter: to disrupt *Arabidopsis* suspension cells.
5. Immobilized pH gradient (IPG; linear and nonlinear pH gradient from 3 to 10, 18 cm length; Amersham Pharmacia Biotech).
6. IPGphor apparatus: for isoelectrofocalization of proteins (Amersham Pharmacia Biotech).
7. Protean II: for sodium dodecyl sulfate polyacrylamide gel electrophoresis (SDSPAGE) electrophoresis (Bio-Rad).

Reagents

Products and Stock Solutions

1. Dextran T-500 and polyethylene glycol (PEG) 3350 are from Amersham and Union Carbide, respectively. Stock solutions of Dextran T-500 and PEG 3350 are made on a weight basis and prepared as *20* and *40%* stock solutions in water, respectively.
2. *0.2 M* EDTA disodium salt dihydrate (EDTA-Na_2) stock solution: dissolve 37.2 g EDTA-Na_2 in 500 mL water (final volume). Adjust the pH with TRIZMA® base (Sigma) in powder until pH 8 is reached. Store at room temperature for several months.
3. 0.2 M EGTA stock solution: dissolve 38.1 g EGTA in 500 mL water (final volume). Adjust the pH with TRIZMA base powder pH 8 until is reached. Store at room temperature for several months.
4. Leupeptin is prepared as a 10 mM stock solution in water (5 mg in 1.05 mL water) and stored at –20°C for up to 6 mo.
5. 0.5 M NaF stock solution: dissolve 10.5 g NaF in 500 mL water. Store at room temperature for maximum 1 mo.
6. 0.2 M phosphate buffer pH 7.8 stock solution: dissolve 1.4 g KH_2PO_4 in 50 mL water. Dissolve 17.4 g K_2HPO_4 in 500 mL water. Mix the two solutions, which gives 550 mL of a 0.2 M phosphate buffer, pH 7.8. Store at –20°C for several months.

Buffers

1. Washing buffer for suspension cells (WBSC): 20 mM KCl, 5 mM EDTA. This buffer is prepared from a 10 times concentrated solution made of 200 mM KCl (14.9 g in 1 L) mixed together with 50 mM EDTA (18.6 g in 1 L). It is stored for several months at –20°C.
2. Homogenization medium: the minimum requirements of a homogenization medium are the presence of an osmoticum to minimize swelling and rupture of organelles, a buffer at pH 7 to 8 to minimize activities of hydrolytic enzymes and to counteract the low pH of the vacuoles, and means to control the level of free divalent metal cations. (β-glycerophosphate, Na-orthovanadate, and phenantroline constitute a cocktail of phosphoprotein phosphatase inhibitors that were shown to help maintain specific cellular activities such as water transport activity at the PM level. NaF is a phospholipase inhibitor,

which, together with EGTA and EDTA, reduces phospholipase activities. Leupeptin is a protease inhibitor. Ascorbic acid is an antioxidant, and dithiothreitol (DTT) is a sulfhydryl group protectant. Polyvinylpyrrolidone (PVP) is added to adsorb phenolic compounds. The composition is given in Table elsewhere in this chapter.

3. Microsome buffer: the micrososomal pellet is resuspended in a buffer compatible with the phase partitioning procedure. The composition is given in Table elsewhere in this chapter.
4. Phase partitioning: the two polymers used for PM isolation are dextran T-500 and polyethylene glycol 3350, 6.4% (w/w) each. The two-phase system also contains 5 mM potassium phosphate, pH 7.8 to buffer the system, sucrose as an osmoticum, and KCl, which modifies phase properties. The composition of the phase partitioning system, used to isolate PM from *Arabidopsis* suspension cell, leaf, and root from *Arabidopsis,* is given in Table elsewhere in this chapter.
5. PM washing buffer: PMs are cleaned of any polymers after phase partitioning by dilution in a washing buffer; the composition is given in Table elsewhere in this chapter.
6. Extraction of intrinsic PM proteins by a urea-NaOH treatment: compositions of buffers required for extraction of intrinsic proteins are given in Tables elsewhere in this chapter. Urea is used as a chaotropic reagent.
7. Solubilization buffers: proteins are resuspended in sample buffer (SB2X) for subsequent SDS-PAGE electrophoresis. DTT is used to reduce proteins. SDS is a detergent used to solubilize, denature, and impart a strong negative charge to proteins.

   Glycerol is added to help sample loading. Proteins are resuspended in 2D solution for subsequent 2D gel electrophoresis. Thiourea is a chaotrope, and a urea-thiourea mixture exhibits a solubilizing power superior to that of urea alone.

   Extensive analyses of nonionic and zwitterionic detergents have revealed that Triton X-100, β-dodecylmaltoside, and ASB14 provide efficient recovery of hydrophobic proteins on 2D gels. Solubilisation buffers, once thawed, should not be refrozen.

METHODS

Plasma Membrane Isolation

Isolation of a Microsomal Fraction

The isolation of a PM fraction from mechanically disrupted leaf or root tissues or suspension cells first requires isolation of a PM-containing microsomal membrane fraction. PM is then separated from the microsomal fraction by twophase partitioning. All the procedures are carried out at 4°C.

Arabidopsis Leaf and Root

1. Leaves and roots are quickly harvested, put on moist paper on ice and then briefly rinsed with ice-cold distilled water. The fresh weight of the material is measured. The homogenization medium to tissue ratio is 2:1 (mL medium/g fresh weight). The entire

amount of homogenization medium is added to tissues in a Waring blender and homogenized for 10 s at low speed and then for 4 × 10 s at high speed.

2. The resulting homogenate is filtered through a nylon cloth (100-μm diameter) to discard any cell wall debris.
3. The filtered homogenate is then centrifuged at 26,000g max. for 25 min, which allows pelleting of chloroplasts and mitochondria.
4. The resulting pellet is discarded, and the supernatant is filtered through two successive filters, 63- and 34-μm diameter each.
5. A microsomal pellet is obtained from the supernatant by centrifugation at 84,000g max. for 25 min. The pellet is resuspended to a total volume of 9 mL microsomal buffer/20 to 40 g fresh weight.

Arabidopsis Suspension Cells

1. Suspension cells are washed with cold washing buffer (1:1, WBSC/suspension cells) through a porosity 2 glass fiber.
2. The fresh weight of the material is measured.
3. Suspension cells are incubated for 10 min in homogenization medium (2.5:1, mL medium/g fresh weight).
4. Cells are then prehomogenized in a Waring blender for 10 s at low speed and then fully disrupted in a cell disrupter that allows cells to be ground by a high-pressure cavitation process. The principle is to impose high pressure (0.54 kbar for Arabidopsis suspension cells) to force cells through a 180-μm-diameter channel. During transfer from the high-pressure compartment to the low-pressure compartment cells acquire high speed. Projection of cells associated with the cavitation effect induces cell bursting.
5. The cell homogenate is then centrifuged at 10,000g max for 10 min.
6. The supernatant is filtered through a 100-μm-diameter nylon cloth.
7. A microsomal pellet is obtained from the supernatant by centrifugation at 50,000g max for 35 min. The pellet is resuspended in a total volume of 9 mL microsomal buffer/20 to 40 g initial fresh weight.

PM Isolation by Two-Phase Partitioning

1. The same protocol is used for PM isolation from Arabidopsis suspension cells, leaves, and roots. Two phase partition is temperature dependent, so it is best to work consistently in a cold room.
2. A 27 g phase system is mixed with 9 g of a microsomal suspension, which is equivalent to a maximum of 40 g fresh weight. Overloading the phase partitioning system will prevent a correct phase separation.
3. The tube is shaken vigorously 15 to 20 times. It is essential that the contents of the tube mix and that a cushion of dextran does not slide along the wall of the tube without getting mixed into the system.

4. The system is allowed to separate out into two phases by centrifugation at 2,000g for 10 min.

   PM-derived vesicles partition preferentially to the PEG-upper phase (up1), whereas membrane vesicles originating from other membranes partition to the lower phase (low1).
5. To purify the PM from the upper phase, this phase is repartitioned against a fresh lower phase (low2).
6. Upper and lower fresh phases are prepared by mixing 9 g of microsomal buffer with a 27-g two-phase system.
7. After homogenization and centrifugation at 2,000g for 10 min, two fresh phases are obtained, up2 and low2. Phases up1 and low1 are then mixed with fresh complementary phases low2 and up2, respectively.
8. After another homogenization/centrifugation step, phases up3, low3, up4, and low4 are obtained.
9. The upper phase up3 is collected.
10. The upper phase up4 is mixed with the lower phase low3.
11. After homogenization/centrifugation, the washed upper phase up4 is collected.
12. The two upper phases up3 and up4 are diluted in 60 mL of PM washing buffer before pelleting for 35 min at 85,000g max. in the case of suspension cells and at 176,000g max. for 30 min in the case of leaf and root.
13. Pelleted PM proteins are resuspended in PM washing buffer complemented with 10 μM leupeptin and 5 mM DTT, frozen in liquid nitrogen, and stored for a long term at –80°C.
14. The protein yield is between 1.5 and 2.5 mg protein/100 g fresh weight.

Despite a carefully adapted two-phase system, complete purification is almost impossible; thus it is necessary to estimate the relative contamination of the PM fraction by other membranes and soluble proteins.

Enrichment in Hydrophobic Proteins

Among alkaline treatment, urea-NaOH treatment of PM gives rise to a better recovery of hydrophobic proteins aquaporins.

1. PM proteins (0.5 mg) are incubated in 15 mL of buffer A for 5 min on ice before being centrifuged for 10 min at 100,000g max.
2. The supernatant is discarded, and the subsequent pellet is resuspended in 20 mM NaOH and centrifuged at 100,000g max for 10 min.
3. Pelleted proteins are then washed with buffer B and then centrifuged at 100,000g max for 10 min.
4. The final pellet is resuspended in PM preserving buffer for protein assay.
5. For SDS-PAGE electrophoresis, the PM protein fraction is diluted twice in sample buffer SB2X.

Protein Separation by 2-D Gel Electrophoresis

Protein Solubilization

1. PM proteins (120 µg; either total PM or urea-NaOH-treated PM) are pelleted at 100,000g max. for 15 min
2. The pellet is resuspended in 350 µL of 2D solution for 1 h under constant shaking.
3. After centrifugation at 10,000g for 10 min, the supernatant is carefully collected and readjusted to 350 µL with 2D solution.

2-D gel Electrophoresis

1. Isoelectric focusing (IEF) is performed with commercially immobilized pH gradients (linear or nonlinear pH gradient from 3 to 10, 18 cm length; Amersham Pharmacia Biotech), using a IPGphor apparatus (Amersham Pharmacia Biotech).
2. The gel is rehydrated in the presence of 350 µL of sample protein for 4 h without voltage and then for 7 h under constant voltage (50 V).
3. The gel is then subjected to focusing with the following running conditions: from 0 to 300 V in 1 min, 300 V for 3 h, from 300 V to 3500 V in 1 h, 3500 V until 80 kV.h are reached.
4. After the IEF run, the first-dimension gel is successively incubated at room temperature in solutions containing 2% DTT and 2.5% iodoacetamide according to Chevallet et al..
5. The second dimension (SDS-PAGE) is carried out on homogeneous 11% T gels (Protean II, Bio-Rad).
6. The first-dimension gel is sealed at the top of the running gels with low-meltingpoint agarose.
7. Electrophoresis is conducted at 20 mA for 1 h and then at 40 mA for 4 to 5 h.
8. For analytical purposes or subsequent MS analysis, gels are stained with silver or colloidal Coomassie G-250, respectively.

Notes

1. Preparation of dextran T-500: because dextran T-500 is hygroscopic, the determination of the exact concentration should be determined. First, 220 g of dextran T-500 are dissolved in 780 g of water under gentle shaking. Complete dissolution requires about 2 h. Then 5 g of this solution are precisely diluted in 25 mL water, and the optical rotation is measured at 589 nm. As the specific rotation is +199°/ mL/g/dm, the final concentration (%, w/w) is given by the following equation: optical rotation × 25 × 100/199 × 5.

   To ensure uniformity of the dextran T-500 used in a series of experiments, a large batch should be made up at one time; this becomes especially necessary if a polarimeter is not used to correct for the water content of the dextran. Here, the stock solution is made assuming a dextran T-500 water content of 5%. The molecular weight distribution differs between different lots of dextran T-500. This means that with every new lot of dextran T-500, membrane separation in the phase system must be evaluated and necessary adjustments of the composition of the phase system made.

2. It is practical to prepare stock solutions of the phase system components and store them in aliquots at –20°C. A two-phase system is constituted on a weight basis. Its size depends on how much membrane material is to be loaded on the system. As an example, Table elsewhere in this chapter shows how to build a 27 g sample system that will be subsequently mixed with 9 g of microsomes, thus leading to a final 36 g phase system. After preparation, the two-phase systems can be stored at –20°C.

3. Protein concentrations are estimated using a modified Bradford procedure and bovine serum albumin as the protein standard.

4. Adaptation of the two-phase system: the two-phase partitioning protocol described in this chapter is adapted for *Arabidopsis* leaf and root and *Arabidopsis* suspension cells. Starting with any other plant material will require modification of phase partitioning. By varying the polymer concentration and the salt composition of the phase system, optimal conditions for separation can be obtained. Using green material enables one to follow the partitioning of intracellular membranes by eye and to evaluate the most suitable polymer and salt concentrations quickly.

   As a starting point, a full-scale experiment should be done according to the protocol described in this chapter. If the upper phases up3 and up4 are green, a series of small-phase systems (10% of the phase system described in Table elsewhere in this chapter) are prepared without changing the KCl concentration. The lowest polymer concentration giving chlorophyll partitioning in the lower phase should be chosen. On the other hand, if the upper phases up3 and up4 are whitish, with a very low protein yield, a corresponding experiment is done with polymer concentrations below those used. Appropriate enzymatic markers are then measured according to Widell and Larsson 1990 (30) to assess the purity of the PM fraction.

5. Quality criteria for PM purity: estimating the purity of a PM fraction can be hard work since such a proteome is not static; in addition to its basic plasticity, the PM proteome may vary in the same tissue according to development and changing environment, and even through protein translocation to another compartment. However, enzymatic markers specific for membranes are currently used to evaluate roughly the presence of other membranes. Protocols for such an evaluation are not the purpose of this chapter; procedures and critical evaluation of enzymatic markers are detailed in Widell and Larsson. The sensitivity of the Mg-ATPase activity to vanadate, oligomycin, and KNO_3 is commonly used to create markers for PM, mitochondria, and tonoplast, respectively, and the presence of Golgi membranes is assessed by IDPase activity. PMs purified with the protocol described in this chapter exhibit activities sensitive to vanadate, oligomycin, and KNO_3 amounting to 83%, less than 1%, and 13% of the total ATPase activity, respectively. IDPase activity represented 4% of the total ATPase activity. These features are similar to those obtained for various other PM-enriched fractions prepared by phase partitioning.

6. A comparative analysis of protocols to extract PM hydrophobic proteins has revealed qualitative and quantitative differences in proteomes according to the kind of extraction, suggesting that different sets of proteins are specific for extraction procedures. In particular, alkaline treatment allowed a better recovery of PM hydrophobic proteins than

treating PM with detergents (Triton X-114, Triton X-100 alone, and Triton X-100 coupled to organic solvents). Comparison of alkaline treatments revealed that carbonate treatment of PM gives a higher protein yield (30%) than urea-NaOH-treated PM (20%), but the latter treatment gives rise to a higher enrichment in hydrophobic proteins as revealed by immunodetection of aquaporins.

7. Because of the high solubilization efficiency of SDS, SDS-PAGE electrophoresis remains one of the best methods to separate hydrophobic proteins. Mass spectrometry analysis of SDS-PAGE bands then allows identification of proteins even if several proteins are mixed in the same band. Thus, analysis by ESI-MS/MS of the 28-kDa band of a urea-NaOH-treated PM reveals the presence of at least five PIP aquaporin isoforms. This result reveals the power of mass spectrometry, which allows one to distinguish between highly homologous proteins. Thus, SDS-PAGE electrophoresis combined with mass spectrometry analysis constitutes a efficient strategy to build an inventory of hydrophobic proteins. However, SDS-PAGE protein separation does not allow one to determine the occurrence of posttranslational modifications that affect protein pI without altering the molecular weight. 2D gel electrophoresis can help to complement this gap, providing good recovery of hydrophobic proteins on the 2D gel.

8. A comparative analysis of solubilization buffers revealed differences in detergent efficiency according to the extraction procedure. In particular, detergents with an aromatic core (e.g. C80) were shown to delipidate poorly but to break protein aggregates efficiently. By contrast, linear detergents (e.g., ASB14) delipidate efficiently but do not break aggregates as well. In a optimized protocol, hydrophobic pelleted proteins are solubilized in the presence of urea, thiourea, and detergent, which is either (β-dodecylmatoside or ASB14. A critical evaluation of solubilization procedures for hydrophobic proteins is given elsewhere in this book.

INDEX

A

B

C

D

E

F

G

H

I

J

K

L

M

N

O

P

Q

R

S

T

U

V

W

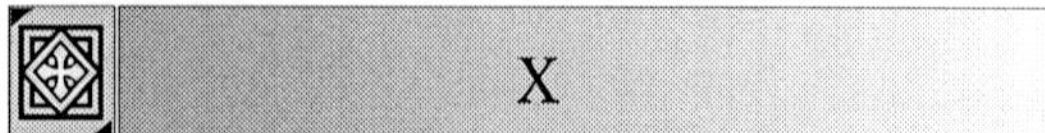

X

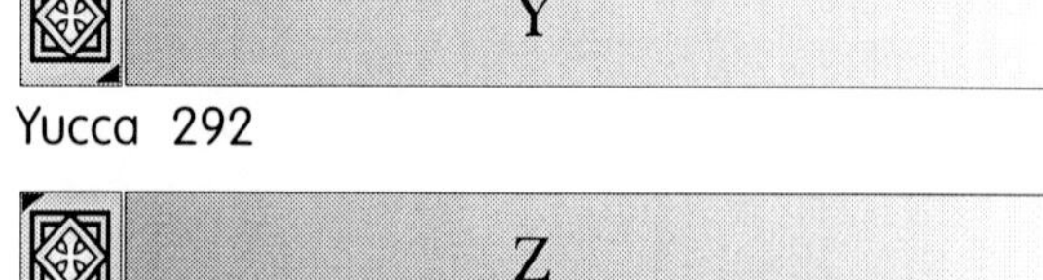

Y

Z